THE BLACK ARAB
And Other Stories

THE
BLACK ARAB
And Other Stories

by

MIKHAIL PRISHVIN

Translated from the Russian by
DAVID MAGARSHACK

1947
Hutchinson International Authors
Limited

LONDON   NEW YORK   MELBOURNE   SYDNEY   CAPE TOWN

Printed in Great Britain at
The Fleet Street Press
East Harding Street, EC4

CONTENTS

THE BLACK ARAB

I. Long Ear

The wind destroys the hills and mountains,
The word destroys the tribe of Adam.

—A Steppe Proverb

WHETHER news in the steppe is self-begotten or whether it comes flying from other countries is a question of no importance: it speeds on wings from one mounted man to another, from one encampment to another.

Sometimes a horseman is overcome by drowsiness and lets fall the reins, and it really seems he needs must miss the news.

But not at all! His horse, seeing another tired and dozing horseman, will turn from its path itself and will stop.

"*Habar bar ?*" ("Is there any news ?")

"*Bar!*" ("There is!")

The horses will have their rest, the riders will have their talk, take a pinch of snuff and go their several ways. Mirages, like distorting mirrors, will reflect their meeting all over the steppe. It is only where the steppe comes to an end and the real desert begins that news wilts, like feather-grass without water.

People will tell you that the earth, deprived of grass and news, becomes brownish-red and that such a great silence reigns there that the stars lose their terror and descend towards the earth.

Good people advised me to call myself an Arab during my journey and to say that I was on my way from Mecca, but that no one knew where I was bound for. "This way," they said, "you will arrive there more quickly; and should anyone attempt to talk to you, say nothing, for an Arab cannot understand a word of Russian or Kirghiz." I spread that rumour abroad and it sped along the Long Ear, "A Black Arab comes riding from Mecca on a piebald pony with a little bald patch on its forehead and not a word does he utter."

The news sped along like a blizzard over the steppe, until it reached the great desert, the great silence, the brownish-red earth, the low stars.

7

But a saddled horse, they say, will run even as far as that.   There wild horses without shoes speed along noiselessly from one oasis to another, like little tawny clouds.   A saddled horse sees them, throws a sidelong glance at his sleeping master, kicks out with his rump and—good-bye!

"*Habar bar ?*" ask the wild horses.

"*Bar !*" the saddled one replies.

And in his own way he will tell them of the Black Arab and the piebald pony.

The horse in his way, I in mine.

The Keeper of the Brackish Lake—there is even such an office—spread a rumour from his little cottage: "The Arab who is travelling from Mecca wants a Kirghiz who can speak Russian, a pair of horses and a small cart."

Soon a man knocked at the window and said, "Is the Arab here ?"

"Yes, the Arab's here," I replied, looking out of the window.

There, on the shore of the brackish lake, stood a little cart and two well-fed horses, and at the window stood a Kirghiz in a wide robe with a riding-whip in his hand.

"What do you want ?   Who told you about me ?" I asked him.

"The Long Ear, dear friend," the Kirghiz replied and laughed.

His snow-white teeth flashed from between the scarlet, juicy "O" of his lips, his yellow face became round like a ripe melon, his eyes disappeared in narrow slits.

Both of us for some unknown reason burst out laughing and we went on laughing for quite a long time.

Everything he had looked good: the horses and the cart, all the wicker baskets and all the ropes—everything was in apple-pie order.

"My horse isn't too fat or dry in the body, the colour of his coat is roan and black."

"Plain words," said Isaac, my future interpreter, travelling companion and friend.

"Yes, plain words," I repeated after him.

"Dear friend," he said to me, "you must trust me.   Another man would start boasting, 'Look at the fine horses I have!'   But I am not in the habit of doing that."

We soon came to terms.

We began to pack my things, making everything ready for a long journey, hundreds of miles from the post-road, along tracks used only by nomads.

"Any danger of being killed ?" I asked.

"Why should anyone want to kill us ?" Isaac replied. "So long as we don't touch their camels, so long as we don't steal their horses, they won't interfere with us!"

So having put our supply of biscuits and our travelling-bags into the cart, having fastened all our baskets and sacks tightly, and made doubly sure by roping everything together, Isaac and I got into the cart. Karat and Kulat ran at a steady trot and behind, fastened by a halter, my piebald pony trotted along. Several horsemen appeared on the horizon. The Long Ear was all agog for news.

"*Habar bar?*" some of them asked.

"*Bar!*" replied the others. "The Arab has got into the cart and the piebald pony with the bald patch is jogging along behind."

The sun warmed this old earth which gets so terribly chilly at night and soon everywhere mirages began to appear. The telegraph poles, lining the highway, receded from us, swaying, like a caravan of camels. The heads of the wild geese on their long necks, on the other hand, looked much longer as they stood on the shore of the brackish lake and flashed in the sun, just as the little china cups on the telegraph poles.

Our nomad road twisted and turned between two ruts, overgrown with green, wayside grass; backwards and forwards they stretched equally far into the distance, like two serpents twisting and coiling on the surface of a dry, yellow sea. The lake, one of those illusory lakes of the desert, glistened like a real lake. A bird rose from the water and flew towards us, flapping its large wings.

Suddenly everything seemed to have blown away. There was no lake, no bird, no camel—everything seemed to have vanished as though by a wave of a magic wand.

A dog came running towards us, its ears swinging about like rags.

"Kah!" Isaac called to the dog in his own language.

The dog ran up to us with a joyful whimper: a steppe wolf-hound, brown and thin like a lath. It gazed at us with that double look of an animal which is panic-stricken, trying to guess, Is it us or isn't it?

"Kah!" I called to the dog.

No, it isn't *us*! The dog gave a whimper and away it ran. But its strength soon gave out, while ahead of it the road went on twisting and coiling far away like two serpents.

The dog sat down on the dry earth and began to howl.

"Kah! Kah!" we shouted for the last time and started the horses.

The dog ran after us, obedient, ours now for good. It looked happy enough, just as if nothing had happened to it: what did it matter which master it served. The one in front was as good as the

one behind.   The steppe-desert looked the same everywhere.   The
big steppe sun shone steadily wherever you looked, without winking,
without lingering behind trees.

Light and silence. . . .   The dog was running after us submissively,
but its howl had been left in the desert as well as its double gaze.
The Long Ear heard the howl and the mirages observed the look of
the dog which had lost its master.

Emptiness!

For whom did that bright and generous sun shine in the steppe ?

The shadow of a solitary cloud, wandering from skull to skull and
from bone to bone, seemed to answer: this is for whom the sun shines
in the desert—they, too, lived and howled in their own way, and the
desert did not obtain its pellucid silence with the mirages so cheaply!

Towards noon the sun in the steppe began to look white.   We
stopped by a well to water the horses.   Isaac spread out his robe and
prayed to God.   Karat, Kulat and the piebald pony, waiting for
Isaac to finish his prayer, bent their heads and looked down into the
opening of the well, just as a star does: did they want a drink so
badly or had they seen in the water, which was the colour of coffee,
a drowned steppe hare or rat ?

"Allah, Allah!" Isaac murmured, prostrating himself on his robe
and rising and again prostrating himself.

Every time he touched the ground his yellow face would merge
with the dry feather-grass, and every time he raised himself on his
knees it would stand out against the blue sky.   So he went on
prostrating himself, passing the palms of his two hands down his
beard, raising his narrow, slightly squinting eyes to the sky and
remaining frozen in such an attitude with his hands crossed.

Even the honey-buzzard was not afraid at such a time to swoop
down on a little bird close to Isaac's robe, but he missed the bird and
soared away into the illimitable spaces of the steppe.   Isaac did not
seem to see anything.   He went on kneeling on his robe, his hands
as before crossed piously, but his eyes were following the flight of the
bird and there was no prayer in them.

A large white turban began to bob up and down on the edge of
the blue horizon.

"Allah, Allah!"   Isaac began to murmur his prayers quickly.

"Is it a mullah coming ?" I asked him when he had hung his robe
on the cart.

"A Sart on a camel," Isaac replied.

And once again everything seemed to have been blown away:
neither a mullah, nor a Sart, but a horsewoman, a white kerchief
tied round her head, came galloping towards us.

She had lost her little boy.

"Haven't you seen a boy anywhere?" the woman asked.

"We haven't seen a soul," replied Isaac, "but we've found this stray dog." Was it her dog by any chance?

"No," said the woman and she asked Isaac—or was it me?—something, throwing a look at our horses.

"She wants to know," translated Isaac, "whether we have met an Arab on a piebald pony and whether it was not that Arab who had carried off her boy?"

To that Isaac replied, "The Arab is sitting just here on the cart, smoking, and the piebald pony is standing by the well."

Then the woman, for all her sorrow, could not help asking, "Where's the Arab travelling to and wherefore?"

Isaac explained to her: "The Arab is travelling from Mecca and he keeps his own counsel, but he has not stolen your boy. If you ask me, it is Albasty, the barren woman with the yellow hair, who has stolen your boy."

As if in reply to that piece of intelligence, the horsewoman whipped her horse and galloped away.

I, too, wanted to mount my piebald pony and become the cause of mirages like that woman.

So I became a steppe horseman. On my head I wore a large fur cap made of the skin of a young ram and covered at the top with green velvet; on my feet were a pair of soft high boots made of felt and leather; the flaps of my long, heavy Caucasian coat were tucked up beneath my legs and held fast against the saddle. A wide black robe covered both my Caucasian coat and the saddle and stretched over half the horse. In my left hand I held a riding-whip and in my right the reins. Thus I sat in those long, wide clothes on a small piebald pony with a bald patch on its forehead. By the look of it a Kirghiz, by rumour an Arab, I went riding along, sowing mirages.

Once more the horsemen of the Long Ear appeared on the horizon. Two of them were galloping straight across my path, as though to intercept me. But I was determined to deceive them. All I had to do was to jab my piebald pony in the ribs with my heavy top-boots and the long ear flaps of my fur-cap would turn inside out like the ears of a bloodhound. The wind whistled in my ears. The steppe came to life. It was not dead: it was alive from end to end and it seemed to rise, it seemed to come up to the horseman.

"*Berge, jiggit!*" ("Come here, rider!") they shouted behind me.

I looked round. The two horsemen had stopped on the road a long way behind me. One had a stick in his hand with a rope in a noose for lassoing horses. Isaac rode up to them from the other side.

"*Habar bar?*" they asked when we met.

"*Bar!*" Isaac replied.

And he spoke to them in his own way, pointing at me with a finger. Now they saw before them a real Arab and not a mirage, they heard with their own ears the story about him and they seemed to be enjoying themselves.

"Ee-yaw!" one of them exclaimed.

"Ah!" replied the other.

All I could hear was just "Ee-yaw!" and "Ah!"

So thrilled were they to meet the Arab that they had nearly forgotten their own business. To be sure, they had lost a she-camel. We had not seen their she-camel by any chance, had we?

"No, we haven't seen the camel. We've found a stray dog and we also saw a woman who had lost her boy, but we have not seen a camel."

For all that, the horsemen rode away satisfied: they had seen a living Arab! Ten years hence, twenty years hence, when they come again to this place, which is called Broken Wheel, they will remember the Arab with all the particulars: that his large fur cap was green and his Caucasian coat grey and his robe was fastened with a red belt, and that his piebald pony had a bald patch on its forehead.

I decided to give my pony a rest and I sat down again in the cart beside Isaac. We jogged off once more, following the nomad road and watching the mirages.

We had several more meetings before the evening. Near the village Buried Well two horsemen stopped us and talked for a long time with Isaac.

"What were they talking about?" I asked.

"All about the lost she-camel," replied Isaac.

Our second meeting took place near a dried-up stream. From every stone and skull on the ground evening shadows stretched across the steppe.

"What were you talking about now?" I questioned Isaac again.

"Still about the lost she-camel," he replied.

At nightfall we saw an abandoned cart with lowered side-shafts in the steppe and we thought: "The woman who lost her boy must have left it there." Afterwards every horseman we met until sunset asked us about the woman who had lost her boy and told us that a wolf had carried off the foal of the she-camel.

When the sun almost touched the rim of the steppe, three geese rose from a bare plot of land, a sure sign that a lake was somewhere near, and when the time came for Isaac to perform his ablutions before his evening prayer, we came to a large sweet-water lake which was, however, overgrown with rushes.

"The sun seems to be ashamed of something in the evening," the Kirghiz Mohammedans say: "it blushes because it was a long time ago worshipped as a god."

Isaac did not pray to the sun, as one might have thought, but to the invisible Kaaba in Mecca.

"Allah, Allah!" He prostrated himself on his robe.

The last two horsemen who had told us about the wolf and the she-camel also dismounted. Their black robes stood out clearly against the red sky. One moment they could be seen with their hands raised to heaven and the next their bodies would be swallowed up by the dark earth.

"Allah, Allah!"

The whole steppe was spreading out its robes and murmuring, "Allah!" The setting sun shed a lustre on every face and only the steppe burial-shrines remained as dark as ever.

I decided to have a walk by the lake while Isaac was praying. The lake was overgrown with rushes for almost a mile from the shore. I entered the forest of reeds by a barely visible path. The reeds hid the whole world from me. There, in those beds of reeds, bustards spent the night, wolves had a meal there on the fat, stumpy tails of the rams, and rested. The tigers were a little farther to the southward. All the same, one could not help feeling frightened in the twilight of that forest of dry reeds.

The footpath took a sharp turn, away from where Isaac was praying, bringing me to a water-hole and then leading me heaven alone knew where.

It seemed to be a blind alley.

A strange bird whistled. "What bird can it possibly be?" I thought to myself. "Never in my life have I heard such a song. I must see that bird!" So I walked on along the footpath that did not seem to lead anywhere. At either side of me in the reeds I could hear startled rustling noises everywhere and in front of me that strange bird went on whistling, her song now dying down, now rising again in the evening air.

I quickened my pace, hurrying away from the growing darkness of the reeds. I stumbled once and fell, but at last I could see clearly the light of the setting sun through the black and thinning curtain of the reeds.

The bird was just there behind the reeds. The dark cupola of a steppe burial-shrine, as tall as a temple, rose between me and the red

disk of the sun.   A flock of rams was passing by the burial-place,
their fat tails glowing red in the sun, and behind them an old shepherd
rode slowly on a bull, whistling like a bird and from time to time
shouting:

"Choo!"

"*Berge!*" I shouted to the old shepherd to ride up to me and to
have a look from the bull's back where Isaac was.

The old man and the bull heard me.

"Choo!" the old fellow shouted at the rams.

The whole flock turned round and began moving in my direction,
and behind the flock came the bull and the old man.

"How are your hands and feet?" I shouted the Kirghiz greeting
to the old shepherd.

"*Amamba!*" he replied.

"And how are your rams and sheep and cattle?"

"*Aman.*"

"And how are your hands and feet and cattle?" the old man
asked me in his turn.

"*Amamba!   Aman!*" I replied.

I could say no more in Kirghiz and I pointed with my hand at the
reeds in the direction where Isaac was.

I kept on stroking the good-tempered steer between the horns,
repeating:

"*Jyaksy, jyaksy!*"

The old patriarch looked over the reeds from the back of the bull
and, seeing Isaac, he understood what I wanted and brightened up.

I patted the old man and said, "*Jyaksy, jyaksy, askakal*, good, good
old fellow!"

And he, good man, got off the bull.   Now I myself mounted the
bull, surrounded by hundreds of hooked-nosed rams with pendent
nether lips, bearded and horned goats, ewes and lambs, and shouted
at the top of my voice over the reeds to Isaac.

Isaac had long ago finished his prayers.   He was now coming by
a side road in his cart, keeping me in sight above the moving tops of
the reeds.   He waved his hand, calling me to him.

I whistled to the sheep.

"Choo!" I shouted at the bull.   "*Berge!*" I called to the old man.

The fat stumpy tails of the rams swung about like rubber cushions
and among them the horns of the goats were like pitchforks; they
moved on, a goat in front, the old Kirghiz behind—and so we walked
in a procession towards Isaac.

Not far away was the encampment of the old shepherd—I could
see it clearly now—a few grimy white tents.   The old fellow invited

us to spend the night at his tents, promising to kill a lamb for our supper, but we refused: the old man was poor and it was dirty in his tents, while here, at the lake, it was fine and the weather, too, was perfect. The old man, who had been telling Isaac a long tale, helped us to gather dry dung for our camp-fire and thanked us profusely for the few lumps of sugar and dry biscuits we had given him.

"What was he telling you about?" I asked Isaac later.

"Oh," Isaac replied, "all about the same Arab, the woman who had lost her child and the she-camel."

Apparently the daughter of the same old man had got up at night to look after her little boy in his cradle and found that the child was missing. She rushed out of the tent and was just in time to see the Arab carrying off her boy into the steppe on his piebald pony. At the same time the she-camel, too, seemed to have discovered that her foal was missing and she began to bray and rushed away distraught into the steppe. The old man's daughter and sons rushed off after her, and so it was that the master of the flocks had to tend them in his old age himself.

Isaac told the poor fellow everything and assured him that it was not the Arab who had carried off the boy, but Albasty, the barren woman with the yellow hair. As for the camel's foal, it was a wolf that had carried him off.

The old man, according to what Isaac told me, in the end believed him and said, "Ee-yaw, Khuday (Oh, Lord), before barren women used to go to the sacred mountains of Aulye-Tay, to spend the night there and to pray, hundreds of miles from here, and the great Khuday gave them children as a reward for their piety, but now, it seems, they have started stealing boys from poor people. Ee-yaw, Khuday!"

With that the old man rode away, shaking his head and murmuring, "A plague on these barren women!"

II. THE PIEBALD PONY

WE did not notice when or how the first star was lit in the sky. While Isaac was talking to the old man, the sun was setting, and all the time two goats were having a fight against the red sunset among the tents.

After the old man had driven his flocks to his encampment, we began to make preparations for spending the night in the steppe. We watered our horses and tied nose-bags of oats over their muzzles. While we busied ourselves with our horses, sparrows came flying from every side to our cart; some of them sat down calmly on the board nailed to its back, thrusting out their little chests towards the red sunset, while others hopped all over the cart, exploring everything they could find and exchanging news about all the events of the day in the steppe. Having finished with our horses, we took a felt rug out of the cart as well as biscuits, tea, sugar and meat and spread everything beneath the clear sky of the steppe. We then raised the side-shafts of the cart, a belt fastened across them and, suspending a bridle from it so as almost to touch the ground, we hung on it a tea-kettle filled with water from the lake. Isaac piled a heap of horse-dung round the kettle, very neatly and almost lovingly, and set a light to it. A puff of the evening breeze which came from under the cart fanned the fire slightly and a bluish flame soon rose under the kettle.

Among the tents the remaining members of the old man's family were meanwhile busy with the flocks. We could not see what they were doing there and we could only suppose that they were milking the goats, the mares and the camels. Somebody was singing there and so simple and monotonous was the strain of that song that it sounded as if a naughty boy were rattling the handle of a pail. To the sound of that song, however, the flocks gradually lay down on the ground. It was after two camels had squatted down and all the animals in the camp had lain flat on the ground and the song had died down that I saw the first star. It looked as if it had been lowered to us on a silver thread—it was so big and so low!

"*Cholpan!*" said Isaac. "The shepherd's star rises when the flocks return from the fields and sets when they leave to graze in the morning. It's our favourite star!"

The star, no doubt, had been in the sky long before, but we had only noticed it now. There was always a second star in the sky when the first one was sighted, and if you looked close enough there were also a third and a fourth.

In a little while whole constellations were telling our fortunes all over the sky above our heads.

Suddenly a change came over everything. The tea-kettle boiled over and a jet of water splashed out of the spout on to the cakes of dung. There was a hissing sound. Isaac gave a start and took off the kettle and it was then that from within that tiny tower, built of small balls of dry dung, a flickering red flame shot up where the kettle had previously been. And the sky, the whole of the sky with its large, low, vacant stars vanished, put out by a little flame on the ground, a flame which was, however, near to us.

Isaac paid no attention to it. He made the tea and then replaced the kettle on the bridle with more water for meat. As soon as the kettle covered up the flickering flame, the sky opened up again.

The tea was brewed. Isaac and I sat facing each other, our legs crossed under us Oriental fashion, and putting lumps of sugar into our mouths, we drank tea from Chinese cups without saucers, holding them from underneath with our fingers. Now we talked of the stars quite simply.

"What would you say about that star there?" Isaac pointed a small lump of sugar at the sky.

"Which one?" I asked. "That one?" And I, too, pointed a lump of sugar at the Pole-star.

Isaac growled assent and nodded.

What could I say about the Pole-star?

"Well," I said, "it is a fixed star."

"We, too, think that it is fixed," said Isaac.

"So you and we agree about it, don't we?" I exclaimed, rather surprised.

"All this was seen in the skies in ancient times," Isaac explained to me. "In our country and in yours, it's the same everywhere. We call it the Iron Stake.

"And what would you say about those two stars, the bright one and the dim one, not far from the Iron Stake?" Isaac asked again.

"Those two stars belong to the tail of the Little Bear. I don't know anything about them."

"Those are two stallions, the White Stallion and the Grey Stallion," Isaac explained to me. "Both of them are tied to the Iron Stake and both of them walk round it just as Karat and Kulat walk round the cart. And those seven large stars," Isaac said, pointing at the Great Bear, "are the Seven Thieves who want to steal the White and Grey Stallions, but they don't let themselves be stolen and just go on walking round the Iron Stake. When, however, the Seven Thieves catch the White and Grey Stallions, the world will come to an end. All this has been seen in the sky since ancient times. Every star means something."

"And what about that cluster of stars?" I asked, pointing at the Pleiades.

"That cluster of stars are sheep," said Isaac, "sheep frightened by a wolf. Have you ever watched sheep crowding together when a wolf is near?"

"But is there also a wolf in the sky?"

"Of course there's a wolf, dear friend."

And he pointed out to me the Wolf in the sky with a lump of sugar.

"In the heavens as on earth!" I exclaimed with surprise.

"As in the steppe," Isaac replied. "You can also find in the sky the mother who is looking for her lost child."

"Perhaps there's also an Arab up there?"

"Ah!"

"And Long Ear?"

"Ah-h!"

We were silent. The stars above our heads twinkled quietly, as though they were breathing, as though they could see us sitting by the cart and were smiling and whispering to each other, and from star to star, along the whole of the Milky Way there was one big family rejoicing.

One star asked the other, like the horsemen in the steppe, "*Habar bar?*"

"*Bar!* An Arab is drinking tea beneath the stars!"

Isaac lit a dry reed on the burning dung. He wanted to look inside the kettle to see if the meat was ready. He cut off a small slice with his knife and put it into his mouth.

The kettle was again taken off. The camp-fire blazed and the sky with the stars seemed to exist no more. The earthly flame lit up our cart and a small circle of dry grass in the steppe.

We spread a dirty rag instead of a table-cloth and ate, Kirghiz fashion, with our hands, throwing the bones to our dog, who was crunching them somewhere in the dark under the cart. Karat and Kulat were rustling in the grass and some large bird kept on screeching over us: the moment he came over us, he would utter a shrill cry, then he'd be away for a long time and then he'd come back and screech again. The bird was called *Yuzak* and it always behaved like a bridegroom who had lost his bride.

Something glittered in the darkness, like the zigzagging glimmer of a glowing match. Our horses snorted. A wolf!

We fired at the glimmering lights: shafts of red flame split the darkness. The barking of dogs and the confused hubbub in the encampment came like an echo of the shots.

"Where are the horses?"

"Here!"

We poured the remnant of our tea over the burning cakes of dung. Now the sky had opened up to us for the whole night, and the moon, like the halo of a saint, appeared at the edge of the steppe. In its light, at the other end of the sky, the Pleiades were extinguished—the frightened flock of sheep, and the wolf, too, disappeared from the sky, and the mother who had lost her child, and part of the Milky Way. Only the largest stars remained.

We lay down on felt rugs at either side of the cart. For a pillow I had my fur cap, on my feet were my felt and leather top-boots, at my side a rifle, on top of me another warm felt rug. On Isaac's side Karat and Kulat were eating their oats, on my side the piebald pony was feeding. At the slightest noise, we had to throw off the rug and frighten the wolf away with a shot.

Now I could clearly see how the bird *Yuzak*—the bridegroom yearning for his bride—made his large circles under the stars: one moment he uttered his harsh cry over our heads, another moment he was gone and I could hear him no more, and then he was back again. He searched, called, screeched, but always within the same circle. Infinitely sad and hopeless were those moans of the bird, yearning for his beloved over the deserted earth, under the stars.

Karat walked up and started scratching himself against the cart.

"Choo, Karat!" Isaac shouted at him.

The horse came over to my side, to the piebald pony. Now there were two horses on my side of the cart. In the sky four of the Seven Thieves lowered themselves slowly to the earth on threads of silver. Were they hoping to deceive the White and Grey Stallions at the Iron Stake to-night?

"Why are the stars here so big and why do they hang so low in the sky?" I could not help asking myself. It seemed to me as I wrapped myself up in the rug that the stars were so low and so big because the earth beneath me was so old and so dry. The older the earth, the lower the stars seemed to be. What had they to fear?

"Choo, Kulat!"

I threw off the rug. The third horse had come over to my side and the piebald pony had walked off a long way and could only just be seen, surrounded, as though by stars, by the sparkling tinsel of hoar-frost on the feather-grass.

Had not the piebald pony gone too far? Should I get up? It was cold. Isaac was asleep.

I put on my fur cap intending to get up, but instead I wrapped myself into my rug, warmed myself by my breath and again the thought flashed through my head: "Hasn't the piebald pony gone too far under those stars? What if a tawny cloud of wild horses came scurrying past? Good-bye to the piebald pony then!"

Again I wanted to get up, but I couldn't.

The piebald pony seemed now to have gone as far as the edge of the steppe-desert. The earth was brownish-red. The stars had descended and lain down. A tawny cloud of wild horses came galloping; they saw the piebald pony and stopped, neighed, called. The stars were swinging to and fro, rising and falling like phosphorescences disturbed by the prow of a ship at sea. The piebald pony bent down his head, threw a sidelong glance at his master beside the cart.

"Is he asleep ? Yes, he's asleep!"

The hoofs flashed high over the steppe-desert.

The wild horses ran from one oasis to another and every time they met, they stopped.

"*Habar bar* ?" the old ones asked.

"*Bar*!" replied the young ones. "A Black Arab is asleep at the edge of the steppe, but the piebald pony with the bald patch is here!"

"It is there on earth that he is piebald and has a bald patch," the old, wise horses corrected them. "Here his name shall be for ever and ever the golden-bay stallion with the white star!"

LITTLE PETERKIN

I.

I OFTEN think that every man's life is just like the outer shell of a nest of painted wooden Easter eggs; the red egg looks so big, but it is only a shell—you take it off and there is a blue one, a smaller egg, inside it, and that, too, is only a shell, and the next one is green and the last one is, for some unknown reason, always a yellow one; that one, however, you cannot open any more: it is your very own. It often happens that during some crisis in a man's life all his thoughts and feelings become fixed on his inner self and then everything that has become attached to him during his life begins to fall away, just like the egg shells. I, too, felt like that once: everything fell away and there remained a little boy, who was standing by the bedside of his sick father.

"Daddy wants you to sit on his bed, dear," mother said. "Do as he says, my sweet."

Father was making some signs with his lips and eyes and his only good hand, signs which mother alone seemed to understand. She immediately gave him a sheet of clean paper and a pencil. Father knew how to draw well and with a few strokes he drew on the paper some strange little animals on small fir trees and he wrote underneath: "Blue Beavers."

The same night Little Peterkin thought he saw an enormous fly on the curtain over his bed. The fly was buzzing so loudly that it could be heard all over the house and everybody seemed to have been awakened by that noise and they were all rushing about with candles in their hands, knocking at doors and whispering to each other. Little Peterkin burst out crying, calling for somebody to come to him in the darkness and biting in his despair the hem of the bed curtain, but nobody came in reply to his cries. So all through the night the giant fly went on buzzing and only towards morning did everything in the house grow still, but, somehow, it was not an ordinary silence: something terrible must have happened!

With that dark foreboding Little Peterkin came out of the nursery. He saw an unknown man standing at the open door of the hall and their village elder waving his hand at him.

"Go away! Go away!"

"I'd like to . . ."

"No time for you to-day: Mikhal Dmitrich is dead."

"May he rest in peace!" the peasant said, crossing himself, and he went away.

Little Peterkin entered his father's bedroom. His father lay on the bed, looking just as he had looked when the little boy had seen him last, except that he was quite naked and nanny was soaping his finger and trying to take the ring off it. There was nothing at all terrifying about that and Little Peterkin just went into another room where he saw Sofia Alexandrovna and some other ladies sitting on chairs, all of them the wives of landowners who were their neighbours.

"Come here, little darling," said Sofia Alexandrovna. "Poor little thing, your father's dead and you're an orphan now."

"I know," said Little Peterkin, "but look what I've got!"

"What is it?"

"Daddy gave it to me yesterday: blue beavers!"

"Always been a dreamer!" the ladies smiled and went on talking among themselves, paying no attention to Little Peterkin.

"I suppose that's about all he's left—blue beavers! Poor Maria Ivanovna! The estate mortgaged twice over and five children. . . ."

"Merchants, if you please! A landlord may be as poor as a church mouse, but he sticks to his land, and quite right, too! He may be ruined, but he sticks to his land and that's as it should be. But why should merchants want to own land? What do they want land for? There's no profit in land, much cheaper to buy your butter in town."

"Want to live like gentlemen, they do!"

"Well, so they did, didn't they? Ran through his capital and left some blue beavers!"

"Oh, you poor little orphan," Sofia Alexandrovna said, stroking Little Peterkin's head. "Poor Maria Ivanovna! I wonder what she will be doing now. Such a young woman, too!"

Mother came in with a handkerchief in her hand. She was in tears and, after embracing the ladies, she said, "Now I shall have to work for the bank for the rest of my life."

"But don't we all work for the bank, dear?"

"You are the gentry," Maria Ivanovna said. "The Government is looking after you."

"But, my dear, just look at you! You're so strong and healthy!"

"Well, I always said that we shouldn't have gone to the country. That was our greatest mistake. The land will anyway sooner or later belong to the peasants."

"Why do you think so?"

"Because they have been freed now, but they've not been given any land. They'll get what they want, you'll see if they don't. The land is sure to belong to the peasants."

From all this talk, Little Peterkin gathered that there were many unpleasant things in the world: someone called Bank had seized his mummy and now she'd have to work for him all her life; also he was now an orphan, which did not seem to be such a good thing to be, and "we are merchants" which was not so good, either, and, last but not least, the land would belong to the peasants, which everybody seemed rather to dread. The only good thing he could think of was the blue beavers, but the grown-ups seemed to think that that was something to laugh at.

LAND AND FREEDOM

Mother used to give parties which were known as "guest nights," and his auntie Dunya used to come to them as well as Sofia Alexandrovna and other neighbours, mostly women. On such an evening dinner used to go on for a long time and everybody tried to entertain Little Peterkin so that he should not fall asleep.

Somebody would sing him a song:

> For thee, O liberty, I'd give my life,
> For thee—sweet and pleasant is all strife.
> Liberty, you're like a hawk soaring so high,
> Liberty, you're like the first gleam of sunshine in the sky!

Mother liked that song very much.

"What a glorious time that was," she said. "I got married in 'sixty-one, you know."

Her reminiscences were interrupted by loud groans and coughing behind the door.

"Who is it?"

"It's me, ma'am."

"Gussyok?"

"Yes'm."

"What do you want, Gussyok?"

"I've come to ask you for a favour, ma'am."

"What is it?"

"A little land, ma'am."

"Mercy upon us! Have you gone off your head? What land do you want?"

"I'd like to have that acre of waste land on your estate, ma'am. I shall work for it."

"Work for it, will you ? I know the way you work. All you do is catch quails."

And turning to her guests, mother said with a face that suddenly brightened up after looking so worried while she was talking to the poor peasant, "Well, my dears ?"

She meant, "Well, carry on with your jolly conversation."

"Please, auntie," Dunya implored her, "why do you always use that common expression: 'Well, my dears ?' It's the wives of our merchants who always talk like that."

"Thank you, Dunya dear, I shan't do it any more, I promise. I know I shouldn't talk like that and I shan't do it again, dear."

But thinking again of that happy time of the emancipation of the serfs, she said to her guests, her face radiant with joy: "Well, my dears?"

The same voice was now singing:

> Am I dreaming of you, dearest ?
> Have you dropped with the dew from heaven ?
> Oh, my prayer has been answered,
> And you the Czar has now forgiven.

Dunya does not like the song, for she hates the Czar.

"Why do you always sing such silly songs ?" she asked.

And she recited:

> Why, dear daddy, must I ever
> Listen to Vanya's vows of love ?
> Why not let me—he's so clever—
> The truth to him by moonlight prove ?

"What truth ?" asked Sofia Alexandrovna.

"What truth? This. There's a Czar in the world and merciless is he. . . ."

"My dear Dunya," the voice that had been singing "For thee, O liberty" said, "you seem always to be worrying about the peasants. You care more about peasants who have no horses or who have only two horses than for Pushkin and Lermontov."

And the same voice began to sing such a sweet song that Little Peterkin never heard anything sweeter in his whole life:

> The angel's wordless song, so sweet and mild,
> For ever haunted the soul of the young child.

But the poor peasant was still moaning in the hall.

"Haven't you gone yet, Gussyok?"

"No, ma'am."

"What do you want now?"

"A little land, ma'am."

"A little land, a little land! What do you go on repeating it over and over again for? If I were you, I should never show my face here again. Have you finished with the ploughing?"

"Yes'm."

"Broke the harrow, didn't you?"

"Me, ma'am? May the Lord strike me dead on the spot if I did it, ma'am."

"Who broke it then?"

"It just broke by itself, ma'am."

"By itself? Go away! I haven't any land for you. Where can I get the land? I can't give land to everybody, can I?"

"Do me a favour, ma'am. I shall always remember you in my prayers."

"Go away, will you? I have no land, I tell you."

"Any piece of waste land will do, ma'am."

"Lord, why don't they shut the door? What's the matter with them to-day? We're just trying to have a quiet time here, but there seems to be neither rest nor quiet for me to-day. Everybody is clamouring for land and when the peasants got their freedom we thought that everything would be all right. Oh, what a glorious time it was!"

She was just about to turn to her guests and say again, "Well, my dears?" when a new noise arose in the hall where a crowd of people seemed to be clearing their throats and blowing their noses. Ivan Mikhalych, the village elder, opened the door furtively.

"What's the matter?"

"The peasants are here, ma'am."

"Well, of all things! Them?"

"Yes, ma'am. Them who been here the other day."

"What do they want?"

"They want land, ma'am. They're after the few acres of fallow land the other side of the cornfields."

"But that's quite out of the question. They can't have it. The others want that piece of land."

"I dare say, ma'am, the others are in a much stronger position."

"Very well, then. In that case tell them Maria Ivanovna has visitors and is too busy to see them."

No sooner had the peasants left the house than Ivan

Mikhalych again opened the door into the parlour and whispered, "The others are here, ma'am."

Mother winked.

The "others" were rich peasants who had most probably brought with them a deposit for the land and they could even be treated to a drink of vodka. The doors opened wide to let them all in and the whole room was filled with the smell of sheepskins. Mother pretended that she did not know what they had come for and even tried to bully them a little.

"What have you come for?"

"We've come to ask you a great favour, ma'am."

"Well . . . what kind of favour?"

"Take pity on us, ma'am."

"Why should I take pity on you? You'd better take pity on me!"

She went on to enumerate all their misdemeanours during the whole of the summer.

"It wasn't us, ma'am," the "others" replied. "It was them, they're real bandits, that's what they are, but we, ma'am . . ."

"Them, them! It's always them!" mother said angrily. "And who's responsible for letting your horses graze in my meadows?"

"It shan't happen again, ma'am."

"I saw their hoofprints in my garden, too!"

"Them's theirs, ma'am."

"Oh, no! Yours!"

However, mother had caught sight of the deposit in the hand of the oldest of the "others" and a bargain was soon struck. Looking very pleased, mother went to another room where the many-tiered stand with the drinks was kept. The expensive drinks were displayed on the top shelf of that stand, but they were there for show only; behind the little doors on the lower shelves stood quarter-bottles of vodka, bottles filled with home-made brandies, bottles of vinegar and medicine bottles. Mother poured the drinks from one bottle to another, added something to the mixture and strained off the flies. Vinegar often got in by mistake into the home-made vodka concocted out of stale bread, and little drops of vegetable oil swam on top of it. Ivan Mikhalych came through the door, which was wide open now, and went back into the dining-room with a large glass which he offered to the peasants. The "others" drank in turn (no snacks were offered to them) and wiped their mouths on their sleeves.

"Have they all had some?"

"All except Nikishka, ma'am. Nikishka drinks only red wine."

Nikishka, it seemed, could only stomach a light wine, but if he only knew what he was drinking! It was the same home-brewed vodka, but to make it look red something was added to it from a bottle of home-made brandy which was so full of flies that it could hardly be called brandy any more. Nikishka drank his "red wine" without turning a hair under the impression that it was a light wine.

"Please excuse me," mother said again to her visitors, "I shall be finished in a moment."

The last thing she did was to give the peasants their orders for the next day.

"Khvatey is to cart away the straw, Kuzma is to chop wood and you're to tell the carpenter to make me a trough and don't forget to make quite sure that they don't graze their horses on my field of clover to-night. You'd better go there yourself to make sure. Do you hear ?"

"Yes'm."

"You can go now."

It was all over. She sat down in her arm-chair and began to shuffle a pack of cards and lay out her favourite patience: "Nicholas dies, Alexander is born." But soon again a shadow passed over her face and she threw a troubled glance at the door.

"Who's there ?"

"It's me, ma'am."

"Who are you ? Gussyok ?"

"Yes'm."

"What do you want ?"

"A little bit o' land, ma'am."

While mother, after having tired herself and Gussyok out, made up her mind to give him a "useless" piece of wasteland to be cultivated in rotation, Little Peterkin took advantage of the noisy discussion to steal away to his divan where, before falling asleep, he murmured a little prayer: "Please, God, I thank you for not creating me a peasant like Gussyok."

GUSSYOK

Little Peterkin always wondered why the peasants looked so poor and unhappy when they came to see his mother, while the same peasants were so jolly and kind when they were in the fields. "It's not their fault," he decided. "It's just because our house is like that: we are merchants!"

Little Peterkin recalled how one day in spring two peasants, Pavel and Gussyok, were pumping water from the well and he got a bit too close to Gussyok's arm.

"Mind, little gentleman," said Gussyok.

"He's not a gentleman," said Pavel, "he's a merchant."

"What is a merchant?" asked Little Peterkin.

"A turkey!" replied Pavel.

Little Peterkin was very hurt at that rude answer.

"Don't look so downhearted, sonny," said Gussyok. "A merchant is a fine fellow, a merchant's as good as any other man, aye, a merchant is a rich man. A gentleman, indeed! Why, what does a gentleman care for except his dogs? But a merchant's different, a merchant loves a bird, that he does!"

"What kind of bird?"

"What kind of bird? Why, sonny, you just come to my cottage and I'll show you the kind of bird a merchant fancies."

So he took the little boy by the hand and brought him to his cottage. The things Gussyok had in that cottage of his! A fighting cock, Kakhetian hens, a talking rook, crested pigeons, cooing doves, a tame partridge and hundreds of quail! Gussyok took him straight to his favourite quail.

"Like him?"

It was a brownish-grey quail with blackish stripes on the back of the neck. It looked a little like Gussyok: Gussyok's face was covered with hair and the quail's face was covered with feathers, Gussyok's nose was hairless and just a tiny bit hooked and so was the beak of the quail.

"Like him?"

"They all look the same to me."

"Go on! Don't you know that this here quail can be heard twenty miles away? You just listen to him start whistling near the priest's kitchen garden or by the Burnt Tree-Stump and, well . . . you'll . . ."

"I'll what, Gussyok?"

"You'll just jump out of your skin, that's what. There are all kinds of quail in the fields, but the really good 'uns are rare and dear. That's why when the merchants hear that there's a real loud-voiced quail in a field, they straightway harness their horses and off they goes to that field. In the old days," Gussyok went on, "lots of merchants used to come to our fields in their carriages with their wives just to listen to a loud-voiced quail. Rich? Aye, that's them! Why, if I was lucky enough to catch a real merchant's quail, they'd shower me with gold!"

"Shower you with gold, Gussyok?"

"Yes, sir. I'd be a rich man and I'd buy myself a fine Tula *samovar* and do nothing except drink tea all day long. That's the kind of folk merchants be. Well, do you like my quail, sonny?"

"He's brown, isn't he?"

"Aye, that's the trouble, my little man. He's a brown one. A real merchant's quail is all white."

"White, Gussyok?"

"Yes, sir, just like a piece of paper. Don't you believe me? I'll show you. Saw one myself the other day, I did. Come along with me to the Burnt Tree-Stump at sundown to-night and I'll show you."

The Burnt Tree-Stump was not far from Little Peterkin's garden. In the evening the little boy went there to meet Gussyok as arranged. It was getting dark. A peasant was riding through a hayfield to the night pasture, looking like a black sail on a green sea. The frog-croaks were silent, but the frog-songsters had started their low, soft trilling which was to go on all during the night. The cuckoos had sung till they were hoarse and fallen silent. A blackbird had just finished his song, but the quails had not started their shrill whistling yet.

"Is it too early, Gussyok?"

"Wait," whispered Gussyok, "the nightingales are sounding the retreat, let them finish and then . . ."

"They'll start?"

"Aye!"

Gussyok's "aye" sounded just like the passionate love call of the quail: "mah-wah!"

One after another the nightingales stopped singing: "chuck-chuck!" and that was all. Then a tight string seemed to hum.

"A beetle, Gussyok?"

"Aye, a beetle's just buzzed off. Wonder why so many beetles should be buzzing to-night," Gussyok whispered.

"Why, Gussyok?"

"Heaven knows why. Hush now, there's a good boy!"

Little Peterkin fell silent, waiting with bated breath for the quail to start whistling, but for some reason the frog-croaks just then woke up and raised a loud clamour, drowning the soft trills of the frog-songsters.

"Qua-qua," Gussyok mimicked them, looking thoroughly fed up.

The frogs fell silent, but the girls in the village raised an awful din.

"Oh, shut up, you!"

The night-watchman struck the bell in the belfry. The first star peeped out of the sky. A whiff of growing corn came floating on the air from the rye fields. The dew was beginning to gather on the grass. It was then that over the whole dew-besprinkled field—from the priest's kitchen garden to the Burnt Tree-Stump—a quail cried and it seemed just as if somebody had cracked a long whip.

"That one has got a loud voice, hasn't he ? Is he a merchant's quail, Gussyok ?"

"Aye, that was a real merchant's quail, that was!"

The two hunters began to steal along the dewy field like two field animals, towards the ditch and then to the other side of it, in the direction of the priest's kitchen garden.

The old night-watchman was still ringing the bell in the belfry and another star peeped out at the very edge of the heavens, and another, and another. . . .

The loud-voiced quail seemed to be in good form to-night: every time he raised his voice, Little Peterkin's ears began to ring. The female bird was silent. Fear suddenly gripped them: what if she should utter her love call at the wrong moment ? They had first to spread out the net and get it into the right shape. Thank goodness, she was silent, only just stirring in her dark bast cage, which was wrapped round with a woman's kerchief. She had been well fed: before going out to catch the white quail, Gussyok had given her some warm milk to drink to make quite sure that her voice would sound extra clear to-night.

The loud-voiced quail went on calling for his mate, but she kept still under the net, in the fragrant, dewy rye.

Gussyok picked up his little leather pipe carefully and blew the female quail's love call softly, for when the female bird was silent, it was always advisable to encourage her.

"Teuke-teuke!"

Then the moment of decision came and the female bird responded beautifully: "Teuke-teuke!"

If only they could roll themselves up into little clods of earth, no bigger than the size of the quail, and become invisible among the other clods of earth in the rye field! If only they could sink up to their necks into the ground and cover themselves up with a corner of the net! How passionately the loud-voiced quail was now calling! He was rushing about all over the field, darting in and out of the rye at the edge like a mouse, lifting up his tiny head and peering between the stalks of rye. Again he uttered his love call in the rye: "Wet-my-feet!" The female bird replied softly: "Teuke-teuke!"

But could they be sure that it was to him she was replying ? There were hundreds of quail in that field and all of them were calling at the top of their voices. She was replying to him! There could be no doubt about it. He was now darting about the edge of the field, standing on tiptoe, but he could not see her. There he was rushing about again, hopping from one mound to another, trying to climb on top of some dead cotton-thistles, but they were too prickly. He tried last year's wormwood, but it was not strong enough to hold him and it bent. Next he wanted to call to her at the top of his voice, but his voice had suddenly gone dead: instead of the former loud "wet-my-feet!" there came a strangled, hoarse cry, deep down in the throat, a barely audible, passionate "mah-wah!"

"Teuke-teuke!" the female bird replied.

He beat his wings against the clods of earth and then he seemed no longer to feel the ground under his feet. He took wing. Where was he flying? Goodness knows: the world's a big place!

"That's right! Fly, fly to us, sweet quail!" Gussyok whispered.

He wanted to shrink into nothingness, to be at least as tiny as the quail himself, but it could not be done. Suddenly the quail dropped by the net, darted into the green corn, whispering passionately, "Mah-wah!"

"Teuke-teuke!" the female bird replied in the cage.

"Come along, sweet quail, come along!" Gussyok whispered and for a breathless moment the sportsman's heart stood still.

The quail was making straight for the net, moving the spikes of the winter corn. There was a bare waterlogged patch of ground in front of the net, barely hidden by the rye. Perhaps the quail had already observed another gigantic quail only ten yards away from him, bent double over the field and the red sunset reflected ominously on his quail beak.

"Does he or doesn't he see me?"—for another breathless moment the sportsman's heart stood still.

But no, the quail saw nothing. He was making straight for the net now. "Mah-wah!" came his strangled cry for the last time and "Teuke-teuke!" came the female bird's reply, and the rye began to wave under the net by the cage.

The female bird poked her brownish-grey head out of her bast prison-cage through the little opening where a china cup with water was fastened and the quail, too, was beside that cup. They were looking at each other, his eyes fixed on hers, beak against beak. The air was heavy with the scent of growing rye, every rye-stalk seemed to call, "Break the bast prison, loud-voiced white quail! Don't waste another minute now!"

But the quail did not dream of wasting any time: he ruffled his feathers, pouted and beat against the dry bark with his chest and wings.

The time for action had come: the net was pulled up quickly and the quail remained hanging in a noose, just in front of the cup of water where he had only a moment ago seen the head of the female bird bent over the cup. Steady now! Mustn't lose him! His warm, fluttering little body must not be allowed to slip through your fingers!

The loud-voiced quail was tied up tightly in a small millet sack. His days of freedom were over. Never again would his song be heard in the fields! It was in the towns that he would be singing in future, in the fish and iron-scrap markets, charming a merchant's ear with his loud song.

The two sportsmen, wet with dew, walked home across the fields, looking like a huge water-sprite striding with his little son across from one lake to another.

The beadle had long since ceased his ringing. Thousands of stars had been twinkling in the sky for hours. The moon had risen. Thousands of the little stars of the earth had also begun to twinkle on the stalks of rye, on their boots, on Gussyok's cossack coat and beard, on the tied-up sack where the loud-voiced quail had fallen silent in the darkness. The frog-songsters alone went on trilling merrily as is their wont from sundown to sunrise.

It seemed to Gussyok that he could see four white horses topping the ditch and drawing a carriage behind them into the field. The merchant came riding full speed across fields, recking naught about trampling down somebody else's corn. Why should he? Had he not money enough to pay for everything? The carriage stopped. Gussyok opened the door.

"I've got him, your honour! Just listen: can you hear him cry?"

The white quail cried at the top of his voice and the merchant in the carriage fell into a trance, forgetting his accounts, his bales of merchandise, his sacks of corn, his inns and his mills. His heart was aflame.

"Catch him, Gussyok! For heaven's sake, catch him for me!"

"At your service, sir," Gussyok replied. "Don't you worry your head about it, sir. I've a lovely female bird, sir. Gave her warm milk to drink to make her voice as clear as a bell. Did it all for you, sir, just to please your honour. I was expecting you, sir. Just a moment, sir."

Gussyok saw himself going away and returning almost immediately with the quail.

"Here he is, your honour."

"A white one?"

"Yes, sir. All merchants' quails are white, sir."

"What do you want for your white quail?"

"I'd be pleased with anything your honour would be good enough to give, sir."

The merchant showered Gussyok with gold and off he rode with the white quail in his carriage drawn by the white horses over fields, over ditches, over the vegetable gardens of peasants and priests.

To round off his dream, Gussyok saw himself treating the whole village to cups of tea from his own samovar and telling them of the honest merchant and the white quail.

Arrived in Gussyok's cottage, the two sportsmen could hardly wait to take the quail out of the sack and put him in a cage. They untied the sack and took out the quail.

"Here he is!"

"Let me see him, Gussyok!"

"A brown one," Gussyok shook his head mournfully. "Missed him again. Been chasing a brown hare, that's what we've been doing."

How did it happen? Weren't there any white quail at all? The small oil-lamp threw a faint light in the room. The fighting cock was asleep, the singing nightingale was asleep, the talking rook was asleep, a whole row of fantails, pouters and tumblers were asleep on their perch, but there was no merchant's quail and gone, too, was Gussyok's dream of a Tula samovar.

"Aren't there any white quails in the whole world, Gussyok?"

"In the whole world? Why, you don't think the world's such a small place, do you? The white quail left for some other place. that's all."

"Which place did they go to, Gussyok?"

"Gone to Siberia, I reckon."

"So there are white quail in Siberia, are there, Gussyok?"

"Why, of course. Every quail in Siberia is white."

"And are the beavers there blue?"

"Aye, there are blue beavers there to be sure, and green ones too, I shouldn't wonder. All sorts of beavers running about all over the place. Time we went there, too, sonny."

The Secret of the Dried Pear

A village now stands where our estate used to be and in our old garden the haymakers are busy. The grass on the parts of the meadow, where the well-manured flower-beds used to be, even now grows taller and the mowers recognise the place and remember that flowers once grew there. But why talk of grass growing on flower-beds? I sometimes come across my father's marguerites in the grass and there is no doubt in my mind at all that they are father's, for mother had no time for gardening. She did employ a lame gardener, though, who was called Yevtyukha and who used to weed the garden

lazily with a rake.   The roses grew in profusion long after my father's
death, whole avenues of roses, and yonder are the cherry trees and the
apple trees.   There were no people under the limes then and young,
yellow-beaked daws used to run about the garden paths, as did
Little Peterkin's brothers, schoolboys who had run completely wild.
The moment they heard the sound of harness-bells or horses' hoofs,
the boys would race from the garden to the yard to see who was
coming or leaving and where they were going to.   But as soon as the
necks of the shaft-horses showed themselves over the other side of the
garden wall behind the bushes and one of the shaft-horses was seen to
turn towards the drive between the stone pillars, they would not wait
another minute, but run as fast as their legs would carry them.
Behind them the children heard their nanny's loud voice shouting,
"Visitors!" but they were too far to be caught by that time.

Mother kept on calling the children to come back, but by the
tone of her voice the boys guessed that visitors were in the house even
if they did not see them themselves.   Little Peterkin usually hid under
the old apple-tree, Rozanka: the trunk of that tree had a cleft near
its roots and he could look through it as through a window down the
long lime avenue and watch the visitors sitting down on the bench at
the end of it and talking to each other.   His heart used to leap with
joy every time visitors came to their house, but he, too, had to run,
for if he didn't his brothers were quite sure to give him a sound
drubbing for being the only one to enjoy a visit from strangers.   On
the sand-strewn path along the lime avenue red-chested bullfinches
and chaffinches ran about, a hare hopped over it stealthily, but as
soon as a human foot stepped on it, everything disappeared, the birds
took wing and the hare ran away.   Perhaps they, too, would have
liked to be in the company of people, the little boy thought, were it
not that the birds in the trees and the insects in the grass seemed to
have a terrible secret, which they alone knew, and that was no doubt
why they all flew or ran away the minute they heard the step of a
human foot.   When every living thing concealed itself, it got very
quiet on the garden path, but however quiet it might be, there was
always some kind of whispering going on behind you. . . .   You
turned round and there was no one there, not a soul, except that
sometimes you caught sight of a pair of little feet scampering away
quickly.   Little Peterkin would get frightened and he'd begin to run,
stopping only when he reached the terrace in front of the house,
where he would start crossing himself rapidly.

"What's the matter?"

"Oh, nothing," Little Peterkin would reply.   "I'm just celebrating
mass!"

One day, however, Little Peterkin's secret wish came true: the visitors rounded up all the children and there they sat at the table covered with a spotlessly white cloth, like perches tied up by the gills.

A plate of soft, sweet, sun-dried pears was very near Little Peterkin and he managed to sneak one without, so it seemed to him, being seen by anyone at the table and he secreted it in his pocket. But his brother Kolya saw him do it and he whispered to him, "Give it to me or I'll tell on you!" Little Peterkin had no option but to obey his elder brother and he gave him the dried pear.

"Now get me one of those biscuits," said Kolya.

"Shan't!" said Little Peterkin firmly.

"All right, if you won't get it for me, I'll show them the pear you've pinched."

Kolya showed him the end of the pear under the table.

"He will never show it," thought Little Peterkin. "He won't dare."

But Kolya raised the hand with the stolen pear higher and higher from under the table.

"Will he do it?" thought Little Peterkin, an awful doubt creeping into his mind. "Not him, he won't half be afraid!"

"I'm asking you for the last time: are you or aren't you going to get me the biscuit?"

"Shan't!"

"All right. Just watch me, will you?"

Kolya put his hand on the table and began to open it slowly.

"Wait a minute!"

"Oh! Changed your mind, have you?"

Little Peterkin contrived to get the biscuit and handed it to his brother under the table. Thank goodness, everything went off all right!

"Give me back my pear now!"

"Your pear? All right, but first get me a sweet!"

Little Peterkin had to filch a sweet for his brother.

Since that day it just went on like that and Little Peterkin became Kolya's slave, blackmailed by him to do all sorts of things under the threat of disclosing the secret of the dried pear to everybody. Once he had even to steal a twenty-copeck silver coin from mother's purse, horrified as he was to do it. Mother was having a nap after lunch and on the small bedside table lay her half-opened, large grey chamois leather bag. Little Peterkin stole quietly up to the bed and, without taking his eyes off his mother, took out the silver coin. The blackmailer was waiting for him at the door. Little Peterkin was jolly glad Kolya let him go without asking him to steal another twenty-copeck bit! So the secret of the dried pear grew more and more terrible with every day and soon another misfortune overtook him.

THE FURIOUS GANDER

Hiding in a cherry bush Little Peterkin overheard a conversation between his brothers.

"Let's kill a goose: the geese are pecking our wheat."

"All right."

"Let's roast him on a spit, just like Robinson Crusoe."

"Which goose?"

"One of the priest's geese, they are the greediest of the lot."

As it happened the priest's geese were just coming along the path across the wheat field. Little Peterkin's brothers got the biggest goose away from the rest—it was a large gander—and in a few minutes they had killed him: they began by throwing stones at him and then finished him off with sticks. The gander was all covered in blood. Then they discovered that they had no matches. One of them rushed off home, but came back almost immediately.

"Let's try to light a fire by rubbing two sticks together," he proposed.

They spent a long time rubbing two sticks together, but nothing happened.

"That's no good. You'd better go for the matches and come back quickly."

One boy rushed off for the matches, while the other mounted guard over the gander. Little Peterkin was all the time sitting in the cherry bush. He was dying to join his brothers and go with them to roast the goose on a spit, but he was afraid that they would give him a good beating with their sticks. "Don't sneak!" No, he decided, it was much safer not to.

Presently one of his brothers came running back with the matches, out of breath and panting.

"Got them?"

"Yes, I got 'em."

"Good!"

The path across the wheat field, made by bare feet, was smooth and hard like a callous heel and it disappeared in the wheat no one knew where. Little Peterkin's brothers also disappeared in the wheat and barefooted Little Peterkin stole after them, the wheat looking like a wood to him and there seemed to be no end to that wood. There was only the blue sky above his head and everything was still, even the ears of wheat did not whisper to each other. It was that awful silence that was so terrifying, for the Big Blue One was looking at them and he saw everything. Little Peterkin felt very frightened and he wanted to go back, but the wheat had long ago closed behind him. Little Peterkin decided to join his brothers, come what may, only not to be left alone. But no sooner did he catch sight of them than his brother who was dragging the goose dropped it and the goose hit the dry, hard path and began to gaggle at the top of his voice! Terrified by the loud clamour of the supposedly dead goose, Little Peterkin's brothers took to their heels and ran back home and, had not Little Peterkin been quick enough and got off the path in time, they would have knocked him down. Luckily, hearing their terrified shouts, he jumped into the wheat and began to run without looking where he was going, leaving a wide path behind him in the wheat. The blood-stained gander was running after him along that path. It was, of course, the Blue One who had seen everything and who now punished the evil-doers by making the gander chase them. While running away, Little Peterkin prayed to him: ". . . and save us from temptation. . . ." He fell down and whispered his prayer, the gander meanwhile stopping and waiting for him to start running again, and as soon as Little Peterkin got up and took to his heels, the furious gander resumed his pursuit, kicking up a row behind and gaggling at the top of his voice. "Mother of God, Holy Virgin, save and protect me!" Little Peterkin tried to defend himself with another prayer and when at last he said, "Oh, Lord, have mercy upon me, miserable sinner!" the wheat field came to an end and he went home, following the familiar path along the high bank.

If Little Peterkin had been like his brothers, he would have made good use of the big secret of the blood-stained gander, by making his own little secret of it against his brothers, like the secret of the dried pear, but it never occurred to him to do anything of the sort. The only moral he had drawn from it was that there were big secrets which you must keep to yourself and little secrets which were always discovered and with which people went on tormenting each other. That awful secret of the dried pear, for instance: it seemed easy enough to make a clean breast of it and get rid of it once and for all, but every time he tried to do so, he realised soon enough that it was not as easy as that. For, after all, it was not a question of the dried pear at all—that admittedly was the least important aspect of it—what was important was the secret itself and that secret seemed to grow bigger and bigger every day. The grown-ups, too, had their secrets: Sofia Alexandrovna had her Old Monk, Dunya had her Pale Gentleman, and the Old Monk and the Pale Gentleman doubtlessly also frightened them with some kind of dried pear. Well, why else didn't they tell everybody about it ?

MARIA MOREVNA

The Blue One hearkened to Little Peterkin's prayer and smiled upon him: a beautiful girl came to their house and she had the sun and the moon on her brow and the stars in her long plaits—a real Maria Morevna, Mary, the daughter of the King of the Sea who saved the Crown Prince from the clutches of the Sorcerer Kashchey whom Death could not touch and who wanted to enchain the whole world.

She came in one day and said, "Mother would like to ask your permission, Maria Ivanovna, to take a stroll in your garden and your park. She wants to visit the places which are so dear to her. So many of her memories are bound up with this estate."

Then the general's widow, the former owner of the estate, herself came in. She was not at all an old woman and she was dressed in black and wore gold spectacles.

For a long time she and her beautiful daughter walked up and down the lime avenue and afterwards they sat down on the bench. Little Peterkin could see through the window of the old apple tree how the general's widow wiped her tears with a handkerchief and he could hear snatches of their conversation.

"Granny's tree was there, wasn't it ?" the young girl asked. "I wonder if the apple tree is still standing ?"

"Yes, darling. There it is!"

"And there was another apple tree beside it, wasn't there ?"

"It's still there!"

"Better run away now," thought Little Peterkin, "or they'll soon remember Rozanka." But it was dangerous to get out of his hiding-place, and, besides, he got such a fine view of Maria Morevna through that window by the spikes of the green grass and it gave him such a thrill to think, "It's *she*, the real one, it is she who has come!"

The general's widow was saying, "We must be fair to these merchants: they are taking good care of the garden. Look how many flowers they have here. We never had so many flowers. Do you remember, dear, there was an old apple tree, Rozanka, in this garden and it had such a lovely window just at the bottom of its trunk."

"Of course, I remember. There it is, mother."

"Let's have a look at it, darling."

Little Peterkin had no time to run away. Maria Morevna looked through the window and exclaimed, "Look, mother, what a dear little boy is lying in the grass here!"

Nanny came out of the house, looking very important. She walked up to the visitors, pulled herself together and summoned enough courage to say, "Maria Ivanovna would be very pleased if your ladyship would have lunch with her."

"Not 'your ladyship,' my dear," the general's widow smiled.

"You can see that they are real gentry," nanny said to Little Peterkin afterwards.

"Aren't we real, too?"

"We don't belong to the gentry, dear, we're just merchants."

No one was more glad to entertain the guests than mother. She beamed with pleasure as she welcomed them into the house and whispered to Dunya apropos of the general's daughter, "She's a real Turgenev heroine!"

Mother did her guests proud and Little Peterkin learnt at the meal the difference between real gentry and common or garden mortals: they ate without any ceremony, asked for a second helping themselves, if they wanted more, and refused any dish they did not like. Little Peterkin had no doubt at all that Maria Morevna was the kind of girl about whom everybody said, "What a beauty!" As for what that exclamation meant and how it was that one look at such a girl made people exclaim, "What a beauty!"—Little Peterkin had no difficulty at all in finding the answers to those questions. "An ordinary woman," he thought, "speaks in a different voice to different people and smiles at them in a different way, but a real beauty behaves the same way to everybody, whether rich or poor, big or small. That is, indeed, where she differs from the rest. But," Little Peterkin thought in dismay, "what if she really were the real and only one? If she said anything to me at the table, I'm quite sure to go red in the face and then everybody will know my secret, everybody will know that it is *she*!" In any event, it was best to be ready for anything and Little Peterkin thought desperately of the gander, covered with blood, so that if the worst came to the worst he could let it loose and thereby call up the dreadful picture of hell and the Last Judgment. The worst, of course, did happen: Maria Morevna looked straight at him and smiled. . . .

"Lord, have mercy upon me, miserable sinner!" Little Peterkin murmured, thinking of his gander.

"Can you read?" Maria Morevna asked.

Little Peterkin muttered under his breath, "Hell and perdition!" and at once let loose the gander.

The rim of the world, where the sky touched it, blazed up in red flames, an immense black mountain was revealed in that crimson conflagration and an angel stood on the top and blew a trumpet.

At the sound of the last trump the dead rose up and those who like nanny had pared their nails all their lives and preserved them carefully in little bags, had long, long nails, for all the little bits they had cut off had joined up and grown together and, clinging to the rocks with those huge nails of theirs, the righteous souls crawled up the mountain to the archangel, while the sinners gnashed their teeth, lost their hold on the rocks and fell headlong into the flames of hell.

Little Peterkin was not red, but deathly pale: he had prevailed.

"What's the matter, darling?" mother asked. "Why are you so pale?"

"I expect I must have swallowed a fly," Little Peterkin replied.

"Why do you always sit with your mouth open? Here, have a drink of water, there's a dear. It'll soon pass off."

Little Peterkin had a drink of water.

"I can read all right," he said calmly to Maria Morevna.

"Good," she said. "I've got a lovely book for you. I simply loved to read it when I was a little girl. It's Andersen's fairy tales. You haven't read them, have you?"

"No, I haven't."

After the meal she went to look for the book among her things and brought it to him. The book had lovely pictures in it.

Ivan's Secret

It was rather warm at noon. Little Peterkin was allowed to go out in the sunshine and knock down the icicles from the roof. It got dark very early—a winter evening. Mother and Dunya, which did not happen very often, had gone out on a visit and nanny, too, had gone out somewhere, to get something for dinner perhaps. Little Peterkin was quite alone in the big old house and, suddenly, he heard somebody saying, "The Czar's been killed!" When he heard that, Little Peterkin at once thought of Dunya. "Now Dunya will be pleased!" he said to himself, but after that loud shout, somebody in the house burst out crying and people started running about and whispering: that was nanny talking to their maid Nastya on the stairs. Little Peterkin felt terribly frightened for some reason.

"Yes, they killed our dear Czar," nanny whimpered.

"Why are you crying, nanny?" Little Peterkin asked. "What's going to happen now?"

"Why, you poor dear, don't you know? All the peasants will now kill their masters with axes."

"Crabs are mowing hay on the stove with axes," the thought at first flashed through Little Peterkin's mind, but afterwards he felt so frightened that he could see everything very clearly as though in a dream: the peasants going to kill their masters with huge axes in their hands, something like a picture of the Last Judgment.

"Oh-oh-oh!" Little Peterkin began to sob suddenly.

"What's the matter, dear?" nanny asked in alarm.

"Didn't you say yourself that now the peasants will be killing their masters with axes?"

"Perhaps they won't do it, dear."

"Of course they will!"

"Why are you so sure?"

"Haven't they killed the Czar?"

"They have, dear, they have."

"Well, so they'll be coming now."

"I dare say they will, dear."

Nastya burst out crying, nanny, too, was crying and Little Peterkin was crying.

"What shall we do, nanny? Shall we hide?"

"We'd better call in the peasants to be in the house with us until the others come back. Nastya, call in the peasants, please."

"The peasants, nanny?"

"Yes, dear. I mean our peasants, of course: they're quite harmless, dear."

Soon the peasants, Ivan and Pavel, came in.

"I suppose," nanny said to Ivan, "they'll finish them all off now."

"Their number's up," replied Ivan.

"Us, too?" asked Little Peterkin.

"You?" Ivan grinned. "What kind of masters are you?"

"Thank God," Little Peterkin said, feeling much happier, and he asked quite cheerfully, "Tell me, Ivan, why won't they touch the merchants? Is it a secret?"

"The merchants live on their capital," said Ivan. "I'm afraid you're too young to understand it. Now, listen carefully and I'll explain it to you. Tell me, did God create Adam out of the earth?"

"Yes, he did."

"But Adam sinned and God drove him out of paradise, didn't He?"

"Yes."

"But do you know what God said to Adam when He drove him out of paradise?"

"No, Ivan, I don't."

"God said, 'In the sweat of thy face shalt thou till the ground.'"

"Well?"

"Now Gussyok is a man, isn't he? Then why hasn't he got any land to till? What's happened to his land?"

"Mummy's got it."

"Your mummy has bought it from the gentry, but how did the gentry get it from Gussyok? Who gave it to them?"

"I expect the Czar must have given it to them."

"The Czarina Catherine. If she liked a man, she'd give him land."

"That's right," said Pavel. "Take that big tree Lim you have in your garden, been there for hundreds of years; well, my granddad used to hang his horse's collar on that tree: the land then belonged to the peasants, but later the gentry got it and you got it from the gentry."

"And now I suppose it will go back to you again?"

"Well, first they're going to survey all the land and then they'll divide it up."

"Survey it? What's that?"

"Can't explain everything to you, Master Peter," Ivan said with a grin, as before. "Master, master has lost his trousers, but he's still dancing!"

"Lost his trousers, Ivan? But I've got my trousers on!"

Everybody burst out laughing and, having finished laughing, Pavel said to Little Peterkin: "That's the kind of problem Ivan has given you for to-night. Think it over when you're in bed—why do our peasants say, 'Master, master's lost his trousers, but he's still dancing'?"

KASHCHEY

Ever since Maria Morevna had gone away (she had promised to come back soon, but winter had almost gone and she had not come back), all sorts of secrets had accumulated; before, Little Peterkin became aware of them only when he was out in the garden or in the fields, but now secrets began to crop up that concerned different people and he could not ask anyone about them, for when he sometimes did ask, everybody laughed at him and told him to find out for himself. Indeed, sometimes it was dangerous to ask any questions, for if you did, all sorts of disagreeable things might happen to you. They were talking about Adam in the village. They said that God had created Adam out of the ground and commanded him to till the land and that it was that Adam who had got the land and that the peasants whom mother used to call "the others" came from that Adam. They were also saying in the village that there was a second Adam whom God had also commanded to till the ground, but that there was no more land left for them to till, and the peasants whom mother called "those peasants" came from that second Adam and that it was "those peasants" who now wanted to survey the land. A police officer came to their house one day and asked who it was who wanted to survey the land. Everybody said it was Ivan, so they took Ivan away.

"Where did they take Ivan to?" Little Peterkin asked.

"They took him where his own mother wouldn't find him."

"Why couldn't she?"

Everybody laughed, which meant: "Find out for yourself!"

They had killed the Czar, but there was another Czar, a grown-up Czar with a beard. Mother was laying out her patience: "Nicholas dies, Alexander is born," but was a Czar born with a beard? That was another thing he had to find out for himself.

"Why is it that everybody finds out everything at once and I only find it out later?" he asked mother.

"It's because you're so absent-minded, dear," his mother replied.

So there was another riddle to solve: everybody seemed to be normal, but he was ab-sent-mind-ed. If he could see Maria Morevna for one day only, he was sure she'd tell him the meaning of all those secrets and solve all his riddles for him.

The long-expected day came at last. The ground was covered with snow, but the clouds in the sky had dispersed and the sun was shining. They were saying, "Aren't the days getting longer?" They were also saying, "This is spring!" And, finally, they said, "To-day Mary's coming!"

"I can't recognise my own children any more," mother said. "How they've changed since the day dear Mary came to see us, how eager they are to do what she tells them. She says, 'Go and gather some flowers!' and off they go and not only do they gather flowers for her, but they spend hours putting them together into lovely bouquets, and she's only to tell them, 'Find me a nice apple!' and they start knocking hundreds of apples off the trees and they search and search until they find the best apple of all for her."

Sofia Alexandrovna did not seem to like that.

"I don't think it's quite right, somehow," she said.

"Why, what's wrong about it? Let them knock off all the apples in the garden for all I care so long as they behave like human beings. You don't know how wild they had become, running away as soon as we had a visitor. Now they're glad when somebody comes to see us. What a talented girl she is! It's such girls who should be educating our children and not old maids and awful frumps."

"She's too proud, my dear," said Sofia Alexandrovna. "I hope you don't mind my saying so, but she seems to infect the children with her pride, give them all sorts of strange ideas, make them wish to do extraordinary things, while life, my dear, demands humility and submissiveness from people."

"Life will teach them that all right, but Mary . . . Mary's a Turgenev heroine."

"If you ask me, dear, she's much too gushing. Can't sit still. One moment she'll be showering flowers on some singers, another she'll be joining the mathe-matic-al faculty, or going to Italy, or milking cows on Tolstoy's estate in Yasnaya Polyana. It's her pride that makes her do all this. I grant you she's a beautiful girl and well bred, too, but she lacks the most essential thing in life. They didn't borrow any money from you by any chance, did they?"

"I don't think it would have mattered if they did: I should have been too glad to be able to show them how grateful I am. You just can't recognise my children. Why, even their schoolmasters praise them!"

"I think she ought to be a governess in an aristocratic family, don't you? But will she? I wonder what she'll make of her life!"

"I shouldn't worry about it, dear Sofia Alexandrovna. A beautiful girl like her shouldn't find it hard to get a good husband."

"I dare say she won't, but will she look for one? Besides, you know yourself, my dear, the kind of prospective husbands we have."

"You're quite right about that, dear. She may find it difficult to find the husband she deserves."

"You know, I'd like to advise her to go and see the dear anchorite. Lots of poor girls from the best families go to him for advice and every one of them finds him such a comfort. It is there, my dear, that she would discover the true spirit of meekness, for she really is much too proud."

Little Peterkin listened to that conversation. He was sitting in an arm-chair and he tried to remember everything Sofia Alexandrovna had said. The chief thing was that Sofia Alexandrovna was quite obviously plotting to deliver Mary to the anchorite and the anchorite was, of course, Kashchey, the immortal sorcerer! But he, Little Peterkin, would never let Kashchey seize Mary. When she came to-day, he would tell her everything. Never, never would he give up Mary to Kashchey, the terrible sorcerer who feared not death!

JUSTICE

Mother was always like that: she did not know how to enjoy herself. She invited all sorts of guests on the occasion of Mary's arrival and she asked Sofia Alexandrovna and her husband to come, too, without stopping to consider whether Maria Morevna would be pleased to meet the Mad Gentleman.

"Besides," Little Peterkin thought, "how am I to tell her of the plot about Kashchey in the presence of visitors?"

While he was thinking about it, somebody called out, "They're coming!" and he immediately rushed out of the house.

"Put on your overcoat!"

But it was too late. Little Peterkin rushed out into the snow without an overcoat or a hat and stood there waving and dancing about, shouting something at the top of his voice. Maria Morevna came out of the sledge and kissed him and he was just about to tell her everything just there on the steps, but he couldn't do it because they were already looking for him and because mother and Dunya had come out to welcome Mary. At home they wasted the whole day talking about all sorts of silly things and then everybody was busy with the preparations for the party in the evening, waiting for the arrival of the visitors, and now they were all sitting at the table. Mother was again laying out the cards and talking.

"What extraordinary changes take place, to be sure," she said. "I'm quite sure about it. He was an atheist, a real atheist."

"No, auntie," said Dunya, "not an atheist. The peasants are quite right: he's just the Mad Gentleman."

"But Alexander Mikhalych did not believe in God, dear. He used to boast about it everywhere and now suddenly . . ."

"How did it happen?" Mary asked.

"Oh, it's quite an extraordinary story, my dear! After the Czar's assassination he began to feel very queer, he even took to bed, his stomach began to show signs of serious excesses. . . ."

"Oh, auntie, you do talk so funnily!" Dunya laughed.

"I'm quite serious," replied mother. "She told me about it herself. You know what a cunning creature she is, don't you? Well, she at once took advantage of his condition and persuaded him to go for advice to that old anchorite of hers. He did and the reply he got was very laconic: 'Eat buckwheat porridge and salted cucumbers!' And what do you think? His troubles came to an end and he's as right as rain now and keeps on saying, 'The Church fasts are a marvellous institution!' "

"So he's a believer now, is he?"

"Well, it didn't happen all at once. After his visit to the monk some time passed without any change and then he suddenly became a very devout Christian: sells candles in the church and hands round the collection plate. Sofia Alexandrovna is beside herself with joy. They're quite inseparable now. You'll see for yourselves, both of them ought to be here soon. A very interesting case."

Dunya sighed and looked very unhappy: they had killed the Czar and another Czar immediately appeared and Dunya found things much worse. She had had to give up her illegal political work and she stood as usual in front of the stove and recited sombrely:

> A policeman with a moustache a mile long,
> And beside him there stands
> A pale gentleman you'd hardly call strong.

Mother could not bear to see anybody looking unhappy or suffering and living a life apart, so she threw a furtive glance at Dunya over her spectacles and asked shyly: "My dear, I just can't understand your point of view. Surely not all policemen are bad, are they?"

"Really, auntie!"

"But take our district police officer, Krapukhin, for instance. He put down horse-stealing in our district. Just think what it means to our peasants."

"But that's quite a different thing, auntie."

"Why is it different and how can you tell which is different and which isn't? A policeman, I suppose, does his duty like everybody else. Why is he worse than anybody else? What has he done to deserve your contempt? The Czar, too, was a nice man. He liberated the peasants and now he's been assassinated. How do you explain all that? Please explain it to me; I'm afraid I haven't had the same education as you."

"You're quite right," Mary said. "Every murder is a terrible thing. No one has a right to plot any murder and if a murder is committed, it is a terrible thing."

"Dear Mary," Dunya exclaimed, "how is it you can't see it? That was not murder!"

"What was it then?"

"That? That was justice!"

Mary wanted to say something, but all the dogs in the yard started barking at the same time and, as usual, somebody screamed as if bitten by a dog, "Visitors!"

"Auntie, darling, please let me go to my room," said Dunya. "I simply can't listen to him and keep quiet."

"No, no, Dunya dear, please stay. We shan't let anybody insult you. And, besides, we have such lovely mushroom pasties to-day and fried gudgeon. Lay the table, nanny!"

A DISCOVERY

It was the first time this had happened since Sofia Alexandrovna had become a regular visitor to their house: Sofia Alexandrovna came in arm-in-arm with her husband, Alexander Mikhalych. But that unusual event made everybody at the table feel very uncomfortable. The conversation flagged and mother went on calling impatiently in the direction of the kitchen door, "How soon will dinner be ready? Won't you start serving?" and again tried to engage her guests in conversation.

"Has your winter corn, Alexander Mikhalych, suffered very badly from blight?"

"Oh, nothing to worry about. We have the blight every autumn."

"Still this autumn the corn did look very wilted. Do you think it will recover in spring?"

"It depends on the kind of spring we have."

"I asked the dear anchorite about it," said Sofia Alexandrovna, "and he also said, 'Autumn rages, spring assuages.'"

"Does your monk know anything about it?" asked Mary.

"Why, of course he does, my dear. He knows everything. It's a gift. I wish you'd have heard the sort of questions our peasant women ask him—in what kind of dress they should get married, a pink one or a blue one, or what pig they're to keep, the white or the mottled one."

"But that's just silly!"

"Well, I don't know that it is, my dear. He says about himself, 'A monk is a dry stake round which the green hop twines. It's the task of the monk to provide a support for the hop.'"

"That's wonderful! What a wise man he must be. I merely asked because I wondered if he should be bothered with such silly questions. What does he tell them in reply?"

"He always says to them, 'Which do you prefer?' and gives them his blessing for whatever they wish themselves."

Maria Morevna's eyes suddenly sparkled and her eyebrows fluttered like the wings of a bird.

"You mean," she said, "that when they go to him for advice, their minds aren't made up, but on the way they seem to come to some decision themselves?"

"Naturally, my dear. It's quite simple, isn't it?"

"And he gives his blessing to whatever decision they have reached themselves on the way to him?"

"Yes, of course."

"So they really re-create the monk in their own hearts, don't they? How beautiful this is! I certainly should like to see him soon."

"If you like, you can go and see him to-morrow, my dear. I shall be able to let you have my carriage. Only do come early, if you can."

"That's done it," thought Little Peterkin. "Now everything's at an end! I shan't be able to tell her anything to-night and to-morrow she'll be leaving very early and Kashchey the Immortal Sorcerer will never let Maria Morevna out of his clutches. I simply must talk to her to-night and warn her not to go."

Full of such alarming thoughts, Little Peterkin began to roll a little bread-ball absent-mindedly between his thumb and forefinger and he thought it very funny that he should be seeing two balls where there was only one.

"Take your hands off the table, darling," said mother. "What are you doing with your fingers?"

"I'm rolling a bread-ball," said Little Peterkin. "Look, isn't it wonderful? It's only one ball really, but it looks like two!"

"How's that?" asked Alexander Mikhalych.

"Look, sir!" said Little Peterkin.

"Well, so it is!"

Everybody was very pleased that a pretext had been found for not going on with their conversation and everybody began to roll bread-balls.

"What a clever boy! Fancy making such a discovery!"

At the word "discovery" Little Peterkin felt as if he were in the seventh heaven, and how lovely it was to be there! "Why shouldn't I ask them now about everything?" he thought. "They're such nice people and even the Mad Gentleman is rolling a ball like a little boy!"

"I'll ask them!" Little Peterkin decided. "Perhaps that, too, will be a discovery!"

He was about to ask them why the Czar was not like other people and why he was born with a beard, and also about Ivan's secret, but mother anticipated him.

"I'm thinking of sowing the fourth field with clover or timothy grass," she said, "but I'd like to ask Dankevich's advice about it first."

"Well," said Alexander Mikhalych, "why not ask him? He had a model farm. He's just returned from St. Petersburg."

"Was he presented to the Czar?"

"Yes. I saw him yesterday and he seems simply delighted with the Czar. He found him such a charming man: 'A Russian face, a big beard.'"

Everybody was silent again. Dunya looked fixedly at her plate and mother felt embarrassed in her presence. Mary, too, felt uncomfortable for some reason. Little Peterkin decided to ask his question about the Czar. "I bet," he said to himself, "that will be another discovery." He felt as if some hook inside him had become undone and he asked in a loud voice, breaking the rather oppressive silence of the room, "The old Czar's killed and then another Czar is born with a beard—how's that?"

Well, that was how he made his second great discovery. Everybody in the room, including Dunya, burst out laughing and Alexander Mikhalych at length explained: "The Czar is born like everybody else and he grows up as a Crown Prince and then, when the Czar dies, the Crown Prince takes his place and becomes Czar."

"But if the Czar is born like everybody else," asked Little Peterkin, "then why do they kill him?"

A fierce look suddenly came into Alexander Mikhalych's face.

"You'd better ask your auntie about it," he said, looking at Dunya. "She knows much more about these things than I."

Dunya reddened and everybody in the room fell silent. The discovery didn't somehow seem to be a very happy one. But Little Peterkin was still in the seventh heaven and he wanted to go on making discoveries. He decided to ask about Ivan's secret.

"Did God create Adam out of the ground?"

"Yes, he did," said Alexander Mikhalych.

"And did He tell him to till the land?"

"He did."

"So why didn't He give him any land?"

"So that's the kind of a little fellow you are, is it?" Alexander Mikhalych said, looking rather surprised. "Did you think of it yourself?"

"No, I didn't," said Little Peterkin. "Ivan told me about it."

"Ivan told you about it, did he?"

"Yes, Ivan, and everybody says about Ivan that he's a second Alexander Mikhalych."

What happened then was what often happened to Little Peterkin in his dreams: he is walking on a glass floor of a huge room and there are lots of people on either side of him and suddenly the glass floor tilts up and—ugh!—down he goes head over heels and bump! wakes up.

The floor tilted up and Little Peterkin went sliding down. He saw his mother making signs to him with her black eyes and waving her white table napkin warningly at him and he heard Alexander Mikhalych saying to him, "It's a bit too early for you to carry on a conversation at table: you're still a very silly little boy!" All got up and thanked mother for dinner, while he was told sternly, "Go to bed!"

A GENTLE VISITOR

That night seemed to go on and on without ever coming to an end. Little Peterkin could not sleep and he kept on fancying that it was he who had touched something he shouldn't and Kashchey had slipped his chain and that now the Immortal Sorcerer would put his chain round everybody and that he, Little Peterkin, might as well say good-bye for ever to Maria Morevna. Mother's bedroom door was open. Little Peterkin could see a faint shaft of light there from the light before the icon and for a long time he could hear Dunya's sobs. Dunya and mother were talking to each other in whispers.

"They say in their letter," Dunya was saying, " 'You must drop your illegal political work now for an indefinite period.' That means that I shall have to go on living in this darkness far away from everybody."

"But why not live in town, dear?"

"There are lots like me in town."

"Well, don't cry now, there's a dear. You'll get used to it. You can't do anything else, can you? Look at me. I have to go on working for the bank and I'm quite alone."

"But you at least have been in love."

"Goodness, dear, who told you I'd ever been in love? They just married me off to him. Brought me out, put me on a green couch and the first thing I saw as I raised my eyes was a black beard. That was all."

"What happened afterwards?"

"Well, it took me a long time to get used to him, you know. You don't want anything of the kind to happen to you, do you? That isn't love."

"Don't say that. At least you have the children and I shan't even have that."

"But you can love the children of other people just as if they were your own, can't you?"

"I know I can, but it isn't the same thing, is it?"

"Poor, poor Dunya," Little Peterkin whispered, "Kashchey has got you all tangled up in his chain. But what am I to do? It was I who set Kashchey free. I must confess everything to Maria Morevna, I must tell her everything and then everything will be all right. I must certainly tell her about that terrible plot against her. But how am I to tell her that? Shall I steal into her bedroom, 'the little room,' and wake her up? She won't be cross with me. She's sure to understand everything. But how am I to get there through mummy's bedroom and then along the passage and how am I to keep awake until they are all asleep?

"I must keep awake! I must!" he decided and from that moment the night began to drag on and on for him without ever coming to an end.

Mother and Dunya kept on whispering to each other a long time.

Little Peterkin purposely did not shut his eyes. He saw himself walking in the snow and the snow was not white, but blue, and he came to a tree where he stood a long time. Jack Frost asked him, "Are you warm, Little Peterkin?" "I'm very warm, thank you," he replied, while a voice from somewhere said, "You must! You must!"

"Do you hear anything?" Dunya asked in the next room.

"He's crying, I think," mother said. "I'd better go and see. The children get so excited when visitors come. Whatever was the matter with him to-day?"

"Oh, it was awful! He's always alone, that's what's so bad. When children are alone there's always something strange about them."

"Are you asleep, darling?" mother asked softly.

Little Peterkin pretended to be asleep and he began to snore.

"He's asleep."

And then as always: a hand touched his forehead.

"I think he has a slight temperature. I suppose it's just nerves. Next time I must send him to bed earlier. Let's go to bed ourselves now. It must be very late."

While they were undressing and going to bed, Little Peterkin was trying hard not to fall asleep, but when everything grew still in the next room it seemed to him as if he were waving his arms in the air like wings and rising. He tried it again and he rose still higher, to the very ceiling of their parlour, then he began to fly round the ceiling, just like a fly. He told everybody about that new discovery of his and crowds of people came to see him fly, the whole yard was packed with people. He went out, waved his arms, took a flying leap and waved his arms again, but the earth held fast to his feet like a magnet and everybody in the yard burst out laughing and cursing: "Came to see a little boy fly? Aren't we fools?" But after they had all gone, he tried it again and he rose in the air and flew higher and higher. He felt so sorry he could not show them all his new discovery. Oh, wouldn't it be lovely, if everybody could fly like that?

"He's crying again. Do you hear?" said Dunya.

"I wonder if I oughtn't to give him a little bromide," mother said.

"Better wait. I think he's gone to sleep again."

Little Peterkin pretended to be asleep again and started snoring loudly, but he did not shut his eyes any more. Once again he saw the white forest glade with the sleeping beauty, Maria Morevna, lying under a pine tree. Ivan the Crown Prince went up to her and wanted to waken her, but he did not know how to do it without touching her and, to make sure that she did not get frightened, he stood there a long, long time and almost fell asleep himself near the sleeping princess. Suddenly there was a loud bang, as though a field gun had been fired: "I must! I must!"

Little Peterkin woke up, but he felt that what he intended doing was so difficult and almost impossible that perhaps the best thing for him to do was to fall asleep, for he was not sure that what he wanted to do had not passed like a bad dream and was no longer necessary. "You must! You must!" the words swam into his consciousness and he listened intently: everybody was asleep, he could even hear Nastya, their maid, snoring in the passage and a rat gnawing there, and in his room a cricket was chirping and it was dark, and in his mother's room there was the soft light of the icon lamp. He must go, he must! He felt cold in his night-shirt, but he could not waste any more time looking for his trousers in the darkness. He opened the door. A floor-board creaked under his feet. He crouched down and crawled between the two beds. Mother was asleep and Dunya, too, was asleep. There was the brass door-knob which nanny always rattled softly from the other side of the door when she wanted to waken mother. Little Peterkin now turned that door-knob himself.

"Is that you, nanny?" asked mother.

"I've got a tummy-ache," replied Little Peterkin. "What shall I do?"

It seemed to him that he had uttered those words in a loud voice, but actually he did not speak at all and mother had spoken in her sleep. He was in the passage now, so long and dark, where Nastya was snoring and the rat was gnawing the floor. There was the "little room" with a door-handle just like a brass pestle, but he was not afraid of making a noise now, for he wanted Maria Morevna to hear him and to ask him who it was. But she did not hear him; she was asleep. He opened the door and—everything was just as if he were seeing it in a dream: Sleeping Beauty lay on a white bed, her dark hair flung about on the pillow, a few strands even hanging down, and he, like Ivan the Crown Prince, was standing there, wishing terribly to waken her, but frightened of doing so: she might scream and waken the whole house and everything would be discovered and then what was he going to tell them? Ivan the Crown Prince stood there a long time, shivering in his night-shirt. "Shall I run back?" he asked himself. "You must! You must!" a voice prompted him sternly.

"Maria Morevna!" he whispered softly.

She opened one eye and closed it again.

"Maria Morevna!"

Again she opened one eye.

"Maria Morevna!"

She opened her other eye.

"Goodness, how long have I been asleep? Who is it? You, Little Peterkin?"

She looked strangely at him and he felt frightened. Ivan the Crown Prince was just about to say, "I've got a tummy-ache; what shall I do?" but again the voice prompted him, "You must! You must!"

The little visitor fell on his knees beside the bed, as if about to say, "Our Father."

"Please don't be cross with me, dear Maria Morevna!"

"What's the matter, darling?" Maria Morevna whispered. "Come to me, sweet. Lie down here on my bed. Well, tell me everything."

Little Peterkin told her about Kashchey the wicked sorcerer whom death could not touch and that there was a plot against her to send her to-morrow to the old monk who was really Kashchey and that he would never let Maria Morevna out of his clutches again. He told her everything, all the secrets he knew, even how he had learnt to fly in his dream and how he couldn't do it when people were about and how they had all laughed at him.

"Don't go to the old monk, please don't!"

Smiling happily and looking—so it seemed to the little boy—like that lovely picture of the beautiful lady with a baby in her arms, Maria Morevna said, "My little darling, you woke me up to tell me all that and I promise you faithfully that no one will ever take you away from me."

"So you won't go to the old monk to-morrow, will you?"

"Why should I go to him, darling, when I know myself what I must do?"

"You mean, you want to become a governess?"

"No, my sweet, I shan't become a governess. I shall be always with people like you, people who love me and who want me to be with them. I shall always go to such as you."

"I shall always love you," said Little Peterkin, "and I want to be with you always."

"And I'll never leave you, my darling."

It was then that Little Peterkin seemed to become conscious of somebody else standing in the room, someone who had entered the room like a gentle visitor.

"Who's that?"

"Who do you mean, darling?"

"Oh, I see. It's the Blue One."

"Oh, it's already getting light. Go to sleep now, darling."

"But why is it so blue outside?"

"It's always like this in spring. The snow looks very blue in the early morning."

"But I thought somebody came in here."

"Don't be afraid of anything, my darling, and don't fly in your sleep without me. One day I will teach you to fly properly and no one will ever laugh at you."

"Will everybody fly?"

"Yes, darling, everybody."

"But where will they fly to? To paradise?"

"No, of course not, darling. Paradise is much too near. They'll be flying much farther than paradise, to the countries beyond paradise."

"Where the blue beavers live?"

"Yes, where everything's blue."

The conqueror of all the terrors slept sweetly in Maria Morevna's white bed. The gentle visitor entered from the blue fields and the beautiful Sistine Lady carried the sweet child through the clouds. The visitor did not come alone. He brought with him from the blue fields all the fathers from Adam and they looked with new and eternal hope in their eyes. "Will not he, that little boy, the conqueror of all terrors, one day remove Kashchey's chain from them?"

STORIES OF GAMEKEEPER MIKHAL MIKHALYCH

THE TALKING ROOK

I'LL tell you of a curious case that happened to me in a year of famine. A yellow-billed young rook began to pay regular visits to my window ledge. The poor chap must have been left an orphan. It so happened that I had a whole sack of buckwheat meal and buckwheat porridge was the only food I tasted during all those days of great scarcity. Well, as soon as the little rook came flying to my window, I'd strew some buckwheat on the ledge and say,

"Want some porridge, you silly fool?"

He would peck the ledge clean and fly away. This went on for a whole month, day in, day out. What I wanted the rook to do when I asked him, "Want some porridge, you silly fool?" was to say, "Porridge." But all he did was to open his yellow beak and show me his red tongue.

"Oh, very well!" I got angry with him and stopped my lessons.

In the autumn I had a bit of bad luck. One morning I went to fetch some buckwheat meal from the chest and found nothing in it. Burglars, it seemed, had paid me a visit during the night and taken away every scrap of food I had. They had even helped themselves to half a cucumber I had left on a plate. That day I went to bed hungry and could not sleep a wink the whole night. In the morning I had a look at myself in the glass and—well, my face had gone all green.

Knock, knock! Somebody was knocking at the window.

My little rook was standing on the window ledge and hammering away with his beak at the pane.

"Well," I thought to myself, "here's some meat for my stewpot!"

I opened the window and tried to grab the rook, but he hopped away and flew into a tree. I climbed out of the window and went after him, but as soon as I reached the branch on which he was sitting, he flew higher. I went on climbing the tree from one branch to another, but the little beggar flew higher and higher until he reached the topmost branch where I could not follow him—it was too dangerous. But what do you think that rogue of a rook did then?

55

Why, he looked at me from above and said, "Want por-ridge, sil-ly fool?"

THE HEDGEHOG

Once as I was walking along the bank of our brook I saw a hedgehog under a bush. The hedgehog also saw me and he rolled up in a ball of spears and began to growl. His growling sounded just like a motor-car passing in the distance. I touched him gently with the toe of my boot; he gave a terrible snort and tried to pierce my boot with his needles.

"Oh, so that's the kind of fellow you are!" I said, and pushed him into the brook with the toe of my boot.

In the water the hedgehog immediately uncurled himself and swam to the bank like a little pig, except that instead of bristles he had needles on his back. I picked up a stick, rolled the hedgehog into my hat and took him home with me.

I had lots of mice at home and I was told that a hedgehog was a good mouser, so I decided to let him live with me and earn his keep by catching mice.

When I came home, I put down that prickly ball in the middle of the floor and sat down to write, watching the hedgehog all the time out of the corner of my eye. He did not lie there motionless long: no sooner had I grown quiet at the table than he uncurled himself, looked round, began to explore the whole room and in the end found a place he fancied under the bed and settled down there, as quiet as a mouse.

When it grew dark I lit the lamp and—hullo!—the hedgehog rushed out from under the bed. No doubt he mistook the lamp for the moon rising in the woods: hedgehogs are fond of running about in the glades in moonlight. My hedgehog, too, started running about the floor thinking it was a glade in a wood. I picked up my pipe, lit it and let a little cloud drift slowly across the moon. So everything was just like in a wood: there was a moon, and clouds, and my legs were like tree trunks and, indeed, my hedgehog seemed to have taken a great fancy to them, for he kept on darting about between them and smelling them and scratching the back of my boots with his needles.

When I finished reading my newspaper, I dropped it on the floor, went to bed and fell asleep.

I am a very light sleeper, and I was wakened by some rustling noise in my room. I struck a match, lit a candle and was just in time to catch a glimpse of the hedgehog disappearing under my bed. The newspaper was no longer near the table, but in the middle of the room. So I left the candle burning, while I myself kept awake, thinking, "What does a hedgehog want a newspaper for ?" Soon my lodger rushed out from under the bed and went straight to the newspaper, began fussing round it, making an awful row, and at last found a solution of the problem that was worrying him: somehow or other he managed to impale a corner of the newspaper on his needles and then he began to drag it, huge as it was, into a corner of the room.

Now I understood what he was about: the newspaper was to him just like dead leaves and he was dragging it to a corner to make himself a nest. And so it was: very soon the hedgehog got himself covered up entirely by the newspaper, making himself a real nest of it.

Having finished that important work, he left his house, darted to the bed and began to look at the moon-candle. I blew several clouds and asked, "What else do you want ?"

The hedgehog did not get frightened.

"Want a drink ?"

I got up. The hedgehog did not run away.

I took a saucer, put it on the floor, fetched a pail of water and kept on pouring the water from the pail into the saucer and then pouring it back from the saucer into the pail, making a noise like a stream running through a wood.

"Well, come on, come on," I said. "Can't you see, I made a moon for you and I blew clouds for you and now here's your water!"

I looked at him and it seemed to me as if he had moved a little nearer. So I, too, moved my lake a little nearer to him. He came forward a little and I moved the saucer a little nearer to him. So very soon we met.

"Drink!" said I to him finally.

He began to lap it up, while I stroked his needles very gently, saying every time I touched him, "You're a good fellow, a good fellow!"

When the hedgehog finished drinking, I said, "Now to bed, old man!"

So I went back to bed and blew out the candle. I couldn't tell how long I had been asleep, but when I woke up I heard some activity going on in my room again. I lit the candle—and what do you think ? I saw the hedgehog running about in the room with an apple stuck on his needles. He rushed to his nest, put it down there and ran off for another. I had a sack of apples in one corner of my room, propped up against the wall and now that sack had fallen over. As soon as the hedgehog reached the corner with the sack of apples, he curled himself up and began to jerk his body about this way and that until he succeeded in impaling an apple on his needles and then he immediately carried it off to his nest.

That was how the hedgehog came to live with me. Now every time I sit down to my tea, I put him on the table, pour some milk into a saucer for him and he drinks it, or else I give him a roll, and he eats it.

BIRDS UNDER THE SNOW

Snow offers two great advantages to the hazel-hen: the first advantage is that it is warm to spend the night under the snow and the second advantage is that the snow carries with it all kinds of seeds from the trees to the ground and on these the hazel-hen can feed. As it is always looking for seeds under the snow, the hazel-hen builds tunnels under it and little windows for fresh air. Sometimes when you go on a run through the woods on skis you suddenly see a little head popping up from under the snow and disappearing again: that was a hazel-hen.

As a matter of fact, the snow offers the hazel-hen not two, but three advantages, for under it the bird finds not only warmth and food, but also safety from the hawk.

The black grouse does not usually live under the snow: it resorts there only in bad weather. Neither has it any spacious runs under the snow like the hazel-hen, but his quarters there are also arranged very neatly: at the back is a lavatory and in the front a little hole for fresh air.

Our grey partridge does not like to bury itself in the snow and in the evening it usually flies off to the villages where it spends the night on the threshing floors. After spending the night with the peasants in the villages, the partridge flies away in the morning to its usual feeding grounds. According to my observations, the partridge has either lost its wildness or is not a clever bird by nature. The hawk notices the partridge's daily migrations from the woods to the villages and it often happens that when the partridge is just about to take wing, the hawk is calmly waiting for it in a tree.

I consider the black grouse a much cleverer bird than the partridge. Once the following incident happened to me in a wood:

It was a fine, sunny, frosty day and I was taking a run on my skis through the woods. I came to a large clearing with tall birch trees and on the birch trees black grouse were busy feeding on the buds. I stood there a long time enjoying that spectacle, when suddenly all the black grouse made a concerted dive into the snow and buried themselves under it, just beneath the birch trees. They had hardly time to disappear under the snow when a hawk swooped down on the same spot and began walking up and down over the heads of the black grouse. The amazing thing was that he did not seem to have enough sense to dig up the snow with his claws and get at his prey. I must confess I found it a fascinating sight. I kept on thinking to myself, "Surely, if he keeps on walking there, he must feel that they are under him! Not that a hawk is a silly bird, either. On the contrary, he is a very clever chap, but it seems he has not enough brains to realise that all he has to do is to dig up the snow an inch or at most two, which means, of course, that nature has not given him more."

Anyway, there he kept on marching up and down.

I made up my mind to come to the aid of the black grouse and I began to stalk the hawk. The snow was very soft, the skis made no noise. But no sooner did I start to skirt the glade round the underbrush than I fell through a juniper bush up to my neck in snow. In scrambling out of the snow I could not help making a noise and I thought to myself, "The hawk must have heard the noise and flown away." I scrambled out and was no longer even thinking of the hawk, but when I had gone round the whole glade and peeped out from behind a tree, there he was right in front of me, still on sentry-go over the heads of the black grouse. He was within easy shot. I fired and he fell. But the black grouse were so frightened of the hawk that not even the shot had made them leave their hiding place under the snow. I went up to them, cleared the snow away with my skis and, goodness! how they did start popping out from under the snow one after another, one after another! It was a sight to make anyone who had never seen it before gape open-mouthed in sheer amazement.

I have seen all sorts of astonishing sights in the woods during my life and I am not so easily surprised, but I cannot help being surprised at the hawk: such a clever bird, and yet here he showed himself an awful fool. But the biggest fool of all is, in my opinion, the partridge: It has got spoilt among the people on the threshing floors; it has not got the sense, like the black grouse, to dive into the snow at the sight of a hawk. All a partridge does when it catches sight of a hawk is to bury its head in the snow, leaving its tail sticking out of the snow for the whole world to see. The hawk gets hold of its tail and pulls it out, just like a cook pulling a bird out of a pot.

A MARTEN IN A HIVE

One day I went into the woods to cut down a bird-cherry to make myself a small tub. I found my bird-cherry in the thirty-first forestry area and next to it was a fir-tree. Round the fir-tree were scattered birds' bones and feathers, a squirrel's fur and bits of skin. I looked up and I saw a decoy hive on the tree and in the hive sat a marten with a little bird in her mouth.

It was summer, marten's fur in summer is cheap and I had no use for her.

"I take it, your ladyship, you live here with your family, don't you?"

At my words the marten darted into another tree and disappeared. I climbed up the fir-tree and examined the hive. It was then that the double-dyed villainy of the marten became as clear as day to me. The decoy hive had been put on the tree to catch wild bees and forgotten. A swarm of bees came, settled in the hive, stored up honey and, when winter came, went to sleep. Then the marten came and gnawed a hole in the bottom of the hive. The frost forced the bees to leave the honeycomb and settle in the top part of the hive, while at the bottom the marten ate up the honey at her leisure. When the frost got to the bees and killed them, the marten finished up the honey and left the hive. In summer a squirrel came and made itself a nest in the hive. In the autumn the squirrel dragged out all the moss from the hive, cleaned it up and settled in it for keeps. Then back came the marten, ate up the squirrel, settled down in the squirrel's nest like a lady and reared a family. And after the bees, the squirrel and the marten I came, found four young martens in the nest, put them in a bag, brought them home and placed them in the cellar. After two days a heavy smell rose from the cellar from the martens and the women in the house began pestering me to get rid of them. What with the smell of the martens and the fuss made by the women, I found it quite impossible to remain in my cottage and I decided to put my martens in a small shed in my garden. I stopped up all the holes and transferred the martens there.

All the summer I looked after them, shooting birds for them and watching them enjoying their food. Young martens have not got a vicious temper: they fight for every morsel of food all right, but they sleep curled up together.

One night thieves broke into my shed. I heard nothing, but next morning my neighbour came in and said, "Quick, Mikhalych, your martens are in an apple-tree!"

I ran out into the garden, but the martens darted from the apple-tree on to a pile of firewood and then across the yard into the wood. In that way I lost them all.

Winter came, the ground was covered with snow and I saw some tracks in the snow: my lost martens, it seemed, were living in a barn in the wood, quite close to the village. Three of them I shot shortly afterwards and sold their skins for twenty roubles each and the fourth one, I could only suppose, the thieves who had broken into my shed must have taken with them. Oh, well, one did not matter so much: after all, a thief, too, must live.

CONVERSATION OF BIRDS AND BEASTS

Hunting foxes with little flags is quite a fascinating sport. A wide circle is drawn round the fox, his earth is found, and along the bushes for about a mile or two round the sleeping fox a rope with coloured bunting is stretched. The fox is mortally afraid of the coloured flags and the smell of bunting and, when roused from his earth, he tries to find some way of escape from the terrible circle. Only one exit is left for him and near that place, under the cover of a tree, the hunter is waiting for him.

Such a fox-hunt with flags is much more profitable than hunting the fox with a pack of hounds. Besides, there were such heavy snowfalls this winter and the snow was so soft that a dog would fall through it up to its ears and to hunt the fox with hounds was quite out of the question. One day, having tired myself and my dog out, I said to the gamekeeper Mikhal Mikhalych, "Let's forget all about our dogs, let's try to catch a fox with flags, for any fox can be hunted down with flags."

"What do you mean by any fox?" asked Mikhal Mikhalych.

"Oh, surely what I mean is clear enough," I replied. "After the next snowfall, let's follow a fresh fox trail, walk round his earth, stretch a rope with flags in a wide circle and the fox is as good as ours!"

"I'm afraid," the gamekeeper replied, "that's not as easy as it sounds now. A long time ago you might have got your fox that way, for at that time a fox used to keep to his earth for three days without daring to run through the circle of flags. But why talk of foxes? Even wolves would not dare to come out of such a circle for two whole days. But to-day the beasts have become much wiser than they were before. Very often they simply run under the flags and you don't see them again."

"I grant you," said I, "that animals which have been in a tight corner and are old enough to know better have grown wiser and are no longer afraid of the flags, but there aren't many such animals about, most of them, particularly the young ones, never saw flags before!"

"Never saw them? Why, sometimes you place a trap and an old, clever animal comes near it, suspects something and—walks off. But the funny part of it is that afterwards no other animal will go near that place. How do you account for that? How do they know about it?"

"What do you make of it?"

"In my opinion," replied Mikhal Mikhalych, "animals can read."

"Read?"

"Why, yes. Read with their noses. You can see that with dogs, too. It's a well known fact that animals leave their own notices everywhere, on tree trunks, on mounds, on bushes. Those who come after them don't take long to decipher them. A fox, for instance, or a wolf always reads like that. We read with our eyes and they read with their noses. A crow flies and caws. It's nothing to us. What do we care? But the fox in the bushes pricks up his ears and rushes out into the fields. The crow flies above and caws and below, following the crow's call, the fox runs as fast as he can. The crow lights on some carrion and the fox is there in no time. But why talk of a fox? Have you never found the cry of a magpie of some service to you?"

Well, naturally, like every other sportsman, I had found the chatter of a magpie jolly useful at times, but Mikhal Mikhalych told me of a special case when a magpie had got him his hare. One day he was hot on the scent of a hare when suddenly his dogs got completely confused. The hare seemed to have sunk through the ground. Then a magpie started cawing in quite a different direction. The gamekeeper stole cautiously towards the magpie, trying his best not to be noticed by it. It happened in winter when all the hares had already grown their white coats, but the snow had melted during a thaw and a white hare could be seen a long way off on the ground. The hunter looked under the tree on which the magpie was cawing and there the white hare was crouching quietly on a patch of green moss, his eyes looking like two shiny black marbles. . . .

The magpie gave away the hare, but it also betrays a man to the hare and any other wild animal: it all depends who it sees first.

"You know," said Mikhal Mikhalych, "there's a little marsh bunting. Every time you go to a marsh after ducks, just as you begin to steal near them, that little yellow bird appears from nowhere, sits down quietly on a reed in front of you and, swaying on it, begins to chirrup. You go on and it flies to another reed, chirruping all the time. That is her signal to all the inhabitants of the marsh: the ducks take wing long before you are ready for them, the cranes fly away, flapping their wings, a wisp of snipe dash into the air, and it is that marsh bunting all the time, nobody but that little yellow bird. So in their different ways birds speak to each other, but the wild animals mostly read the tracks left on the ground."

The Treacherous Sausage

Yarik became very friendly with young Ryabchik and played about with him all day. He spent a whole week like that and then I took him away from town to a little cottage in a wood about six miles from Ryabchik. I had barely time to settle down in my new place and look round properly when quite suddenly Yarik disappeared. I spent a whole day looking for him everywhere, and I kept awake most of the night, stepping out on the little veranda every now and then to whistle for my lost dog. Next morning, as I was about to go back to town to inform the militia about the loss of my dog, my children arrived with Yarik who seemed to have been on a visit to Ryabchik. Now, I have nothing against friendship between dogs, but I could not possibly let Yarik leave my service without permission.

"That won't do," I said to him sternly. "That, my dear sir, isn't fair, running off without notice. You can't leave your master's service like that, sir. And, besides, you ran away without your muzzle and every man you met had a right to shoot you. You're a very naughty dog, sir!"

I said all that in a very stern voice and he looked very sorry for himself as he listened to me, lying on the grass with a guilty look in his eyes, not at all like Yarik, the proud, golden Irish setter, but like some reddish, insignificant, flattened-out tortoise.

"You won't go any more to Ryabchik, will you?" I asked him in a more kindly voice.

He jumped up and put his paws against my chest. That meant in his language, "Never again, dear master!"

"Stop pawing me, sir!" I said sternly.

So I forgave him. He rolled in the grass, shook himself and became the usual, good-tempered old Yarik.

But our friendly relations lasted only a short time, just one week, in fact, and then he again vanished somewhere. My children, who knew how worried I was about him, soon brought the runaway back: he had again been paying an illicit visit to Ryabchik. This time I did not waste any time talking to him, but straightway sent him to the dark cellar; and I told my children not to bother to bring him back next time, but just to let me know that Yarik was back in town. I further told them that if Yarik ran back to Ryabchik again, they were not to give him anything to eat. I wanted to make him come back of his own free will.

The adventurer spent a day in the dark cellar, then I had my usual heart-to-heart talk to him, after which I forgave him. The solitary confinement in the cellar kept Yarik away from Ryabchik only for a fortnight.   My children came running from town: "Yarik is with us," they said.

"All right," I said, "remember, you are not to give him any food. Let him get properly hungry and he'll come back by himself.   I'm going to prepare a fine welcome for him!"

A day passed.   Night came.   I lit the lamp, sat down on a divan and started to read a book.   Hundreds of moths and flying beetles, attracted by the light, began to circle round the lamp, dropped on my book, got entangled and buzzed in my hair, but I did not want to close the veranda door, for that was the only way through which Yarik, whose arrival I was expecting, could enter the house.   I did not really mind the moths and beetles, the story I was reading was very thrilling and the gentle breeze which came from the woods rustled pleasantly in the trees.   I read my book and listened to the music of the woods at one and the same time.   Suddenly I noticed something out of the corner of my eye.   I raised my head quickly, but whatever it was vanished even more quickly.   I now tried to read my book so that I could see the door without having to raise my head.   Soon I caught a glimpse of some reddish creature at the open door.   In the twinkling of an eye Yarik stole round the table and, I am sure, a mouse would have made more noise in darting across the room than that large dog did in crawling under the divan.   Only the familiar breathing told me that Yarik was not only under the divan, but was just under where I sat.   I went on reading for a while, waiting for Yarik to announce his presence, but my patience soon gave out.

I got up, went out on the veranda and started to call Yarik in a stern voice, then I began to whistle for him, loud and then soft, and I even blew an imaginary horn for him.   In this way I wished to assure the dog under the divan that I suspected nothing of his return.

Then I closed the door to keep out the moths and said aloud, "Well, I don't suppose Yarik will come back to-night.   It's about time I had my supper."

Yarik knew the word "supper" very well, but it seemed to me that after my words he even stopped breathing under the divan.

In a drawer of my hunting-table I always kept a supply of smoked sausage, a delicacy that becomes more and more palatable the longer it is kept and the drier it gets.   I am very fond of dry hunting-sausage and I always share it with Yarik.   Sometimes I had only to pull open the drawer for Yarik, who had been asleep curled up on the floor, to unroll himself like a steel spring and run to the table, a fiery glint in his eye.

I pulled out my drawer: not a sound from under the divan.

I parted my knees, looked down to see if there were not a reddish nose on the floor, but no! there was nothing there. I cut off a piece of the sausage, chewed it noisily, looked down again—no! no tail was wagging there. I was beginning to be afraid that I had imagined the reddish apparition because I was so eager to see it and that there was no Yarik under the divan. I could hardly believe that he, guilty though he was, should not be tempted even by the sausage of which he was so fond. Why, it was quite sufficient sometimes for me to take a piece of it, cut it up, tear the skin off so that I could hold it by one end with a finger, leaving a little piece of it hanging down as if on a thread, for Yarik to raise his nose, watch it a long time and then suddenly jump up. And that was not all by any means: if I was quick enough to raise my hand before he had snapped up the sausage, Yarik would remain standing on his hind legs like a man. I used to take a walk round the room with the bit of sausage in my hand and Yarik would follow me on his hind legs, his fore-paws drooping like hands and so we would walk round the room once or twice or even several times. Why, I had even considered the idea of teaching Yarik to walk like a man with the help of the sausage and to take a walk in our public park one day arm-in-arm with my reddish canine friend.

So knowing how much Yarik loved that sausage, I could not help thinking that it was hardly likely that he was under the divan. I therefore made my last experiment. I threw on the floor not a piece of the sausage, but just a bit of its skin, and waited to see what would happen. But however much I looked, I could not see any-thing: the skin seemed to vanish as if by magic. Next time, though, I did succeed in seeing something: I caught a glimpse of a disappearing tongue.

Yarik was there all right: under the divan!

Now I cut off the sharp, pointed end of the sausage, tied a thread to it and let it drop quietly between my knees. The tongue shot out, I pulled up the thread and the tongue disappeared. There was no more any need to go on playing hide and seek: I saw him and he saw me. I raised the piece of sausage higher, Yarik raised himself on his hind legs, followed me, walking like a man on two legs, to the veranda, came down the steps on all fours like a dog, raised himself again on two legs, and so we came to the cellar. It was only then that the poor dog understood my terrible intention and lay down flat on the ground like a tortoise. But I opened the trap-door to the cellar and said, "Down you go, young man!"

A POINTER PUPPY

The name of my pointer puppy is Romul, but I usually call him

C

Roma, or simply Romka, and occasionally more grandly Roman Vassilyich.

Romka's paws and ears seem to grow more quickly than any part of his body. He has grown such long ears that every time he looks down, they cover up his eyes, and his legs are so huge compared with the rest of his body that he cannot help getting in the way of things and tumbling head over heels.

To-day this sort of thing happened: coming up the stone steps from the cellar, he brushed against half a brick with one of his big paws and the brick rolled down the steps, counting each step on its way, until it came to rest at the bottom. The puppy followed the progress of the brick down the steps with great surprise. He remained a long time on the top of the steps, his long ears trailing over his eyes, looking down the steps and turning his head now one side and now another, to get one of his ears out of his eyes so that he could watch the brick at the bottom of the steps.

"Goodness gracious me, what a wonder, Roman Vassilyich!" said I. "Fancy a brick jumping about as if it were alive!"

Roma glanced at me with a clever twinkle in his eyes.

"Don't you look at me like that, old man," said I, "and don't go woolgathering like that, either, or he'll pluck up courage, come jumping up the steps and punch you on the nose!"

Roma shifted his glance. I expect he wanted very badly to run down and see for himself why a dead brick should come to life suddenly and start rolling down the steps.

"Well, sir," I asked, "what are you going to do now? Not run away, by any chance?"

Roma just glanced at me for a second, and I understood him perfectly. What he wished to say to me was, "Of course I don't intend to run away, but what if he catches me by the tail when I turn round?"

So that, too, seemed impossible and Roma remained standing at the top of the steps for a long time, and that was the first time he came to a point for a dead brick, just as dogs do when they find game in the grass.

The longer Romka stood there, the more perilous did his position appear to him and the more scared did he grow; for to a dog an enemy that feigns death more realistically than is possible will be more terrible when he suddenly comes back to life and springs to attack.

"I'll outstand him," said Romka to himself.

And it seemed to him that the brick, in reply, whispered, "I'll outlie him."

But a brick can lie in one place for a hundred years without the slightest discomfort, while a live puppy finds it difficult to stand motionless even for as many seconds. Romka soon got tired and began to tremble in every limb.

I asked him, "Well, what are you going to do about it, Roman Vassilyich?"

Romka replied in his own way, "Shall I yap?"

"By all means," said I, "yap to your heart's content!"

Romka barked and jumped back. I suppose, in his fright, it seemed to him that he had wakened the brick and that the brick had made a slight movement. He stood still, watching the brick from a safe distance: no! the brick did not even dream of crawling up the steps. So Romka stole back to the top of the stone steps and looked down apprehensively: it was still lying there.

"Shall I yap again?"

He yapped and sprang back.

Kate, Romka's mother, came running across the yard in reply to her puppy's yapping. She stopped beside Romka, eyed the brick critically and began to go down the steps slowly, one step at a time. By that time, of course, Romka stopped barking, leaving everything to his mother, and just looked down: he felt much safer now.

Kate recognised the cause of Romka's alarm by the scent of the puppy's paw on the brick. She sniffed it all round: the brick was as dead as a doornail and, needless to say, quite harmless. Then, just in case, she sniffed everything round the brick, taking her time over it, and finding nothing suspicious she raised her head and said to her son with her eyes, "I'm pretty sure, Roma, there's nothing wrong here."

After that Romul quietened down and began to wag his tail. Kate walked leisurely up the steps. Romka overtook his mother and pulled her ear.

KATIE'S IN THE 'TATERS

We did not hire a herdsman in our village until last year. The task of minding our pigs, sheep, cows and horses was left to the village children, while old Grandpa Mikhey sat on a little hill, plaiting bast shoes and minding the children, seeing that they did not play about and did their work conscientiously as good children should.

Now Grandpa Mikhey was very old and it often happened that while his hands went on pulling at the thin strips of bast, his wits went a-birds-nesting and he would not notice that the children were up a tree, looking for Moscow. When old Grandpa Mikhey came back to life with a start and looked to see where the children were, they

were all up a tree. He looked to see where the sheep were, and
the sheep were all scattered among the growing oats. The horses
were afloat in the rye as in the sea, the cows were in the hayfields and
the pigs were all busy digging up the potatoes with their snouts on
grandpa's own potato patch. So the naughty children would catch
it good and proper. They were lucky if they were in time to jump
down the tree and run as fast as they could in different directions.
Woe to him who was too slow, for he would fall straight into Grandpa
Mikhey's shaggy paws.

One day our shepherds thought of this sort of game. There is a
lovely little flower, the daisy, which has a little sun in the middle
and lots of white rays all round its little yellow sun. By tearing off
all but one of those rays, the children got a priest with one pigtail, if
two rays were left—a priest with two pigtails, three—with three
pigtails, as many priests could be made, as there were children to
play the game, only one priest being left with no pigtail, and that
priest was known as the bald-headed one. Having got all the priests
for the game, the girls and boys dug little holes in the meadow, as
many little holes as there were children, each hole representing a
trunk, and each trunk had its own bit of turf to represent its lid.
After every girl and boy had dug his or her trunk, they chose one of
them as leader and gave him all their priests. It was then the leader's
task to put the priests in the trunks, without, of course, letting anybody
see which priest got into which trunk—that had now to be guessed.
Every girl and boy whose turn it was to guess had a little crooked
stick. Now, suppose my priest with one pigtail lay in the second
trunk. If I guessed right, I hung the hook on the first branch of a
tree, but if I was wrong I kept the stick until I guessed right. If
I guessed right a second time, I hung my stick on the second branch
of the tree, and so on; the higher I got up the tree, the nearer I was to
Moscow. The lucky one got higher and higher up the tree and in
that way journeyed to Moscow faster than the rest, who, of course,
also journeyed to Moscow, some faster, some more slowly.

This time the first to start on his journey to Moscow was a boy by
the name of Antosha Komar and the last one was a girl by the name
of Rybka. However, soon their luck changed: Rybka was on top and
Komar remained at the bottom.

So on they journeyed to Moscow until, at last, Rybka shouted from
the topmost branch of the tree, "Moscow!"

Farther nobody could possibly journey, for there were no more
branches on the tree.

Meanwhile old Grandpa Mikhey's wits had wandered off goodness
knows where. There he sat dreaming on the little hill and he did not

see the children journeying to Moscow on the tree, while the largest sow, Katie, all black except for a white ring round her middle, went off to old grandpa's potato patch and started to dig it up. That sow Katie was a very wicked old sow and as soon as she wandered off, all the other pigs wandered off after her, and so did the horses, and the cows, and the sheep. Rybka was the first to notice it from the top of the tree and she yelled, "Quick, let's climb down, Katie's in the 'taters!"

So all the children at once climbed down the tree and got Katie out of old grandpa's potato patch back to where she belonged. Then they began to punish the sow in the way naughty pigs are usually punished: they put Katie with her face to the stream and one of the boys or girls sat down on her back, while somebody hit her from behind with a twig, the pig being supposed to give the boy or girl a ride on her back to the bank of the stream. They put Katie with her face to the stream so that she should not run any farther, otherwise no one could tell where she would take the little rider on her back.

Rybka, having been the first to get to Moscow, ought to have had the first ride. Besides, had she not been the first to notice that Katie was on grandpa's potato patch? But all the children had had their rides and poor old Katie was quite out of breath with so much running about, while Rybka was still waiting for her turn to have a ride on the sow's back.

Poor old Katie! She looked so tired out that it seemed unlikely that she would be able to run another race and old Grandpa Mikhey, funny old chap, did not see a thing, dreaming of his past life, poor fellow. Rybka, however, made up her mind to have her ride, come what may, and she climbed on the back of the sow and sat down with her bare legs dangling at either side of Katie.

It was just then that Antosha Komar, the boy who was the first to start on his journey to Moscow, but arrived there last, played a dirty trick on Rybka. It was Komar, of course, who was to blame for everything that happened.

Pigs are awfully sensitive about their tails: if a fly alights on a pig's tail, the pig immediately hides it between his legs. Well, knowing that, what did Komar do but put a piece of rolled-up bark on Katie's tail and, making sure that it had stuck firmly on it, give it a big pull at the end! Katie, of course, ran off as fast as her four fat legs would carry her, and feeling the rolled-up bark sticking to her tail, she took it into her head that it was the bark that was hurting her and the minute she reached the bank of the stream, just opposite a big whirlpool, in she went—plop straight in the middle of the whirlpool with Rybka on her back, and there she disappeared. "Plop!"—into the water.

"Ugh!" gasped the little shepherd boys and girls.

All that could be seen on the surface of the water were rings and round the spreading rings the little piece of rolled-up bark was floating.

Old Grandpa Mikhey was still plaiting his bast shoes; the poor old chap saw nothing, heard nothing, his mind still lingering among his memories.

The children were struck dumb with fright. They stood on the bank of the stream without moving, staring at the terrible place where the little piece of rolled-up bark was still floating. Suddenly bubbles appeared on the surface of the water, then a whole fountain spurted up, then the penny-shaped nose of Katie emerged, then her ears with little hands clutching desperately at them and after that her back and on her back was Rybka.

All the girls and boys cheered for joy.

They all thought that when the sow swam to the bank, Rybka would jump off, but the immersion in the whirlpool seemed to have added to Katie's strength and no sooner did she jump out of the water than off she streaked into the woods. Rybka had no time to jump off and she vanished in the forest together with Katie.

People say that our forest stretches for over a hundred miles, but those who say that cannot count more than a hundred. Our forest is much, much bigger than that, and there are all sorts of wild beasts in it, hundreds and hundreds of them: wolves, bears, lynxes and goodness knows what else. And it was in that big forest that Katie had taken Rybka for a ride!

The little girl disappeared in the dark wood and it was only then that old Grandpa Mikhey raised his old grey head from the bast shoes. . . . He looked and, poor old fellow, nearly fainted: all the village pigs were busy digging up his potato patch, the sheep had trodden down half an acre of oats, the horses had run into the rye to escape from the horse-flies: the rye was very high and all one could see was the horses' heads.

Grandpa Mikhey ran as fast as his old legs would carry him to the children, who stood crowded in one place, staring into the wood on the other side of the stream.

Grandpa gaped speechlessly.

"What's the matter with you ?   Got no eyes ?"

But the children still went on staring into the wood, as if they did not hear him at all. It was only then that grandpa noticed that Rybka was not among the children and he asked, "Where's Rybka ?"

The children were silent: they were afraid to tell him what had happened to Rybka, for the little girl was old Mikhey's granddaughter.

So old Grandpa Mikhey picked up a big stick and went straight for Komar, and Komar told him everything except that it was he who had put the rolled-up piece of bark round Katie's tail and given it such a pull that it hurt the sow terribly.

Grandpa did not waste any more time and ran quickly to the village where he collected a search party. All the peasants left their work and rushed into the fields to save the rye, the oats and the potatoes and when they had done that, they lost no time in getting to the other side of the stream and they scattered in all directions in the forest. They kept up the search for Rybka all through the night and it was only after the sun had risen high in the sky that Uncle Mitrofan raised a halloo for all of them to come to him. Uncle Mitrofan had noticed a child's white frock on a bush and, glancing under it, he saw little Rybka, who had taken off all her clothes and covered herself up with moss and was now having a nice sleep. Oh, what a clever little housewife that Rybka was! She had hung up her frock on a bush to dry and during the night it had dried beautifully.

The whole search party gathered round the bush, attracted by Uncle Mitrofan's cries, and all of them went back happily to the village. One thing, however, they were very sorry about: poor old Katie seemed to have been eaten up by a wolf. But there they were mistaken, for as it happened the sow was safe and sound and had run back from the forest to her mistress during the night.

It was decided at a village meeting the same day that our village, like every other village, should have a herdsman of its own and that the children should be relieved of the hard task of minding the pigs, the sheep, the cows and the horses. One task, though, was still reserved for the children: they had to look after the geese. But the geese spent the whole day in the stream, it was easy to look after *them*. So now our children go on their journey to Moscow without any fear of an accident.

ERUDITE HARES

We have hundreds of sportsmen in our town who go hunting hares with hounds. From the very first day of the opening of the hare-hunting season the hare is given no respite, so that in a month's time when the real fun of the chase starts, along the footpaths in our woods where the trees are still covered with yellow leaves and the paths are still free from snow, not a hare can be found within miles of our town. After the first snowfall, however, the print of the hare's pad can be seen everywhere on the snow, and it really seems as if the white hares have come tumbling down with the flakes of snow from the clouds. Now I am going to tell you where they really come from.

Only one in ten of our sportsmen possesses a well-trained hound which, having picked up a hare's scent, will follow it to the bitter end; the other nine are either busy training their young hounds or have to put up with stupid hounds all their lives. While the hounds are being trained, the hares are not wasting their time, either, being busy undergoing an intensive refresher course in deceit. I shall never forget one case which sticks in my mind as an example of the utter guilelessness of the first young hares which run in regular circles straight where the hunter is lying in wait for them. Once a friend from Moscow came to stay with me and he asked me to show him how to lie in wait for a white hare. I pointed out a hare's footprint to my friend and told him to wait there. Laughing up my sleeve, I left him there, convinced that he had not a chance of ever killing a hare, But after a few minutes I heard a shot, followed by a shout of triumph: the hare was killed just on the spot I had pointed out. Those first young hares are just silly! But little by little they learn such tricks that they make both hound and sportsman look silly. That is why hunting the white hare is such good sport; for each hare works out his own plan of flight and it is not always easy to uncover it. The hares learn how to screen themselves from observation after their nightly feed and that is why it looks as if all the hares had disappeared at the end of the autumn and why they seem to come tumbling out of the sky after the first snowfall.

When the pad of the hare appears on the virgin snow, all the sportsmen leave the towns and, young and old, go hare-hunting. This is the most fearful examination the hares have to pass and afterwards only the graduates remain in the woods. That is why all our sportsmen always refer to them by that name: "Hare-Scholars."

I have long had a great weakness for the erudite hare and I only begin hunting with hounds when all the other sportsmen have given up the chase and only the hare-scholars are left in the woods. All day long, from dawn to dusk, I never tire of following one trail after another, always keeping pace with my hound, or lying in wait for hours in the thick fir underbrush of a swamp. I can't possibly tell all my adventures with the erudite hares during the past fifteen years, for one case calls up thousands of others in my memory and is irretrievably lost among them. But one very difficult year when all the "scholars" had gathered in one swamp stands out in my memory apart from the rest and I shall tell you about it.

That year the "scholars" had learnt the trick of running along a straight line as soon as roused for about three miles and then running in circles in one large swamp which was overgrown with dense fir brushwood. The hound experienced the greatest difficulty in creeping through the thickets, while the hare—hop, hop!—just went jumping from mound to mound quite calmly, sitting down to listen for a minute and then hopping off again and then again crouching down behind a mound. By the time the hound got anywhere near him, by the time it could make up its mind what to do next, the hare would have had a good rest, then off he'd go again, hop, hop! all over the swamp.

However, I was not going to give up so easily and I just carried on after him through the most impassable thickets. But it was impossible to stand in that swamp for long in one place. During the first frosts it became covered with a sheet of ice and the water under the ice had sunk, leaving a thin crust of ice: the hare and the hound could run over it without falling through, but every time I stepped on it, I fell through. Thus it stayed until the hard frosts when the swamp was covered with snow. Such a thin crust of ice is one of the most difficult things during a chase: it breaks with a terrific crack and, besides, how long is it possible to stand in icy water in leather topboots?

I did my best, but every time the "scholars" scampered off to that swamp where on account of that thin layer of ice I could not follow them. I was almost on the point of giving it up altogether when one day Vasska Tomilin came to see me and began insisting that I should go hunting the hare with him. My friendship with Vasska went back to the time when he had my Karay and my own dog Anchar had been killed during a hunt. Vasska very generously came to my assistance at the time and the two of us went out hunting with Karay. Later Karay died and Vasska persuaded me to make him a present of my Solovey. Now out of respect for Karay's memory I could not refuse Vasska's request and off we went to hunt the "scholars," Vasska in his ordinary felt boots and I in my topboots. Incidentally, Vasska's felt boots were rather famous: he wore them in winter as well as in summer and he even went out fishing in them so that his feet should not be cut on the sharp stones on the bottom of the stream, and when one sole wore out, he sewed on another and so *ad infinitum*: a most economical footwear.

Well, so off we went after the "scholars," got on their trail, let Solovey follow it, roused them almost immediately and drove them into the swamp. What were we to do now? I kept on walking round and round the edge of the swamp. An hour passed, two hours, three. . . . There was quite a sharp frost at the time, my feet began to freeze even on dry land and it was quite hopeless to attempt to walk over the thin crust of ice, for I was sure to fall through. There was the further difficulty that it was quite impossible to call Solovey back until a hare had been shot and we could not go away and leave the hound behind, for the wolves were quite certain to get him if we did. In the end I got so frozen that I began to break off twigs to light a camp-fire. I stopped even thinking about the hares: what chance was there of catching a hare! Suddenly a shot rang out in the very heart of the fir thicket and the ice-covered swamp, followed by a cry, "Hop-hop!" which in our language meant that a hare had been shot.

Solovey soon got the hare and stopped barking. There could be no doubt that a hare had been killed, but how had it happened? That remained a complete mystery to me. The thin ice over the swamp broke with a thunderous crash and if one wanted to lie in wait for a hare, one simply must not stir. Vasska was wearing felt boots and the question was how on earth he could stand in icy water in felt boots for any length of time?

I heard him coming a long way off, creating a frightful racket as he crept through the fir underbrush in reply to my call. I took one look at him after he had crawled out of the thicket and just gasped: his legs were legs no more, but big columns of ice.

"Take them off quickly," said I, "and warm your legs by the fire."

"Thank you," said he, "but I'm not cold and my feet are quite dry."

And, to be sure, he took a leg out of that column of ice and it was bone dry. I put my hand into the felt boot and could feel the warmth inside.

Then it dawned on me that in the keen frost the felt boots were covered by a crust of ice immediately they got wet and as the ice did not melt in the icy water, it did not let any water through.

I could not help expressing my astonishment, but Vasska just said, "I always do that."

So from that time I, too, began to dip my felt boots into water at night and put them out in the frost, then after another dip, I'd leave them in the passage for the night. Next morning they were covered by a solid crust of ice and I would walk off in them to the swamp.

So it was that Vasska had outwitted the most erudite hares and become professor-in-chief over them.

A DOUBLE TRAIL

Anyone seeing the black grouse for the first time will hardly believe that the cock and the hen belong to the same family. The hen looks just like a little grey hen, while the cock has blue-black plumage, large vermilion wattles over his eyes, a lyre-shaped tail and, beneath the lyre, an under-tail as white as snow.

Their family life is nothing to boast about. The cocks spend all the spring in fights in some open space and after that they are rather off colour for a time, some from the punishment they have received during the fights and others from moulting. Having lost a large quantity of their feathers, they get very timid and spend the summer in inaccessible thickets in the woods. The whole worry of hatching, rearing and guarding their fledglings falls upon the grey hen. But how she treasures her fledglings because of that! She becomes quite fearless when she has to defend her young brood. But the laws of sport take special care of the grey hens and it is strictly forbidden to kill them.

One day I was very unlucky when out shooting. I was ashamed to come back home without any game and, on top of that, not only meat, but also bread was very scarce in the village just then: we had to feed on what we shot. As I was getting near my village, I remembered that not far away from it, in a fir and juniper spinney, I had often flushed an old black grouse and that in the same spinney there also lived a grey hen with a young cock of quite a decent size.

I should have preferred to kill the old black grouse: his meat, to be sure, was not as palatable as the meat of a young bird, but, on the other hand, there was more of it.

The moment I unleashed my dog, she picked up a strong scent in some cranberry-bushes, then she raised her head and inhaled the air. Her nostrils twitched, her eyes sparkled. I guessed at once that the cock was somewhere about. Then my dog lowered herself on her hind legs, becoming very small, and stepping stealthily on her paws, led me straight to the cock. We had only to walk a short distance. Kent froze in her tracks near a bush and bent one of her forelegs, wishing to tell me by that gesture: "He's here!"

The black grouse is far from being a silly bird. Hearing the approach of a dog, it often runs to the other side of the bush and flies out of it there: the sportsman cannot shoot it there because he cannot see behind the bush and all he hears is a whirr of wings as the bird flies away. But I know that habit of theirs and when my dog comes to a point, I walk quietly round the bush, so that my dog stands on one side of it and I on the other with my gun raised, while the black grouse is between us.

I walked round the bush and raised my gun. Then I said softly to Kent, invisible to me on the other side of the bush, "Go on, Kantaria!"

The word Kantaria is quite meaningless and I don't know myself how it originated from Kent's name, for Kent itself is really a derivation from Kate and Kate comes from Kitty, the name her first master gave her. He was not a sportsman and he did not appreciate the fact that it was impossible to shout out a name which only had the short "i" sound in it. I, therefore, substituted the vowel "a" for "i" and her name became Kate and Kate, somehow or other, grew into Kent, while at moments when something much grander was required, when the dog had to be encouraged and entreated to make a move, it became Kantaria. But now even the grand name Kantaria failed to do the trick, for the dog refused to move, but just stood there trembling, and for some unknown reason when I called her again her name was changed into Funtaria. This time when I commanded, "Go on!" she just stepped from one foot to another and showed herself to me through the bush.

"Kentaria!"

She again shifted from one foot to another and once more became motionless.

"Funtaria!"

Now she just went straight through the bush and we met. There was therefore no cock between us.

"Where is he?" I asked.

She, looking as puzzled as I, seemed to ask me the same question, "Where is he?"

She was so dumbfounded that she just kept on looking at me, refusing to leave me.

"You silly girl," I said, "you don't think I've got him in my pocket, do you? He made fools of us, that's what he did, my dear girl! Go on, look for him!"

She twitched her nostrils and, suddenly, got it! While I was walking round the bush, the bird rushed out, crossed the glade and hid itself in some juniper bushes.

So we resumed the hunt. In front of us, somewhere in the juniper bushes the black grouse was hiding. He did not want to take wing because he was moulting and he did not have sufficient confidence in the strength of his wings. He probably said to himself, "With a pair of wings like that, I shall get entangled in the bushes and then the fox will be upon me in less than no time!"

For the bird, no doubt, thought Kent was a fox.

He was a fast runner, though, and if he started running at full speed, we should never be able to overtake him. But he was afraid that if he began to run fast, the long grass would begin to stir and that that would betray him. I had on many occasions watched a black grouse run: he'd run a little, then stop and look round and listen, and then set off again. . . .

Kent followed him, neither lagging too far behind, nor pressing too close on his heels. She could scent him in the air: when he stopped, she stopped, and when he resumed his run, she went after him.

"Will it never end?" I thought to myself, my heart in my mouth, trying to walk as softly as possible behind Kent.

For he was liable to take wing any moment and I had to be ready to level my gun and shoot at any dark spot that might appear for only a fraction of a second in the bush. The suspense was getting so great that it seemed to me that we were not hunting a black grouse, but some enormous wild animal, such as an auroch or an elephant.

But at last the juniper bushes came to an end. Behind it was a swampy clearing overgrown with high carex-sedge. He had to fly out of the bush any moment now, but would he venture out on the marsh where the movement of the tall sedge would betray him? I levelled my gun, but Kent ran straight into the sedge.

So the black grouse seemed to have decided to cut across the marsh through the tall sedge, hoping, no doubt, to reach the safety of the large wood beyond. I could even see his "run" on the grass: a recent drizzle of rain had made the sedge look quite grey, but a green strip could be seen where the bird had passed—that was where he had shaken off the raindrops.

It often happens that in moments of great suspense when you are, say, about to pull the trigger, you see two sights on your gun: you begin to see double. So it happened now. I must have begun to see double, for I could distinctly see two "runs" on the grass. Another thing I saw was a beautiful new belt with a clasp lying on the grass in a circle. Any other time I should have been very glad to pick up a belt somebody had dropped, but now I just glanced at it from the corner of my eye and instantly forgot all about it. It is only now when I am telling about it that I remember about the belt. The "run" continued in a double line up to the very edge of the wood.

I had no time to make up my mind whether I was seeing double or whether there really was a double trail on the grass or how one bird could have left a double trail behind it. I was running fast now and I purposely made a great noise hoping that the fleeing black grouse would get frightened and take wing and that I should then be able to aim at him while he was still close to the ground. But all was of no avail: the bird reached the wood and disappeared in it. My manœuvre, though, succeeded all the same, for the bird did get frightened and stopped in the first alder-bush, thinking it its last refuge. Kent came to a point, her eyes burning: the black grouse was there!

I walked round the bush. I could just see Kent standing opposite me: the black grouse was between us, he was here!

"Go on, Kent!"

The dog did not move.

"Go on, Kantaria!"

Still she did not move.

"Go on, Funtaria!"

Kent turned her eyes slowly to the right, her nose following her eyes. Was it possible that the bird would dare to run out at the side of the bush, right under our eyes? No. No black grouse would do such a thing. Now Kent moved her head again, back to its original position.

"He's here!"

In cases like that my dog was never wrong. Why didn't I say again "go on!" at that moment? I was too slow and Kent again moved her nose to the right, again asked me with her eyes what she was to do. Her eyes, bloodshot from the strain of the chase, again moved to the right as she shifted from one paw to another.

What a fool I was not to have got her meaning earlier? Why, she was telling me plainly enough: "He is here, but *that* is moving about and I must go after it, for *that* is more important. since it is moving about, while the bird in the bush is sitting down and won't run away from us, but *that* will be gone soon."

I failed to get her meaning earlier, I did not even remember that the trail on the grass was a double one.

We did not have to go far. Kent came to a point and I went round the bush. This time Kent pressed forward at the first word of command and then the bird flew out of the bush with a loud cry and whir of wings: but it was not the black grouse, it was the grey hen.

Her grey feathers would not have saved her, for I would have had no time to control the automatic movement of my hand, but her cry reached me in time to make me realise that it was not a cock, but a hen, which it was forbidden to shoot.

Her cry, however, was not a cry of terror, but the cry of triumph of a mother rejoicing at having saved her young. It was also a signal, for it was followed by a whir of wings over the alder-bush where we had stood waiting such a long time: that was the young cock who had been saved by his mother and who was now beyond the reach of my gun.

Everything then became clear to me. From the very beginning I had been stalking the grey hen and her fledgling and not the black grouse at all. Nor had I been seeing double from excitement, but there really was a double trail made by two birds. They were together in that alder-bush: mother and son. At the last moment the mother took a risk and rushed out of the bush under my very eyes and the eyes of my dog, her intention being to entice the dog away from the young bird and force Kent to follow her. Kent was deceived and so was I. The hen had saved her young cock and I returned home without any game.

A School in the Bushes

When the snow had melted I began to teach Romka the right way to go in search of game. A young setter must be taught to run in the field round the hunter and not further than a gun-shot from him, fifty paces at most, and in the woods even nearer; the chief thing such a dog must be taught is never to forget about its master and not to be diverted from the business of the chase by its own affairs. All this taken together—to run in regular circles in the field and not to lose sight of its master in the woods—constitutes the right way of searching for game.

When the snow had melted I took Romka with me outside our town to a small hill covered with bushes. The bushes have been set aside for the inhabitants of the suburb for fuel, the whole hill being divided into allotments, each inhabitant taking as much firewood as he requires, and hence it is known as *the allotment*. Some people obtain their firewood from elsewhere and their plots remain dense islands of tangled shrubbery; others only cut down the bigger trees and leave the smaller ones to grow; others again cut everything down and on such a plot only a pile of rotting brushwood remains. That is why that hill looks like a head of hair cut by a blind hairdresser.

It was hard to believe that there would be any game in such a place so near to the town, but for a trainer of a young dog such an empty plot of land is of greater value during the first lessons than a place rich in game. For on a plot of land practically devoid of game the dog learns one thing, namely, how to run the right way without for a moment losing sight of its master.

I undid Romka's lead and just stroked his coat a few times. He did not notice that I had undone the lead and he remained standing beside me as if he had been tied to me. I waved my hand and said, "Look for it!"

He understood and off he went. Another minute and he would have disappeared in the bushes, but as soon as he lost sight of me, he got frightened and came running back. He stood still for a few seconds and looked strangely at me; it seemed as if he were photographing me so as to carry away with him a mental picture of my figure and to keep it in his head among the bushes and tree-stumps which have no human outline. Having done with that mysterious task of his, he turned his constantly wagging tail to me and ran off.

In the bushes it is quite different from the field where a dog can always see everything. In the woods one must teach a dog to disappear on one's left, describe an invisible circle and come back on one's right, and so turn round and round like a spinning top. For I have to know that if my dog has not come back from my left-hand side, it means that he has picked up the scent of some game somewhere near. It is perhaps best never to lose sight of your dog when walking through a cutting in a wood, for then your dog should keep crossing the footpath every now and then.

After disappearing in the bushes, Romka did not return. That did not worry me. On the contrary, I was glad that at first his feeling of freedom had proved stronger than his attachment to his master. In fact, I sympathised with him entirely, for as a sportsman I, too, love freedom. All I intended was to teach him to use his freedom in accordance with my wishes, for so both he and I would be more likely to be satisfied. In order not to leave my scent at too frequent intervals so that he should not find me too easily, I purposely took long leaps and so ran through the bushes to another clearing, in the middle of which stood a big juniper bush. I took a flying leap into the middle of that bush and hid myself there.

I could not hear the patter of the dog's paws on the wet ground which had only thawed a few days ago, but instead I could clearly hear from a distance the cracking of twigs and the quick panting of the dog. I realised the meaning of those quick pants at once: the dog had discovered that I was gone, rushed head over heels to find me and immediately began to gasp for breath from great excitement. However, he was not far wrong about my present whereabouts: he cut across the first clearing where I had begun to take my long leaps.

When everything got quiet again, I gave a sharp whistle: my usual signal to him.

The whole thing was now very much a game of hide and seek.

My whistle reached Romka's ears when he was probably standing rather lost in the middle of a clearing and, puzzled, was listening for a signal from me. He guessed where the whistle came from right enough, rushed headlong in that direction, again making a noise like a railway engine and stopped dead at the edge of the clearing with the juniper bush.

I held my breath. Romka's tongue was hanging out at the side of his mouth from his fast running and excitement. In such a state he could scent nothing and he relied entirely on his sense of hearing to enable him to find me; he had pricked up his ears, but the tip of each ear was hanging down and covered up his earholes. He bent his head sideways, but again he could not hear anything, whichever side he tried. At last he realised what was wrong: he could not hear his master's voice because of the loud panting which was coming out of his open mouth. So he shut his mouth and, being in a hurry to do so, he closed his teeth upon his nether lip, and with one lip inside his mouth, he was now listening.

To prevent myself from bursting out laughing at the sight of so comic a face with pursed lips, I covered my mouth with my hand. But the poor dog did not feel funny at all. Bereft of his master, nature had become a desert to him, a desert where only wolves, his forefathers, roamed. They would never forgive him for betraying their cause by attaching himself to a man, for receiving shelter from his master, for enjoying the food his master gave him. They would tear him to pieces and devour him. To live with wolves, a Russian proverb says, one has to howl like a wolf. And so Romka tried it. . . . Raising his head high, he began to howl. . . .

Such an awful sound I had never heard from him. He seemed really to have got an inkling of the desert life of the wolf without man. His howl was exactly like the howl of wolf cubs in the forest when their mother has gone for some prey and does not return. . . .

It does happen exactly like that. The she-wolf kills a sheep and carries it to her cubs. A hunter gets on her trail and, lying in wait for her, kills her. The man then finds the wolf cubs, takes them home with him and feeds them. Nature's store of tenderness is infinite: the cubs transfer their feeling for their mother to the man, they lick his hands, jump up to his chest. The cubs do not know that that man has killed their mother. But the wild wolves know everything; they are man's mortal enemies and they are also the mortal enemies of the dog, this traitor to the wolves' cause.

Romka's howl was so plaintive that my heart was seized with pity, but I must not show any pity, for was I not his teacher? So I held my breath.

He turned with his tail to me and pricked up his ears again for any sound that might come from the other direction. Perhaps somewhere in the wide heavens a snipe, flying past, uttered a whistling sound. Could it be his master that had got up there and was he now calling to him from the sky? Then a cow probably frightened a lapwing in a nearby field and, as he soared upwards, he uttered his "pee-wit." That was neither so high, nor so far—that might very well have been his master's whistle.

Romka rushed headlong in the direction of that "pee-wit," but I whistled sharply after him: "Here I am!"

He came back immediately. In less than fifteen minutes I had tired him out completely and now for the rest of his life he would carry with him the dread of an empty forest, a forest without man, for I had planted in his heart a terror of the life of his ancestors, the wild wolves. When at last I purposely made a movement in the bush, he heard it, and when I lit my pipe, he smelt the tobacco smoke and recognised it, he dropped his ears and his head became as smooth as a water melon.

I got up. He lay down with a guilty look in his eyes. I came out of the bush and stroked him. He began to yelp and jump about with joy.

YARIK

After that I went out hunting along the "runs," that is to say, I followed the trails left by the birds in the grass on dewy mornings and I hunted down the game just like a dog; I could not swear to it, but it did seem to me as if I began even to scent the game a little.

At that time a veterinary surgeon about twenty-five miles from our village succeeded in mating his remarkable Irish setter bitch with a dog of the same breed, both dogs belonging originally to the owner of a large bankrupt estate. So it was that one day when life became particularly difficult a friend of mine presented me with a six-week-old Irish setter puppy. I did not refuse the gift and I acquired a real friend for myself. Training a dog without a gun gives me as much pleasure as a real shoot. I remember once. . . .

On an old tree-felling site there were among the black tree-stumps hundreds of tall red flowers, rising from the ground like diminutive firs, and they made the whole place look red, in spite of the fact that there was an even greater quantity of cow-wheat there—John and Mary, our peasants call it—half-blue, half-yellow flowers, and also hundreds of white daisies with their yellow buttons for hearts, blue harebells and purple orchis, every imaginable kind of flower!—but from the spiky red flowers the whole clearing looked red.

By the black tree-stumps one could also find ripe and very sweet wild strawberries.

In summer a shower does not bother me at all and on that day I sheltered under a fir where thousands of gnats also came for shelter from the rain. I lit my pipe and blew clouds of tobacco smoke to get rid of them, but they still went on plaguing my dog Yarik. So in the end I had to light a camp-fire of fir cones and the dense smoke that rose from it soon drove the gnats back into the rain. But no sooner did we get rid of the gnats than the rain stopped. A summer shower is just a sheer delight!

We had nevertheless to stay under the fir-tree for another half hour to give the birds time to come out to feed and leave their trails on the rain-drenched grass. When, according to my calculation, the time had come for us to go, we went out on the red glade with the black tree-stumps and saying, "Go on, Yarik! Look for it, old man!" I sent Yarik to hunt out the game.

Yarik was now going through "the third field," that is to say, he was, under my supervision, going through the most advanced course for an Irish setter and, if everything went as I hoped, I should possess by the end of summer one of the best hounds in the world, an Irish setter trained by me, a dog that knew no fatigue and whose nose could pick up a scent for miles.

I often envied Yarik his nose. "Oh," thought I, "if only I had such an apparatus I should run to the blossom-smothered red clearing with the soft breeze blowing on my face and inhale, inhale and inhale all those ravishing smells!"

Lacking a dog's sense of smell, we are deprived of many great delights. We always ask each other, "How is your eyesight?" or "Is your hearing all right?" but no one ever asks us, "How is your smelling? Is your nose all right?" I have been training dogs for many years and every time a dog picks up a scent, I cannot help feeling thrilled and frequently I cannot help asking myself, "What would it be like if it were not Yarik but myself who scented the game?"

"Well, go to it, citizen," said I to my friend.

And away he went, running in circles, all over the red clearing with the black tree-stumps.

Very soon Yarik stopped under some trees at the verge of the wood, sniffed all round the place vigorously, cast a sidelong, earnest glance at me, inviting me to follow him: we understood each other without words. He led me on very slowly, himself walking very close to the ground and looking very much like a fox.

In this manner we came to a dense thicket, through which Yarik alone could creep. But I should not have let him go by himself, for, left to his own devices, he could easily be carried away by his own enthusiasm, fall upon the birds when they were wet with rain and ruin all my labours in training him. I decided regretfully to call him back, but suddenly, with a wag of his lovely tail, which looked so much like the wing of a bird, he turned round and looked fully at me. I understood him to say, "They have spent the night there, but they were feeding in the clearing with the red flowers."

"What are we to do?" I asked.

He sniffed round the flowers: the birds had left no scent on them. Then everything became clear to me: the rain had washed away all the traces left by the birds except those we had followed and which were preserved because they were under the trees.

All that was left for us to do now was to describe another circle on the glade in the hope of stumbling on a new scent left after the rain. But before Yarik had time to walk round half the circle, he stopped dead near a small, but very dense bush. He had caught the scent of the black grouse and he came to a point at once, fast though he had been running. His pose, as he stopped dead in his tracks, was for that reason rather extraordinary: he twisted himself almost into a ball and, had he wished it, he could have given himself up entirely to the contemplation of his gorgeous tail. I hurried to him, stroked him a few times and said in a whisper, "Go on, old man, if you think it worth while."

He straightened himself, went forward a step rather hesitantly—yes, it was worth while, only he had to walk with great circumspection. Having gone round the whole bush like that, he seemed to say to me, "They have been here during the rain."

Then he led me along the freshest possible trail, along the "run," the green track over the grass which but for that narrow strip of green was grey from the rain, and as he followed that plainly visible "run," the wisp of hair at the end of his tail touched the ground.

The birds must have heard us, for they, too, were running now. I guessed it by looking at Yarik who reported to me in his own way, "They're running in front of us, very near."

The birds ran into a large juniper bush and it was there that Yarik came for the last time to a *dead* point. Before, he still could from time to time open his mouth and pant, his long, pink tongue lolling out of his mouth; but now his jaws were firmly clenched and only the tip of his tongue, too slow to go back into his mouth in time, protruded from under his upper lip like a pink petal. A gnat lighted on that pink tip of the tongue and began to suck the blood, and I could see the dark-brown blotch on Yarik's nose, which looked almost like a tiny piece of oil-cloth, writhing with pain and at the same time twitching, as he kept on inhaling the scent of the black grouse, but he could not get the tip of his tongue inside his mouth, for if he did so, he was sure to give a loud gasp and frighten away the birds.

However, I, who was not as excited as Yarik, went carefully up to him, brushed off the gnat by a quick flip of a finger and, standing alongside of Yarik, could not help feeling a thrill of pride at the sight of him: he stood there as if he had been cast in bronze with his wing-like tail stretched out in a line with his back, while in his eyes all life seemed to be concentrated in two tiny points.

I walked round the bush very quietly to prevent the birds from flying away behind it without being seen and to force them to rise over the tops of the trees.

We stood there for a long time and the birds inside the bush, of course, knew perfectly well that we were standing at either side of it. I took a step towards the bush and I caught the voice of the grey hen. She just clucked once and by that one sound she told her brood, "I'm going to fly out of the bush and have a look round, but you'd better stay where you are for a while."

If she had flown straight at me, Yarik would not have moved, and if she had flown over him, he would not have forgotten that the game we were after was still inside the bush, or what a great crime it was to run after a flushed bird. But the large grey bird, nearly the size of a hen, turned a somersault in the air and, after almost touching Yarik's nose, flew off in a straight line slowly and just above the ground, luring him on to follow her by a low clucking: "Come on, catch me! I can't fly properly!"

Then, feigning sudden death, she flopped down on the grass within ten yards of him and, as he approached her, ran away quickly, creating a stir among the tall, red flowers.

Such provocation Yarik could not endure and, forgetting the years I had spent in training him, rushed after her. . . .

The trick succeeded: the grey hen had lured away the dog from her nestlings and with a final cry to her little ones, "Fly, fly in all directions!" she herself suddenly soared over the trees and vanished out of sight.

The young birds obeyed their mother's call and ran off in all directions and Yarik seemed to hear their mocking cries from afar, "Fool, fool!"

"Back!" I shouted to my fooled friend.

He came to his senses and with a guilty look began to sidle up to me slowly.

I asked him in a special, rather complaining voice, "What *have* you done, old man?"

He lay down on the ground.

"Well, come on, come on!"

He crawled forward and, looking the picture of contrition, put his head on my knee, beseeching me to forgive him.

"Oh, all right," I said, sitting down inside the bush, "I'm going inside this bush and you come after me. Right. Now sit still, don't start panting, we shall make fools of them all presently!"

In about ten minutes I started to whistle softly, imitating the call of the young birds.

"Phew, phew, phew . . ." which meant, "Where are you, mummy?"

"Cluck, cluck," she replied, which meant, "Coming, coming!"

Then from all over the place there came the same kind of soft whistling: "Where are you, mummy?"

"Coming, coming!" she replied to them all.

One nestling was whistling quite near me. I replied to him and he set off at a run. In another minute the grass began to stir near one of my knees.

I gave Yarik a stern look and cautioned him with a fist to make quite sure that he would not harm the little bird. Then I quickly covered the moving ball of fluff with my hand and picked up a grey nestling, as big as a pigeon.

"Come on, sir, smell!" I said in a soft voice to Yarik.

He turned away his nose: afraid to give a sudden pant.

"No, sir, no!" I said to him plaintively. "Have a smell!"

He sniffed the little bird, panting like a railway engine.

That was the biggest punishment I could have inflicted on him.

After that I went on whistling loudly, for I knew that the grey hen was quite sure to come to me now; she would collect her brood, miss one nestling and come running for him.

There were altogether seven of them, not counting the one I had caught. I could hear how one after another they had found their mother and then fallen silent, but I, the eighth one, went on calling, "Where are you, mummy?"

"Come along to us," she replied.

"Phew, phew, phew. . . . No, I don't want to come! Bring them all to me!"

In another minute I could see her coming. She was running fast and I could see how here and there her neck would pop out of the tall grass like the neck of a bottle, and behind, where her chicks were coming after her, the grass stalks were astir.

They were now sitting in the grass only a few yards away from me. I said to Yarik with my eyes, "Don't you dare to behave like a fool!" and I let go the young black grouse.

He rose over the bush with a whirl of wings and after him the rest went flapping their wings as they rose into the air.

But Yarik and I just could not help laughing as we followed them with our eyes from inside the bush: "That's how we fooled you, citizens!"

THE ROOT OF LIFE—GINSENG

I

THE animals of the Tertiary period remained faithful to their native land when it became covered with ice; but if it had happened all at once, how terrified would the tiger have been to see his own tracks in the snow! So it was that the dread tigers stayed in their native land as well as one of the sweetest, most tender and most graceful creatures in the world—the Spotted Deer and a number of the most wondrous plants: the tree-fern, the aralia and the far-famed Root of Life—Ginseng. One cannot help reflecting how great man's power on earth is when the freezing of a sub-tropical zone did not drive the wild animals out of it; yet the roar of man's guns in Manchuria made them flee in panic and, I have heard it said, people came across tigers as far north as the Yakutsk *taiga*, the primeval forest belt on the southern reaches of the river Lena. So I, too, like the wild animals, could endure it no longer. I heard and I can still distinctly remember the dreadful whine of the shell as it came screaming through the air towards our dug-out, but of what happened after that—nothing! It is thus that people sometimes die—nothing! During a space of time, of which I shall never know the duration, everything had changed around me: there were no more living men to be seen anywhere, neither friends nor foes. On the battlefield dead men lay and dead horses; the earth was strewn with shell cases, torn bits of metal and empty *makhorka* packets, and the ground was pitted with shell-holes, like the one by my side, as if it were pockmarked. Armed only with a revolver, I selected the best seven-point-six rifle I could find and I filled my knapsack with live cartridges. Unknown nature had beckoned to me since the early days of my childhood and now I found myself in a paradise which seemed to have been specially created for me. Nowhere in my native country have I seen such vast open spaces as in Manchuria: wooded mountains, valleys covered with grasses so tall that a horseman entirely disappeared in them, enormous red flowers like fiery beacons, butterflies as big as birds, rivers whose banks were smothered in flowers. Would I ever have another chance of living free as a bird in such an earthly paradise? The Russian border was not far from where I was, and nature was just as beautiful on the other side of it. I set out to walk in that direction and soon I noticed on the sand along the bank of the river countless tracks of wild goats: those were the wild Manchurian goats and musk deer which at that time of the year migrated in their thousands northward across the border from Manchuria into Russia. I did not overtake them for many days, but one day, after crossing a mountain range and reaching the gorge where the little stream My-hé rises, I saw a wild goat high above me on the spur of a mountain. He stood on a rock and, so it seemed to me, got scent of me and began to swear in his own language. By that time I had run out of all my army biscuits and had been sustaining myself for the past two days on little round white mushrooms which, when fully grown, exploded under my foot; these mushrooms were apparently quite a tolerable food and they exhilarated me almost like wine. Having been on short commons for some time, I was very glad to have the wild goat within rifle range and I took special care in aiming at him. While letting the sights of my rifle wander all over the goat, I happened to observe a big, wild boar lying below him beneath an oak and I realised now that the goat was swearing at him and not at me. I got the boar in my sights and, after I had fired, a whole herd of wild boar appeared from nowhere and stampeded madly away, while on the topmost crags of the mountain where the winds had free play, thousands of migrating wild goats came suddenly into view and fled headlong towards the Russian border along the banks of the My-hé. Looking in that direction, I could see two Chinese farmsteads, the peasant cottages perched on little hills, surrounded by small patches of Chinese ploughland. The Chinese farmers readily consented to take the boar from me. They gave me a good meal and, in exchange for the boar, let me have some rice, goat's cheese and other foodstuffs. Having made the discovery that in this wooded mountain district my cartridges were as good as any money, I began to feel easier in my mind, crossed the Russian border very soon afterwards and, having climbed over another mountain range, saw the blue Pacific in front of me. Oh, for just one glimpse of the blue ocean from the peak of a mountain I'd gladly put up with the hardships of many nights when, like a wild animal, I had to sleep with my ear to the ground and eat whatever I was lucky enough to get with my gun! I stood there for a long time, admiring the view from the top of the mountain and regarding myself in very truth as the happiest man in the world. Then, after a hasty meal, I began the descent from the bare, stone-strewn mountain-side into a cedar grove and from the cedar grove emerged by and by into a broad-leaved wood in which there was every imaginable tree of the Pacific coast. One velvety tree at once caught my fancy by its homely look: it looked almost like our mountain-ash, except that its bark was not at all like the bark of the mountain-ash, but as soft as velvet: it was a cork tree. On the greyish bark of one of those trees there was a notice in Russian which had gone black with time: "No man go—chiki-chiki be." What was I to do? I re-read the notice on the tree, pondered for a while over its threat of death by beheading and, obeying the law of the *taiga*, turned sharply on my heels, intending to look for another footpath. Meanwhile, a man, who was hiding behind one of the trees, was watching me. As I turned back after reading the notice, he realised that I was not a dangerous man, left his hiding place and began to jerk his head violently from side to side to re-assure me that I had nothing to fear from him.

"Come along, come along, mister," he said to me.

And he explained to me in broken Russian that Chinese hunters had taken possession of that narrow valley three years before: there they hunted the large Manchurian red deer and the spotted deer and they carved the notice on the tree to frighten away strangers in order to prevent them from coming there and disturbing the game.

"You can walkee this-side, mister, much as you likee!" said the Chinese with a smile.

I was quite charmed by his smile, but at the same time it made me feel a little embarrassed. At first the Chinese struck me not only as an old man, but even as an ancient one: his face was all wrinkled, his complexion was of an earthen colour and his eyes, hardly visible, were hidden in that furrowed skin of his, which looked so much like the bark of an old tree. But when he smiled, a pair of beautiful human eyes suddenly blazed forth with a black fire, his skin became smooth, his lips regained their colour, his teeth, still white, flashed and his whole face, in its inward sense, became as fresh as a boy's and as trustful as a child's. It is always like that: some plants in bad weather or at night cover themselves with their grey sepals, but when the sun shines, they open up again. He looked at me with a kind of special intentness, as if I were his kith and kin.

"Me getting hungry, mister," he said, and he took me to his little Chinese hut by the stream in the narrow valley, under the shade of a Manchurian nut-tree with enormous large-lobed leaves.

The Chinese hut was a very ancient one with a roof made of rushes, covered with netting to prevent them from being blown away by the typhoons; the door and windows were covered with paper instead of glass; there was no kitchen garden round the little hut, but instead there lay near it the various implements used for digging out Ginseng: small spades, pickaxes, scrapers, little boxes made out of bark and small sticks. The stream could not be seen near the hut, for it was flowing somewhere under the ground, beneath a heap of piled-up stones, and so near that, sitting in the hut with the door open, I could always hear its uneven murmur, which sometimes sounded very like some happy, though rather muffled, chatter.

When I listened to the stream's talk for the first time, I could almost believe in the existence of the next world, and it seemed to me that now all the people who had loved each other, but had been parted for a long time, had met again and could not have enough of talking to each other day and night, weeks, months. . . .

I was to spend many years in that little Chinese hut and during all those years I could never get used to this happy chatter. After a time I stopped noticing the concerts given by the thousands of grasshoppers, crickets and cicadás: their music was so monotonous that after a very short time you were no longer aware of it—they seemed to have been created for the sole purpose of distracting your attention from the circulation of your own blood and of making the silence of the desert more silent than it would have been if they had not been there. But I could never for a moment forget that subterranean talk; for it was never the same and the sudden exclamations with which it was punctuated were most unexpected and never repeated themselves.

The seeker after the Root of Life gave me shelter and food and he forbore to ask me where I had come from or why I had come to his valley. It was only after I had had a good meal and had given him a goodhumoured look that he smiled at me just like a friend and almost as if I were a near and dear relation of his. With a wave of his hand towards the west, he said, "Lussia?"

I got his meaning immediately and answered, "Yes, I come from Russia."

"Which place you belong Lussia?"

"My Lussia," I said, "is Moscow, and which is yours?"

He replied, "My Lussia—Shanghai."

So it happened quite by chance in our "me—you belong" language that he, the old Chinese gentleman, and I, the Russian, seemed to have one country—Lussia.

Only about twenty yards from the Chinese hut the impassable jungle began: oak-woods and the velvety cork-trees, small-leaved maples, hornbeams, yews, firmly intertwined with the vine lianas and lemon trees, the thorny stems of huge, seven-foot wormwood and the same lilac which in our country is only found in gardens.

Lu Wen, on his frequent journeys down the steep side of the valley to fetch some water from the stream, had made a path, and that hardly discernible footpath, skirting the thicket, soon brought you to a ravine where all the conversation, which near the Chinese hut seemed to come from the next world, burst out into the open; then, as it appeared from underneath a cliff, the stream at once dashed itself against a rock, standing right across its path, and was precipitated downwards in a mist of rainbow-tinted spray. The whole broad side of the sheer cliff was oozing water; it was always wet, it always glittered and all its countless streamlets united below in a wildly rushing, gay torrent. Never in my life shall I forget the thrill of happiness that went through me when I first beheld that stream! What a reward for my weary trek across the mountains just to bathe in that stream! There, behind those mountains, the insects never gave me a moment's respite, but here, so close to the sea, there were no mosquitoes, no gad-flies, no midges. A little below the place where I was bathing was a whirlpool among some rocks: it was on those stones that I spread out my clothes to be washed in the shoots of the rapids, while I myself squatted under the waterfall, letting the drops of water fall upon my head like a shower. The noise of falling waters silenced every sound, and the wild animals, to whom the sound of man is the most terrible of all the sounds in the world, approached the rushing stream fearlessly to drink, and for the first time on this Pacific coast I was lucky enough to see something of them.

Under the shelter of the broad-leaved trees, on the shady patches of sward, leaf-shadows danced continually, a tremulous maze of irregular spots of light from the golden sun of the forty-second parallel. Summer is the time of mists on those eastern shores of the Pacific, and only rarely does the sun show itself in all its might and glory, but on that day it showered that happy welcome on me.

Among the dancing leaf-shadows it would have been quite impossible for me to notice similar spots on the red coats of animals unless they had moved: the spotted deer, having rested somewhere very near, no doubt, had got up and come to the stream to drink.

Who, on visiting the Far East, has not heard of this rare animal of the jungle of the Pacific coast which is supposed to preserve in its antlers, when they are still new and filled with blood, a medicinal virtue which restores to men their youth and gladness? I had heard so many legends about those growing, soft, velvety antlers, deemed so precious by the Chinese, that I could not help ascribing a certain significance even to those absurd fairy-tales. And now a pair of those renowned antlers were pushed through two enormous leaves of a Manchurian nut-tree quite close to the water. They were velvety, of a reddish peach colour and they branched out from a living head with a pair of beautiful grey eyes. The moment Grey Eye bent down to the water, there appeared beside him a hornless head with a pair of even more beautiful eyes, which, however, were not grey,

but black and sparkling. By the side of the hind was a young deer
with a pair of thin, awl-like brow-tines and also a fawn—a tiny
creature, but with the same kind of spots as the grown deer. The
fawn walked right into the stream with all its four little hoofs.
Gradually, moving forward slowly from stone to stone, he stopped
between me and his mother, and when the hind wanted to see whether
he was all right or not and looked up at him, her eyes straightway
met mine as I squatted there like a stone idol in the spray of the
waterfall. She, too, became rigid and seemed to have turned to stone,
looking full at me, trying to make out whether I was really a stone or
whether I could move. She had a black mouth, extraordinarily
small for an animal. Her ears, on the other hand, were unusually
large, alert and sensitive, and there was a little hole in one of them:
the light was shining through it. I did not notice if she had any
other peculiarities, so entirely absorbed did I become in looking at
her lovely pair of sparkling black eyes, hardly eyes at all, but each of
them a flower of rare beauty. I understood at once why the Chinese
called this so precious deer Hua-lu, which in Chinese means deer-
flower. I found it difficult to imagine the man who, on catching
sight of such a flower, had brought himself to level his gun calmly at
it and fire the terrible bullet: the sunshine came streaming through
the hole of that bullet.

I could not say how long we stared into each other's eyes like that:
it seemed a very long time to me. I did my best not to breathe and
with every minute that was passing I was finding it harder and harder,
until, from excitement, I suppose, there must have been a twinkle
of movement in my eyes. Hua-lu noticed it and she began to lift
her foreleg with slow deliberation, a very thin leg with a pointed,
sweet little hoof. Having bent it, she straightened it forcefully and,
suddenly, stamped. Then Grey Eye raised his head and he, too,
began to look at me, but with an expression in his eyes, as if he were
examining some rubbish from a great height and, it being against his
nature to notice life's flotsam and jetsam, he kept on staring at me,
preserving his majestic air as the lord and master of the deer. The
only thing he did not do was to say as people of importance sometimes
say to the little men who come to ask them for a favour: "I'd gladly
do anything for you, if you'd only tell me in a few words what you
want. You really can't expect me to tell you what you want, can
you?"

When Hua-lu stamped her foot and Grey Eye, looking puzzled,
raised his majestic head with the short, velvet-covered antlers, something stirred a little further downstream and, among the other heads
of deer, one head, a large one, was thrust forward, and presently a

stag came into full view, a stag with a black stripe along his spine, as distinct as a leather thong. Even from a distance it was clear that Black Spine harboured some evil design in his head and that in his black and sombre eyes there lurked some wicked purpose.

It was not only the deer near Black Spine who, at the signal from Hua-lu, began to contemplate me with motionless stares, but also the fawn, in imitation of the full grown deer, tried his utmost to stare motionlessly at me from the stream. But little by little he began to get tired of that rigid pose of his and, besides, like the other deer he was all the time being bitten by ticks, so that at last he could bear the strain no longer and, lifting a leg, scratched himself. That, I am afraid, put an end to my endurance, for I could not help smiling. Now Hua-lu immediately realised who I was and she stamped her foot with such determination and vigour that a stone fell into the stream with a loud plop, raising a spray. After that she suddenly moved her black lips and emitted quite a human whistle, and when she turned round and fled, she raised aloft her unusually broad, white stump of a tail to show her fawn, which followed her, the way she was taking through the bushes. The pricket also rushed after his mother, followed by Grey Eye, Black Spine and the other deer.

When they had all gone, a pretty hind rushed straight into the middle of the stream, stopped dead in her tracks and seemed to ask with her beautiful little face, "What's the matter? Why have they all run away?" All of a sudden she streaked across the stream quite in the opposite direction, was soon half way up the steep side of the narrow valley, threw a glance at me from above, stopped to cast another look at me when she had reached the top and then disappeared beyond the line of black cliff and blue sky.

II

Lu Wen had hidden his little Chinese hut at the bottom of the deep coomb as a protection against the terrible typhoons of the Pacific region, but it was sufficient to climb about three hundred and fifty feet up the side of the valley to see the sea, the Pacific Ocean. Our deep and narrow valley entered a large gorge not far from the place where I had first met the deer, and at the bottom of that gorge flowed the river Zu-Su. The river ran more quietly there and, as the gorge gradually widened into a big valley, it flowed on solemnly and calmly, after having completed its tortured course over mountainous valleys and gorges, into the ocean.

The day after my arrival, a steamboat entered Zu-Su bay and she remained there for the following two weeks, while the immigrants were settling down. It was during those two weeks that the great event of my life took place which forms the subject of my story.

The valley through which the Zu-Su flows is carpeted with flowers, and it was there that I learnt to understand the touching simplicity of the story each flower has to tell about itself: each flower in the Zu-Su valley is a little sun in itself and each of them embodies the whole story of the meeting between a sunbeam and the earth. Oh, if only I could tell the story of my life as simply and with as touching a frankness as those flowers of the Zu-Su valley! There were irises there—from pale blue to almost black, orchids of every imaginable hue, lilies—red, orange and yellow, and among them all over the valley gilliflowers were scattered like bright red stars. Over those dales, like so many beautiful flowers, hundreds and hundreds of butterflies fluttered, looking for all the world just like flying flowers, yellow apollo butterflies with black and crimson spots, brick-red and rainbow-tinted tortoiseshell butterflies and enormous swallowtail butterflies of a remarkable dark blue colour. Some of them (it was the first time that I had seen it) could light upon the water and float, then rise again and flutter away over the sea of flowers. Bees swarmed among the flowers, wasps, hairy humble-bees with black, orange and white bellies raised a noisy hum in the air. Sometimes when I looked into the cup of a flower, I found something there I had never seen before and the name of which I don't know even to-day: it was neither a humble-bee, nor a honey-bee, nor a wasp. And among the flowers on the ground nimble-footed beetles scurried to and fro, the predatory ground-beetles, scavenger-beetles crawled about, enormous ante-diluvian beetles, relics of ages past, suddenly took wing when disturbed and flew straight ahead, without swerving either to the right or to the left. Among all those flowers and amid all that swarming life of the valley, I alone, so it seemed to me, could not look straight at the sun or give as simple an account of myself as they did. I can talk of the sun only while avoiding it with my eyes, for I am a man and I am blinded by the sun; I can talk of the sun only while looking upon all the different objects upon which it sheds its beams, deeply conscious of the kinship of all nature, and by gathering all their beams into one whole.

I caught a glimpse of the steamship from the top of the cliff above our hut and I wanted to have a look at the people. By the time I reached the spot where our stream Chiki-Chiki flowed into the Zu-Su river, it got very hot and I felt tired and wanted to rest. Where the little stream and the river Zu-Su met, on one of the banks, the supple stems of the vine had twined themselves so thickly round the young Manchurian nut-trees that some of the trees had been transformed into dark-green tents, impervious to the rays of the sun. I was greatly tempted to get inside one of those tents and, should it be nice and cool there, to sit down and have a rest. But I did not find it so easy to penetrate through the solid mass of vine stems which trailed to the ground and were very thick. Pushing aside the vine stems, however, I saw quite a spacious, dry place, and in the sweet coolness of that shady retreat I sat down on a stone, leaning against the grey trunk of the tree. Inside the tent it was not, of course, as dark as it seemed from outside: the rays of the sun did find a way through the thick foliage which seemed to gleam with a light of its own, and everywhere there were dancing leaf-shadows. The air was absolutely still, and for that reason I was rather surprised after a time to notice a curious movement, a changing over in the dancing spots of sunlight, as though somebody outside kept on shutting out the sunbeams and then again admitting them. I parted the vine shoots very carefully and a few paces away from me I saw a hind, covered with her own spots of sunlight. Fortunately the wind blew in my direction and at such a distance even I could *scent* the deer. But what would happen if the wind suddenly blew in the opposite direction? I felt quite terrified lest she should discover my presence by some unintentional movement of mine. I hardly breathed, while she was getting nearer and nearer. Like all timid animals, she would take a step and then stop dead, pricking up her extraordinarily long and alert ears in the direction where she scented something in the air. Once I thought that it was all over: she turned her ears straight at me, and it was then that I noticed the little hole in her left ear, the hole from a bullet and I was overjoyed, as though I had met an old friend, when I recognised in her the same hind which had stamped her foot at me on the verge of the mountain stream. Now, as then, she, either in hesitation or just lost in thought, lifted a foreleg and stayed like that, and if my breath had moved even one vine leaf, she would have stamped her foot and disappeared. But I held my breath, and she put down her foot slowly and took one more step towards me, then another. I looked straight into her eyes, marvelling at their beauty and imagining such a pair of lovely eyes in the head of a woman, or on a stalk, as flowers; it was as startling a discovery as any I made among the flowers of the Zu-Su. And once again I realised how inevitable the name of deer-flower was, and I felt a thrill of happiness at the thought that many thousands of years ago an unknown yellow-faced poet, seeing those eyes, thought of them as flowers and that I, a pale-faced man, too, thought of them as flowers; I also felt happy that it was not I alone who had made that discovery and that there were things in the world about which there could be no disagreement. I could now understand why the

Chinese preferred the growing antlers of just that species of deer and not of the coarse Manchurian red deer or the Persian red deer. No doubt there were many useful and even medicinal substances in the world, but how often did it happen that the useful was at the same time also perfect from the point of view of beauty ?

After taking a few more steps in the direction of my tent, Hua-lu suddenly raised herself on her hind legs, placing her forelegs high over me, and through the intertwined vine stems there appeared straight before me a pair of delicately moulded little hoofs.

I could hear how Hua-lu was tearing off the juicy vine leaves, a favourite food of the spotted deer, which is quite pleasant even to our human palate. Looking at her large udder from which drops of milk trickled, I remembered her fawn, but I did not dare to lean forward to look for him through the small gap I had made in the foliage. I knew, however, that he must be somewhere near.

As a sportsman, who is, I suppose, a kind of animal, too, I was greatly tempted to get up very quietly and take hold of the hind's hoofs suddenly: I was a strong man and I felt sure that were I to grasp the hind's forelegs above the hoofs firmly in my hands, I could easily have overcome her resistance and tied her up with my leather belt. Every sportsman will appreciate the almost irresistible desire that came over me to capture the beautiful animal and make it my own. But there was another man in me who, when the sweet moment came, hated to grasp it, who, on the contrary, wanted to keep it unsullied and thus preserve it for ever in his inmost heart. We are all human, of course, and every one of us has a little of that feeling: even the keenest sportsman would find it difficult to remain unmoved at the sight of a wounded animal that was dying, and the most gentle of poets would like to possess both the flower, the deer and the bird. I had a pretty good idea of myself as a sportsman; in fact, I never considered myself to be anything else. I certainly never dreamt that deep inside me there dwelt another person and that beauty, or whatever it was, would render me, the sportsman, as helpless as a deer that has been captured and tied up.

Two men and two wills fought within me. One said, "If you let slip this chance, it will never come again and you will never forgive yourself. Come on, bestir yourself! Grasp her! Hold her! Don't you want to possess the female Hua-lu, the most beautiful animal in the whole world ?"

But the other voice said, "Keep still! A beautiful moment can be preserved only by not desecrating it by a touch of your hands!"

I was conscious of a curious similarity between me and the hunter in the fairy-tale who took aim at the swan and suddenly heard a voice imploring him not to shoot and then it appeared that the swan was really an enchanted princess. The hunter did not shoot and, instead of a dead swan, a beautiful, living princess stood before him!

So did I, too, struggle with myself, straining every nerve. But what a price I had to pay for it and what the struggle had cost me! Controlling the irresistible impulse to seize the animal, I could not control the violent shaking of my body. I was trembling like a dog that comes to a point, and it was quite likely that that animal tremor had communicated itself to the hind as a signal of alarm. Anyway, Hua-lu freed her hoofs quietly from the vine stems, stood still for a moment on her thin legs, cast a meaningful glance into the depths of the dark thicket and, for a moment, seemed to look full into my eyes. Then she turned round, took a few steps, stopped and looked round. Her fawn appeared from somewhere and went up to her. With him at her side, she looked full at me for some time and then disappeared into a clump of meadowsweet.

III

Every spring and during the summer and autumn flood seasons the river carries down to the sea-shore a large number of giant trees, uprooted by the floods or the typhoons—poplars, cedars, hornbeams and elms—and covers them up with sand. So much sand is silted up and so many years pass that the sea itself is forced to recede and a bay is formed.

How many centuries must have passed for the ocean and the river Zu-Su to have transformed the straight line of sea and shore into a semi-circle? How many sea creatures had visited the small, rocky islet in the middle of the bay until, at last, the siren of a steamer rent the silence of the sea wastes and all the frightened seals jumped from the island into the sea?

A huge tree, half covered with sand and looking like the back of a monster turned to stone, lay at the very edge of the sea; two large boughs were all that remained of the top of that tree and there they protruded starkly into the sky, black and knotty, rending the azure heavens to the horizon. On the small branches of this dead tree hung pretty little round white boxes: these were the skeletons of sea-urchins thrown up by the typhoons. On that tree a woman was sitting with her back to me, gathering in a small basket those gifts of the sea. I must still have been under the strong influence of the graceful animal near the tree entwined with vine-stems, for something about that unknown woman put me in mind of Hua-lu, and I could not help feeling that as soon as she turned to me I would see those beautiful eyes in the face of a human being.

D

Even now I cannot understand how such a thought should have occurred to me, how I should have formed such a queer idea in my head. For if one considered it coolly, if one were to draw a picture of that woman on the sea-shore, there would be nothing at all resembling a spotted deer in her figure; but I could not suppress the curious feeling that the moment she turned round to me, the deer-flower would appear before me, Hua-lu embodied in a woman. And, as if in answer to my premonition, it happened just like that: the transformation took place as in the fairy tale about the Princess-Swan. Her eyes were so like the eyes of Hua-lu that everything else, the deer parts—the spotted coat, the black lips, the alert ears—seemed to have imperceptibly taken on a human appearance, preserving at the same time, as in the deer, that enchanting unity of truth and beauty, which seemed to have been decreed from above.

She looked at me, amazed and mistrustful, and I had the strange sensation that in another moment she would stamp a foot at me like the deer and run away. How many different feelings overwhelmed me at that moment, how many thoughts rushed like some misty exhalations through my brain, and in those thoughts and feelings how many decisions were born in a world that was to me then totally incomprehensible and vague! But even now I cannot find the words, the exact and absolutely truthful words, in which to describe what I felt at the time, and I doubt if I shall ever be able to find them, or, if I do, whether they will bring my hour of liberation. The word *freedom*, perhaps, best describes the peculiar state of mind when, having grasped the beauty of an uncommon animal, I suddenly found in myself power to project it infinitely in man. It was as if I had emerged from the narrow coomb into the broad valley of the Zu-Su, covered with flowers and stretching far into the infinity of the blue ocean.

But the most important thing was this: when Hua-lu had pushed her hoofs through the vine thicket there were two men in me: one was a hunter who desired to seize her above the hoofs with his strong hands and the other was a man unknown to me, a man whose dearest wish was to preserve that ineffably sweet moment for ever in his heart. That is why I can say now without hesitation whatever that the man who approached the woman on the sea-shore was the man unknown to me and that he approached her in a state of breathless ecstasy, infinitely strong in that agony of heart, and . . . and that she understood him at once. She could not fail to understand me or respond to me. If such a thing happened more than once in a lifetime, or if such an experience could be lived through at will, then all of us would be able at any time and in any place to transform every flower, every swan and every hind into a Princess and live with her as I lived with my hind turned into a woman in the Valley of Flowers of the Zu-Su, in the mountains and on the shores of rivers and streams. . . .

I took her to the top of Misty Mountain which had once been a volcano (now the priceless spotted deer are born there) and to the little Chinese hut where I listened with her to the subterranean talk of our ancestors. It was in that hut that Lu Wen, the seeker after the Root of Life, told us about the wonderful properties of that root which had the power of endowing man with eternal youth and beauty. He even showed us the powder made out of the Root of Life, the crushed new antlers of the spotted deer, and some medicinal mushrooms; but when we laughingly asked him for the powder of eternal youth and beauty, he suddenly got angry and would not talk to us any more. Most likely he was annoyed that we did not take him seriously and laughed at him, but, perhaps, convinced that to be successful in the quest for the Root of Life one ought to have a clear conscience, he wished to indicate to us that we, too, like him, the seeker, must think about the purity of our consciences. It was, of course, also possible that old Lu Wen perceived the lightning which rent our happiness here and there: for two men lived in me, the same two men who had striven for the possession of the beautiful Hua-lu—one of them a hunter and the other—a man still unknown to me.

On the way to my vine tent where we intended to lie in wait for Hua-lu, I did the wrong thing, or rather not the whole of me, but the hunter in me. She was hurt and her attitude towards me suddenly changed: it was as if a flash of lightning had rent our union; but I soon collected myself and regained my usual mastery over myself. While we were sitting in our vine-tent we suddenly saw, through the little opening in the foliage, Hua-lu in all her beauty. She crossed a glade with her fawn and ate the vine-leaves quite close to us and then she disappeared somewhere in the meadowsweet and Thuya bushes. Calmly I told her of my meeting with Hua-lu, how she had raised herself on her hind legs and pushed her sweet little hoofs through the vine thicket and how an uncontrollable tremor had shaken my limbs and how I had tried to overcome the temptation to grasp her by the hoofs and how another man, a man who was quite unknown to me, had helped me to preserve that moment of beauty and how, as a reward for that, the deer-flower had been transformed into a princess. . . .

I wanted to prove to her by that story that she could trust my ability to control my impulses and that my mistake before had been unintentional and would never, never recur. I spoke without looking

at her, my gaze fixed upon the green space that surrounded us.
I wanted to lay bare the inmost places of my heart to her, without
looking into her eyes, and when I thought that I had achieved what
I had set out to do and should now be able to look straight into her
eyes where I should see. . . .

I thought I would find there the blue serene, but suddenly quite
the opposite happened. I could not understand it at all: there was
no blue serene there, it was a blazing fire that I saw there. Her
cheeks flamed red and her eyes were half closed when she fell back
on the grass. Just then the siren of the steamer reached us. She
must have heard it, yet she did not seem to have heard it. I, however, just as it had happened with the hind, sat there motionless.
Then I, too, like her, was on fire and, presently, my whole being was
at white heat, but I went on sitting there motionless. When the
steamer hooted for a second time, she got up, smoothed her hair and,
without looking at me, went away. . . .

IV

Why does the sound of the sea soothe you as you stand on the shore?
The regular beat of the incoming tide tells of the vast periods of time
of our planet earth, the ebb and flow of the tide are the clock of the
planet itself, and when those great spans of time impinge upon the
minutes of your all-too-fast life among the sea-shells, sea-stars and
sea-urchins cast up upon the beach, your mind is overwhelmed by
great thoughts about life and your little personal sorrow fades away
and you are conscious of it only faintly as if existing somewhere far
away. . . .

There was a rock at the very verge of the sea, a rock shaped like
a black heart. One of the fiercest typhoons must have knocked it
off a cliff and apparently flung it rather unsteadily on top of another
rock. If you lay down quite flat upon that stone, which so much
resembled a heart in shape, and pressed your own heart against
it, remaining motionless like that for some time, it seemed to sway
softly with the tide. Still, I cannot say for certain whether it really
did so. Perhaps it was not the sea or the stone, but myself who was
swaying because of the beatings of my own heart; I found it so hard
to be alone, however, and I yearned so badly for the company of
some human being that I began to treat that stone as if it were a man
and I sought its company as if it were a man.

The stone heart was black on top, but the half of it which was
nearest the water was very green: that was because when the tide
came in, the whole stone was covered with water to the top and the

green sea-weeds had time to live for a space and, when the tide went out, they remained hanging helplessly in expectation of the next tide.

It was on that stone that I sat watching the steamboat until she disappeared from view. After that I lay down on the stone and listened for a long time: the stone heart beat in its own way and, little by little, everything around me seemed to become part of me through this stone and I conceived of everything as my own, as something alive. Little by little everything I had learnt about nature and life from books—that everything belonged to separate compartments, that men were men and animals only animals, and that the same was true of plants and stocks and stones—all that I had taken out of books and that was not mine, became meaningless and I began to look upon everything as an inseparable part of myself, and everything in the world grew to be like people to me: the rocks, the sea-weeds, the tides and the cormorants, which were drying their wings on some rocks yonder just as fishermen dry their nets after a catch. The incoming tide set my mind at rest, lulled me to sleep and, when I woke up, I was cut off from the shore by the sea. The stone was half submerged, the sea-weeds round it moved about as if they were alive, and the cormorants on the spit were now within reach of the tide water: there they sat, drying their wings, when suddenly a wave would roll over them and even fling them off the rocks, but back they went where they had been sitting before and they went on drying their wings, spreading them out wide, like the wings of eagles on coins. Then I put this question to myself, a question which seemed very important to me and to which I felt I must find the right answer: why do the cormorants stick to just that spit and refuse to fly up a little higher on the cliffs to dry their wings?

Next day something else happened. I came there again to listen to the incoming tide and I looked for a long time in the direction where the steamboat had disappeared the day before, and then I must have fallen asleep again, for when I woke up a mist covered both land and sea. I could just see how the new settlers were busying themselves on the shore. Ask any one of them, I thought, and he would tell you that I was a tramp, a homeless creature, and he would be quick enough to hide his axe and spade from me. How mistaken they were! I *was* a tramp, but now that my heart had been pierced, now because of that, because of that pain of mine I felt everywhere the same: any spot on earth was now my native land; to me, somewhere deep inside me, all the creatures of the earth were the same, and now I had nothing more to seek, for no outward change could bring anything new to me—there! deep inside me. "No," I thought to myself, "your native land is not where you happened to be born,

but your native land is there where you have reached that understanding, where you have found your happiness, where you have gone
forth to meet it, where you have put your trust in it, and where, yes!
where they opened fire on you, aiming at the very spot where your
happiness was!"

The sea was warmed by the summer sun and the vaporised water
rose, cooled down on reaching the top of the mountain range and then
descended in a mist and a drizzle of rain.   But I felt as if giant white
hunters, clad in flowing white robes, advanced upon me, swaying,
and opened up a murderous fire upon me, not with bullets at first,
but with small shot, so that I, shot through and through, entirely
annihilated, should henceforth live entirely within myself and should,
through that inevitable pain, come to the understanding of all things.
No!   I was no longer a tramp and now I understood the cormorants
well!   Now I understood why although they found it hard to dry
their wings on that spit, they refused to fly up higher and sit down on
top of another rock: it was there that they happened to catch their fish
and there they remained, for, they must be thinking to themselves,
"if we fly to another place, higher up, we may be able to dry our wings,
but it is ten to one that we shall lose our fish.   Oh, no!   We shan't
fly anywhere, for it is on this spit of land that we intend to remain."
So that was why they lived there, in spite of an occasional drenching
by the waves, and made their permanent home on that spit at the very
edge of the breakers.   And one other thing I felt: this stone heart,
I thought to myself, lies here, swaying gently as the waves
dash against it, and so it will lie here for perhaps a hundred years or
more, for a thousand years, and all the time it will keep on swaying—
so why should I enjoy any particular advantages over it ? why should
I seek to find consolation by going to some other place ?   There is no
consolation!

Well, the moment I said to myself with all the force of conviction
and with the greatest possible determination that there was no
consolation, that the past could never be brought back and that all
hope or expectation of better things from a change of place was futile
and vain, my pain seemed to abate for some little time and for a
minute I even imagined that life could go on for me even after my
execution.   It was then that I remembered Lu Wen and I entered his
little hut as if it were my own dear home.

That night countless hosts of flying insects were borne up by the
hot, moist air at the bottom of our deep coomb and, in their bridal
flight, millions of them lit their night lanterns, as though borrowing
the light for them from the invisible moon.   I sat beneath the
projecting roof of the Chinese hut and tried to follow from beginning

to end of the journey of some firefly. Each of them was granted only the tiniest fraction of time for carrying their light about with them, a second or, maybe, two—and everything came to an end in darkness, except that immediately a new lantern was lit. Was it the same insect which, after a rest, re-lit its lantern and carried on with its illuminated flight, or did its journey come to an end when the light in its lantern went out and another insect took up the torch, as it happens in our world of men ?

"Lu Wen," I asked, "what do you make of it ?"

Quite unexpectedly Lu Wen replied, "Me makee same's you, mister."

What did it mean ?

Just at that moment something happened under the ground where the continuous, but desultory talk had gone on as always: something fell with a terrific crash. Lu Wen listened for some time, looking very grave.

"I suppose," said I, "a piece of rock must have fallen down."

Lu Wen did not seem to have grasped the meaning of my words. I drew a semi-circle with a sweep of my arms, thus representing a cave, and then indicated in dumb-show how a rock must have fallen into the stream and stopped the flow of the water. Lu Wen apparently was of the same opinion as I, for he again said, "Me makee same's you, mister."

But although he had said it a second time, I could still not be sure that I understood what he really meant. Suddenly Lu Wen's dog, Ly-Bah, rushed back into the hut with his tail between his legs. I supposed a tiger must have passed quite near, or perhaps he was still lying in wait among the rocks, intending to spring upon Ly-Bah at the first favourable opportunity. We had to kindle a fire as a precautionary measure and no sooner had the fire been lit than thousands of moths came fluttering round it: there were so many of them in that hot, damp night that we could hear distinctly the rustle of their wings. I had never seen such a sight before: so many moths that a constant rustle could be heard in the night air. Had I been as healthy in mind and body as I was only a short time ago and had I been as guileless as I was then, I should not have ascribed any special significance to that rustling as I did now: the rustle of life! I listened intently and, large-eyed and greatly amazed, I asked Lu Wen about it: what did he make of it ? And for the third time Lu Wen said significantly, "Me makee same's you, mister."

It was only then that I looked closely at Lu Wen and, suddenly, I understood him! What Lu Wen was interested in was not the life of the flying fireflies, nor the fall of rock under the ground, nor the rustling of millions of moths. What he was interested in was myself. He had long since taken all the living creatures to his heart and he lived in them as well as with them and, of course, he comprehended everything in his own way; but what he was interested in was how to understand me through my understanding of all that. No doubt he realised perfectly well whom the steamer had taken away from me. He now picked up the leopard skin, his constant companion in his quests for the Root of Life, and spreading it just there beside me under the projecting roof of the Chinese hut, he curled himself up on it, like a dog. He always slept like that and one could talk to him all through the night and even in his sleep he would reply to an intelligent question as well as to the incomprehensible murmur of a drowsing person.

Now that many years have passed and I have gone through every kind of experience, I cannot help thinking that it is not sorrow that brings us an understanding of life, the whole of life in all its manifold implications of kinship between every living creature upon earth, as I had understood it on that night, but happiness, yes, happiness; sorrow, like a plough, merely turns the clods of earth and opens up new possibilities for the development of our vital forces. But there are still many simple-minded people who believe that our understanding of the lives of other people, our kith and kin, is due only to suffering. I, too, felt that it was only through my pain that I suddenly attained to the understanding of everything. But it was not the pain, it was the joy of life that welled up within me from the deeper recesses of my heart.

"Lu Wen," I asked, "have you ever had a woman ?"

"Me no savee," Lu Wen replied.

"One sun," I said, shaking my head and wishing to indicate by that gesture of negation that I was taking away one day, that is to say, to-day, thus leaving yesterday. And two fingers meant that we were two yesterday, then one finger and, pointing to myself, I said, "I am alone to-day."

And pointing in the direction where the steamer had gone, I said, "The woman's there!"

"Lady," Lu Wen exclaimed joyfully.

He understood: every woman was "lady" to him and so was mine, too. Then he showed me: a head lying with closed eyes.

"Lady sleepee-sleepee."

I guessed that he meant that *his* lady had been dead long since. "You mean your wife ?"

Again he did not understand me, so I showed him in dumbshow how two grown-ups sleep and little ones are born.

Lu Wen understood and beamed at me: that was old lady,

meaning wife, whereas lady, it seemed, meant sweetheart. He indicated by gestures a man of medium height, then another—smaller, a third one—smaller still and so on and so on, until he came to a baby, carried in a bundle on the back.

"Plenty, plenty, me must work all light."

That old lady was the wife of his brother and the little ones were her children and his brother himself was " sleepee-sleepee," while Lu Wen had to work and send them money to Shanghai.

So it went on all through the night. I muttered in my sleep, "Sleepee-sleepee, lady!"

But Lu Wen replied, "Live, live, lady!"

Perhaps I liked hearing him say that, for, quite involuntarily, I repeated the same sentence and received the answer I desired, "Live, live, lady!"

V

Quite likely the tiger did not stay long near our hut, but went on his way, for Ly-Bah soon came out of the hut and curled up beside Lu Wen. The camp-fire, of course, went out. The rustle of wings ceased, but until dawn the lanterns of the fireflies which seemed to have borrowed their light from the moon traced lines across the darkness in their bridal flight, and the trees, gathering the moisture from the air in their broad leaves, as though in saucers, would suddenly spill it. . . .

When dawn came, the white hunters again rose from the sea in their flowing robes and again began piercing me with small shot.

Yonder is a cliff. Water oozes out of its countless crevices, gathers into big drops, and it really seems as if that cliff were shedding tears. It is not a man, it is a rock and I knew well enough that a rock could not feel, and yet when my heart was full to overflowing, I could not help sympathising with that rock every time I saw with my own eyes that it was weeping just like a man. Once more I lay down on that rock and it was *my* heart that was beating, but it seemed to me that what I felt was the beating of the rock's heart. Don't tell me, please, don't tell me!—I know it is a rock. But my heart yearned so badly for a human being that I took that rock for a friend, and that rock alone knows how many times I, our hearts beating as one, exclaimed: "Oh, hunter on the hill, hunter on the hill, why did you let her go, why did you not grasp her by those sweet little hoofs of hers ?"

How ingenuous, how naïve I was at that time! For I was absolutely convinced that if only I had seized my bride like a deer everything would have been all right: the question of the root of life would have been answered. Dear children, beloved youths and you, sweet girls, in those days I, too, like you, attached great importance to what you are now discussing *quite frankly;* I, too, believed that love could exist and could mean something without shelter or, as you express it, without roses and bird-cherry blossom. To be sure, the root of our life is in the earth and, looked at from that point of view, our love is just like the love of all animals, but that does not mean that we should cover up our stalks and flowers with earth and lay bare the mysterious root and so deprive the source of human life of that which shields it from exposure. Alas, all that becomes clear only after the danger has passed and, unfortunately, the rising generation trusts the experience of their elders least of all, and in this respect what they desire most is to be left to their own devices. I, however, was lucky to have had Lu Wen at my side, the most tender-hearted, attentive and, I make bold to say, *cultured* father one could wish for. Yes, my faith in my wilderness is so unbounded that I cannot help regarding things like scented soap and nailbrushes as the very trash of civilisation, for I hold its essence to lie in the genius for understanding and in friendly relations between people.

Slowly I realised that Lu Wen's chief purpose in life was to provide medical treatment for people—what it actually amounted to from the medical point of view is not for me to say. But I saw with my own eyes that whoever came to him for a cure, left him with a happy face, and many came back later just to thank him. Chinese hunters, trappers, seekers after the root of Ginseng, natives of every description, khunkhuzes, tazes, goldas, oroches, ghilyaks, with their wives and children, covered with scabs, Russian tramps, convicts, settlers. He knew hundreds of people in the primeval forest belt of Siberia and Manchuria and, it seemed, next to the Root of Life and the new antlers of the spotted deer, he considered money to be the best medicine. He never wanted for that medicine: all he had to do was to send a message to one of his numerous friends and the medicine arrived. Once, in midsummer, the river Zu-Su overflowed its banks and flooded the countryside, ruining the crops and leaving the new settlers without any means of subsistence. It was then that Lu Wen sent a message to his friends and the Russians were saved from starvation by Chinese assistance. It was here, therefore, that I learnt the lesson which I have never forgotten—not from books, but from life—that civilisation is not a matter of boiled shirts and tails, but of brotherly intercourse between the peoples, which transforms even money into a medicine.

At first I could not help smiling every time Lu Wen said that money was a medicine, but the conditions of our lonely existence soon made me realise that he was right and I, too, began to look on money as medicine.

Besides Ginseng, the young antlers of the spotted deer, and money, Lu Wen's medicines included the blood of the Manchurian antelope, the musk secreted by the musk-deer, the tails of the large Manchurian red deer, the brains of the long-eared owl, all sorts of mushrooms, growing on the ground or on trees, and various herbs and roots, among which were many of ours: camomile, mint and valerian.

One day, while watching the old man's face as he was carefully sorting out some herbs, I plucked up courage to ask him, "I say, Lu Wen, you know such a lot, don't you? Tell me, am I well or am I sick?"

"Ev'ly man," said Lu Wen, "is numpa one all light and vely sick same time."

"What medicine ought I to take?" I asked. "The new antlers of the spotted deer?"

Lu Wen laughed heartily: he prescribed the antlers for the awakening of passion in cases of lost virility.

"Maybe Ginseng will help me?" I asked.

Lu Wen stopped laughing and stared at me long and hard. He did not say anything that time, but next day he propounded this riddle and left it to me to solve it: "Your Ginseng, mister, grow-grow, me soon makee you see all light."

Lu Wen never spoke in vain and I was eagerly waiting for the promised opportunity of seeing with my own eyes not only the powder of that famous Chinese medicine, but the root itself which grew somewhere in the jungle. One night, it was long past midnight, Ly-Bah rushed out of our hut and, barking, disappeared in the pitch darkness. Lu Wen went after it and I followed him with my rifle. Emerging presently out of the darkness with Ly-Bah, Lu Wen said, "No want gun, our people."

Soon six well-armed Chinese appeared before our hut, handsome Manchus with aquiline noses, armed with rifles and long knives.

"Our people," Lu Wen said to me again and, speaking in Chinese to our visitors, he must have repeated the same thing to them about me: "Our people."

The Manchus bowed politely to me and, stooping, for they were very tall men, entered our little hut one after another. There they sat down in a circle, placed something on the floor, did something to it and, after a minute or two, all froze into contemplation of the mysterious object at their feet.

"I say, Lu Wen," I said softly, "may I have a look at it, too?"

Lu Wen again said in Chinese: "Our people," and all the

Manchus turned round to me, made room for me very respectfully and invited me to join them in contemplating the object on the floor.

It was then that I saw Ginseng for the first time—the Root of Life, so rare and precious that six strong and well-armed young men had been detailed to transport it. A small box had been made out of cedar bark and in it, on a handful of black earth, lay a small root of a yellowish colour, which looked to me just like our parsley. Having made room for me, all the Chinese resumed their speechless contemplation. As I began to examine the root, I was surprised to recognise human features in its shape: I could clearly see a pair of legs forking out of the trunk, and there were also hands, a tiny neck and, on it, a head, and the fibres on the hands and legs looked like long fingers and toes. But what made me, too, lose myself in the contemplation of the Root of Life was not the coincidence of its resemblance to, a human body—after all aren't there hundreds of cases where the arbitrary formation of roots assume an extraordinary similitude to all sorts of figures ?—what made me, too, contemplate the root was the silent influence exercised on my consciousness by those seven men, sunk into the contemplation of the Root of Life. These seven living men were the last of the millions of men who during countless centuries had become dust, and those millions and millions of men had believed in the Root of Life, many of them had perhaps even contemplated it with the same veneration, and many had drunk it. I could not resist the influence of such faith. Just as on the sea-shore the brief hours of my human life got utterly lost in some limitless cosmic time, so also now individual human lives were to me like waves, which broke against me, the living one, as on some shore, and all of them seemed to ask me to conceive of the power exercised by the root not in terms of my own existence, which was also soon bound to dissolve into a wave, but in terms of a cosmic conception of time, or, perhaps, a conception of time that went much further than that. Later I learnt from scientific books that Ginseng is a survival of the aralian species of herbs and shrubs and that the different species of animals and plants which surrounded it in the Tertiary period, had undergone unimaginable changes since then; but this knowledge did not, as it often happens, banish from my heart the thrill of excitement which the faith of men aroused in it. Even to-day, for all my knowledge, I am thrilled at the thought of the fate of that herb which during the past tens of thousands of years had seen incandescent sand change to snow and lived to see the coniferous trees and among them the bear walking. . . .

After a long period of silent contemplation, the Manchus suddenly fell to talking all together and, as far as I could make out, they were discussing the various minutest details of the construction of that root. Perhaps the argument revolved round the question whether a certain fibre was more appropriate for a masculine root and suited it better, while, on the other hand, it did not suit a feminine root, and that it might therefore be better to remove it carefully altogether. There could have been hundreds of questions of such a nature, and many of them, no doubt, arose in the course of the discussion, interfered with its main theme and provoked heated arguments. But however heated the argument, Lu Wen had only to smile for calm to be restored, for everybody accepted his opinion unquestioningly. Lu Wen no longer got excited, his authority was supreme, it was as unchallengeable as is the authority of any man who has attained to the perfect mastery of his subject. Lu Wen's decision was regarded as law by everyone. When passions were laid and a quiet argument ensued, I made up my mind at last to ask Lu Wen what they were discussing now.

"Plenty, plenty medicine," replied Lu Wen.

The conversation, therefore, turned upon the subject of money: how much that rarest of treasures was worth ? Lu Wen told me that a poor seeker after the root Ginseng had found the root and had been killed and that the treasure had been seized by "a numpa one lascal," that is to say, a great rascal, and another man had bought it from him and sold it to a third for more money, and the third one would sell it to a fourth for still more money and so on and so forth, for every man who engaged in this business was a "lascal."

"And how will it all end ?" I asked.

"No end," replied Lu Wen. "Such root walkee-walkee. Such root has plenty, plenty medicine. Little man find it, sleepee-sleepee, but big man walkee-walkee."

Having entrusted the precious root to the care of Lu Wen, the Manchus lay down to sleep on a cold stone floor and, I suppose, must have left before dawn.

VI

A strange noise wakened me. It reminded me of the hum of telegraph wires in a high wind. But there were no telegraph wires in the wild jungle of the Pacific coast. I opened my eyes and saw Lu Wen. He, too, was listening to something.

"Me and you must go now, mister," he said "Your Ginseng grow all light. Me show you."

He was dressed in blue clothes like one of the Chinese seekers for Ginseng. As a protection against the dew he wore an oilcloth apron, while his back was covered by a leopard skin, to make it possible for him to sit down on a wet day. On his head he wore a conical little hat made out of bark, in his hand he had a long stick for clearing away the dead leaves and grass under his feet; a knife hung at his belt as well as a little stick made out of bone for digging up the root and a little bag with flint and tinder. The blue colour of the cotton material out of which his shirt and trousers were made recalled to my mind those desperadoes who engaged in the hunting down of the seekers for the Root of Life and who called their sport a pheasant shoot, if it was the blue-clad Chinese seekers they were after, and a swan shoot, if it was the white-clad Koreans.

"What's all this noise, Lu Wen?" I asked, pointing in the direction of the noise which reminded me of the humming of telegraph wires in a storm.

"War!" Lu Wen replied without a moment's hesitation.

We struck a light. I went upstairs and there I discovered the cause of the war in a heap of rubbish: a large death-head sphinx moth had got herself entangled there and, trying to free herself, she fluttered with her wings so rapidly that the noise produced was just like the hum of telegraph wires. I showed it to Lu Wen, but he paid no heed to the cause of that humming noise.

"Such hoo-hoo belong war," he repeated. "War come plenty quick."

Superstition, the irremovable residue of far-away, once perhaps living beliefs, does not in my view degrade a person any more than a hankering after certain middle-class comforts degrades the people who cannot live without them: even while remaining superstitious or showing a preference for a certain kind of hair lotion or a particular size of notepaper, a man can remain a living, civilised human being. But this time Lu Wen's superstition stung me to the quick. "Do not the papers," I thought to myself, "or, under the conditions we live here, the rumours brought by the new settlers, testify a thousand times more about the imminence of war than any wild guesses from some natural signs and portents? And does not the rustle of life produced by the wings of moths flitting over a camp-fire at night speak of the boundlessness of the creative force of the earth more eloquently than some superstitious notion?" Reflecting more deeply on the reasons for my special disrelish of superstition at this time, I came to the conclusion that the legend of the Root of Life, in which a people of so many millions had believed for several thousands of years, fascinated me so greatly that I was a little afraid to subject it to the test of personal experience, a test which I fearlessly applied to every kind of legend. This fear aroused my temper and made me feel exasperated at the slightest contact with superstition.

We left the Chinese hut in pitch darkness, walking along the verge of the coomb in the direction of the sea. Even if we had left after daybreak we should not have been able to see anything because of the dense mists which are prevalent here in summer-time. The only light we had was the light that came from the lanterns of the flitting fireflies and that, too, only just at close quarters. And here I myself had an opportunity of testing the power of inherited superstition: looking at the luminous flies as they flitted here, there and everywhere I could not help remembering the countless dead on the battlefield. I remembered them as, dying in horrible agonies, they seemed to *pass out* somewhere. "Aren't they those fireflies?" I asked myself, just like some savage aborigine. And calling to mind some of my dead comrades, I became aware of a pain deep inside me which seemed to have lain dormant there all the time, a pain I had accepted from them because of the great compassion I had felt for them, and so it came about that, having passed out, they were now flitting about as fireflies, while I still carried their pain in my heart and, perhaps, at certain times acted quite unconsciously under the influence of the pain I was harbouring because of the loss of friends in war. But Lu Wen's goodness was so great that at the sight of the flitting fireflies he began, not altogether by chance, to guess something of the pain I felt and, having guessed everything in a flash, he took all that pain upon himself; for his faith in a better life was part of his belief in the vital force of the Ginseng root and he had therefore quite naturally dedicated himself to the succour of the sick.

So, looking at the flying insects, I tried in my own way to purify the legend of the Root of Life and to detach it from the dead and, in the conditions of our modern life, often harmful superstitions which had come down to us from a far away past. The flying insects disappeared so suddenly that it seemed quite uncanny and the impression left on my mind was as if they had left behind them some of their light. In that light we began to discern various objects lit up from below and not from above, as usually happens at dawn on a clear morning, when the first thing you see is the sky and only a long time after are you able to distinguish the things lit up on the ground by the sun. We were in the mountains near the sea-shore and the cliffs appeared to us like gigantic black figures looming out of the mist. Those ghostly figures of cliffs brought back to me the strange transformation of deer-flower into woman; for peering at them through the mist, I seemed to be able to read in their book of magic and see that transformation again. Lu Wen, too, no doubt, was pondering over some dear memory of his own. There was no need for us to tell each other our thoughts, and that was why we walked along in silence and did not in the least feel constrained in each other's company. The morning breeze sent a cold shiver down my spine and, through my body, which seemed to have become one with the rest of nature in that one sensation of chill at dawn, I got the impression as if all nature had divested herself of her clothes and was bathing. Lu Wen, too, seemed to want to tell me about it, for he suddenly stopped me, began to rub his hands together as if he were washing them and, spreading out his hands in the sense of "everywhere! everywhere!" he said, "All light, all light, plenty all light!"

But it soon became apparent to me that Lu Wen was merely trying to convey to me what the weather was going to be like shortly: it frequently happens in those parts of the Pacific Coast that even the thickest mist suddenly becomes invisible and the air, although still saturated with vapour, becomes entirely transparent. We saw the sunrise from a high cliff on the sea-shore, on a path surrounded by some dense bushes. Occasionally beautiful Mongolian pheasants with white rings round their necks flew out of the bushes, and as they rose with a whirl of wings, they looked back at us and called to us in their own language: "Ker-ker-ker." Soon I understood why the scrub here was so terribly dense and why it was so stunted: the sea with its typhoons had for thousands of years struck furiously against these cliffs and, in the end, life had succeeded in striking roots here—all sorts of flowers began to grow in the crevices of the cliffs, soon to be followed by oak saplings. Thus it was that the sea had let life obtain a foothold here. But, oh, what a wretched life it was at first! The oak saplings which grew nearest to the sea dared not even think of raising their heads: they grew in a kind of recumbent position, crawling away from the sea on their thin trunks and looking very much like smoothly brushed back hair. But the further we walked away from the sea, the higher and higher did the oak saplings raise their heads, although even then they dared not rise beyond a certain limit: as soon as they reached the height of a man, they withered at the top, forming an impassable thicket with their intertwined branches, and the pheasants took advantage of it at that season when their fledglings had to be carefully shielded against attack by all sorts of beasts and birds of prey.

As we walked away from the sea and went further and further into the jungle, we did not lose sight of it all at once: we kept on descending and ascending, now the sun would disappear and now we would hail it again, as though experiencing afresh a new dawn; the sea-shore, cut up by bays and blocked up with rocks and inlets, provided more and more screens for the sun, and as a result every new sunrise revealed more and more features of the land and sea-scape to us. On the top of the last cliff, from where a distant prospect opened up across miles and miles of ocean, there grew a group of funereal pines of a remarkable shape, looking like Japanese parasols or the stone-pines on the Mediterranean coast. These were of so intense a blue that it seemed to us that even if there were hundreds of them on that particular spot, we should still be able to see the sea through them. From the top of that cliff, through the pines, we could distinguish with the naked eye, the heads of a great number of creatures in the sea.

Even in the darkest part of the forest, after we had finally lost sight of the sea and had descended into a deep gorge, we could clearly see an ant crossing our path with its prey. We were following a path which was entirely bare of vegetation and which had been made by the hoofs of the Manchurian red deer, the spotted deer, boars, antelopes and goats, and only later adapted by man for his own purposes. From that path we turned into a deep coomb with a nameless spring which kept on appearing and disappearing under heaps of stones and which only betrayed its existence to us by its perpetual subterranean talk. It was across these piles of stones that the barely visible footpath crossed the brook in one direction and then in another, but we soon left this meandering path and strode from one pool to another, often jumping from stone to stone. Every now and again Lu Wen pointed out to me some notch on the bark of a cork-tree, or a broken twig on an aralia thorn, or a piece of moss which had been purposely stuck into the hollow of a poplar, and asked me to remember all those primitive signposts. They had not been put there for any traveller that might pass that way, any trapper, hunter or jungle tramp; no, all those were pointers left for other seekers for the Root of Life, as an indication that the locality had been thoroughly explored and that they would be wasting their time in searching for it there. But that footpath did lead to my own Root of Life and Lu Wen pointed out those guideposts to me so that I, inexperienced root hunter that I was, could find it myself without his aid.

"But what am I to do," I asked, "if a typhoon should tear the moss out of the hollow of the tree or the spring floods wash away the marked cork-tree or if even this whole hillside should crumble and block our path with stones?"

"Must have clear conscience in head, mister," Lu Wen replied.

I understood that he meant that I must have my wits about me and I pointed at the rugged side of the gorge, the trees and the sward: everything, I meant, would be blocked up and no wits would be of any avail.

"Head no good," I said, "no good."

"Head no good," Lu Wen repeated. "No want head. Here's

where head belong," and he pointed to his heart. I understood
him to mean that in searching for the Root of Life one must have a
clear conscience and never look back in the direction where everything
had been trampled down; for if a man had a clear conscience, no
obstruction could bar his way to the goal.

Slowly the lofty sides of the gorge began to decline and we came
to a small depression with a little swamp out of which the little stream
issued which had caused that deep gorge among the cliffs. From
here, at the end of the pass, we passed into a wide valley with line
upon line of majestic cedars, so widely dispersed and with so low an
undergrowth, that it was possible to see a long way between their
trunks and obtain an unobstructed view of the sward between each
tree. Everything in the Valley of Song—the dancing leaf-shadows
the constantly flitting silhouettes and shadows of birds—spoke of a
rich life: countless numbers of little songbirds chirruped among the
different trees, for, besides the cedars, the valley abounded in ancien
poplars, at least three hundred years old, stooping, hunch-backed
gnarled, with huge hollowed out trunks in which bears hibernated in
winter, giant lime-trees, tall elms and cork-trees.

The Valley of Song with its giant trees, sufficiently dispersed to
assure enough light for the numerous creatures living in the under
growth, was so beautiful that the thought of the need of a clear
conscience for the quest for the Root of Life came by itself. As we
walked on, we soon cut across the Valley of Song in a north-westerly
direction and, suddenly, we came to an ancient river terrace which
took us down to another valley, covered with a different kind of
vegetation: among the stocky trunks of the black poplars there were
black birches, spruce firs, silver firs, hornbeams, small-leaved maples
and further on, after we had passed through that dense wood in which
the trees were intertwined with the lianas of vine and lemon-tree, the
vegetation changed for a third time on the bank of some unknown
stream, broad-leaved nut-trees here and there intermingling with
cedars; the wide-spaced big trees were smothered in thickets of buck
thorn, elder-bushes, bird-cherry and crab-trees, beneath the shade of
which among the intertangled shade-loving grasses we had to look
for the Root of Life—Ginseng.

Here Lu Wen and I sat down for a rest and neither of us broke
the silence for a long time. What was happening in the stillness
during our long silence? A countless multitude of insects, thousand
and thousands of grasshoppers, crickets and cicadas as well as other
musicians of the insect world built up that stillness, created it them
selves, while playing their different instruments for all they were
worth: for you don't hear them at all once your thoughts have

attained that calm state of equilibrium where one thought follows on the heels of another freely and unimpeded. Or, maybe, you just fall under the spell of the music of those countless musicians so that after a time you cease noticing it and you yourself, as it were, take part in it without knowing it, and it is because of that that a real, curiously alive, creative silence is born. The stream, which was somewhere near, also seemed to glide along in complete silence; and yet should your calm thoughts be interrupted by some quite random memory and should you be overcome by a sudden desire to say something to someone near to your heart, a desire so irresistible that it broke from your lips in a suppressed moan, then a voice would suddenly burst out of that little stream, which probably ran over a bed of pebbles, and the voice would say, "Speak, speak, speak!" And the countless millions of musicians, the whole inaudible throng of them, suddenly caught up that refrain and all together burst forth: "Speak, speak, speak!"

And so Lu Wen and I began to talk about some bird which was said to guard the Root of Life—Ginseng. I assumed that Lu Wen had in mind one of the three species of cuckoos which inhabited that region; this small, dusky-hued cuckoo is said to mount guard over the Root of Life, but is visible only to the man who, immediately he sees the Root of Life, pushes in his stick beside it. For it often happens, indeed it is said to happen almost invariably, that no sooner has the seeker after the Root of Life caught a glimpse of it than it vanishes: in the twinkling of an eye Ginseng is transformed into some other plant or animal. But if, on catching sight of it, you immediately push in your stick beside it, it will never vanish from you. However, we had nothing to worry about, for the root we were after had been discovered about twenty years ago: it was very young then and it was left to grow for another ten years. But it chanced that a big Manchurian red deer passed that way and stepped on the head of the Ginseng and, because of that, the root had stopped growing. A short time ago it began to grow again and in another fifteen years it would be ready.

"You run-run now," Lu Wen said, "but time come you understand all light."

We were silent for some time. During that silence I tried to think what would happen to me in fifteen years' time and I imagined a meeting. Fifteen years of our separate lives had passed and it was with difficulty that we recognised each other, feeling somewhat apprehensive and looking rather embarrassed, standing beside each other and unable to think of anything to say.

Oh, the sharp pain in our hearts! But as that "Oh!" escaped our

lips, the stream suddenly called out, "Speak, speak, speak!" and after
it all the musicians and all the creatures of the Valley of Song, struck
up their instruments and burst out into song, the whole living stillness
suddenly opening up and calling out, "Speak, speak, speak!"

"Another fifteen years," Lu Wen said, "you still young man,
your lady also young."

Then we got up and crossed to the other bank of the stream over
the trunk of a crab-tree which lay across the stream. There Lu Wen
soon knelt down on a patch of matted sward and, putting his hands
palm to palm, remained in that position a long time. I felt so excited
that I, too, knelt involuntarily beside him: I was conscious of kneeling
at the very source of the creative force of life. My thoughts, in
harmony with the beatings of my heart, were crystal clear, and my
heart beat in unison with the whole music of stillness. But presently
the right moment came by itself: Lu Wen parted the grasses and—
I saw . . . a few tiny leaves, looking like human hands with
five elongated fingers on a short and thin stalk. Not only the
Manchurian red deer with its coarse hoof could mortally injure such
a tender plant, but even an ant, if it were so minded, could in a short
time stop its growth for many years. How many hazards might not
that plant and my own life, too, for that matter, incur during the next
fifteen years!

Before we left the place Lu Wen showed me a notch on the trunk
of a cedar. It was exactly an ell from the ancient cedar to the root
and, from the other side, from the trunk of a cork-tree, it was also
an ell, while on the third side there was a notched oak, and on the
fourth side—an acacia.

VII

One day I went into the jungle to hunt the stag of the spotted
deer or the Manchurian red deer while his antlers, still filled with
blood, were quite large, but had not yet matured and turned
into bone. Such a hunt is very lucrative: there are immature
antlers which fetch as much as one thousand gold roubles.

At the time when the hunters set out to get those antlers, the hinds
are already taking out their fawns on the hillsides; the stags, however
seldom show themselves and usually keep to the northerly slopes of
the mountains, while during the season of the cold, north winds
and rains, they take refuge in the underbrush where they often stand
motionless for a long time, afraid, no doubt, to injure their new antlers
which are very sensitive to the least touch.

Misty Mountain, which was my destination that day, was
almost entirely clear. Only its very top, black and rugged, loomed

indistinctly out of the mist. This mountain was flanked by the sea on three sides and reminded me very much of an extinct volcano, which, I surmised, it must have been not so very long ago: I often found pumice-stones on the beach. The mountain was, of course, greatly eroded and its sides were everywhere cut up into deep gorges and big hollows. It was in those gorges that every kind of game could be found as well as all sorts of curious plants which belonged to species that had long ago vanished from the earth; all those ravines, which were invaluable to the hunters, met at the top of the mountain and the mountain as a whole was the central point of all those deep valleys which were so rich in game and rare plants.

I was walking along the sea-shore in a south-westerly direction where three of the most beautiful valleys of Misty Mountain—the Blue Valley, the Forbidden Valley and the Leopard Valley—ran down to the sea. At the bottom of each valley a stream flowed, a stream which, of course, had in the course of time scooped them out of the sides of the mountain, from top to bottom. It was at the very bottom of those valleys, along the course of the streams, that the precious plants, relics of past ages, had been preserved, for there they were well protected from all the winds except the south wind which blows from the sea; on the top of those valleys, along their sides, grew the funereal pines, which seemed to enjoy sporting with the typhoons.

I ascended to the very top of Misty Mountain from the sea, keeping to the left side of the Blue Valley and I was walking along the ridge quietly, just as the tigers and leopards do, so as to be able to see everything on every side. Here and there, both in the Blue Valley and in the Forbidden Valley, I caught sight of deer, but they were all hinds with their young. Only occasionally was a pricket to be seen among them, a stag in his second year with his thin 'brockets.'' Suddenly I heard a bellow, a growl and a snorting at the bottom of the valley which I was later to call the Leopard Valley. I ran down the ridge very quickly along the sandy bank of the stream, trying my best not to knock against or precipitate any stones, took a flying leap over some bushes, stole along cautiously and soon espied on the other side of the gorge, across some bushes, some kind of a brownish animal. He got scent of me and ran reluctantly, at a lazy trot, up the other side of the deep valley, now appearing, now disappearing in the oak underbrush. I was waiting until I could see him clearly when he reached the sandy ridge near the top of the mountain, but it seemed that, before reaching it, he lay down behind some stones, as beasts of prey of the feline species usually do: all I could see from behind the rocks were his eyes. At such a distance

the target was covered by the sights of my rifle and I could not possibly
have killed him.   I then made haste to cross over to the other side
of the gorge to see what prey the brown animal had got.   Not to
lose my way, I fixed a certain object of an unusual form as my guiding
post, namely, a tree under which there lay suspended almost in mid-air
a huge rock which, it seemed, had only to be touched to be precipitated down the side of the gorge, knocking over whatever lay in its
path.   I thought that behind that boulder the life and death struggle
between the two animals had taken place.

I could reach the tree with the stone only by climbing up the
precipitous side of the gorge on my stomach, grasping the stone-pine
saplings with my outstretched hands.   I was not mistaken: behind
that boulder I found the carcass of a young stag with beautiful and
fortunately, entirely undamaged new antlers.   I had often heard
Lu Wen say that the value of the antlers depended not so much upon
their size as upon their configuration, the main thing being that the
right and left branches should be a perfect match.   It seemed that
that was neither superstition, nor a whim of fashion; for if any part of
the deer suffered the slightest injury, the corresponding branch of those
bony outgrowths on one or the other side developed in a different way
and, consequently, if the medicinal value of the antlers depended upon
the animal's health, that could be partly judged by their formations.

I gathered as many boughs of stone-pines as I could break off,
covered up the killed stag with them as a protection against the sun,
and then went to track down the leopard.   The rock behind which the
wild animal had hidden itself looked like an enormous eagle.   I made
a long detour along the ridge and, recognising the rock, began to
steal my way towards it, ready at any moment to get the leopard in
the sights of my rifle.   But the leopard was no longer behind the
rock.   Then I went along the ridge round the whole plateau, which
had once perhaps been the crater of a volcano, but the leopard was
nowhere to be seen.   I sat down for a rest near a remarkably smooth,
as though polished, slab of mountain schist and, as I looked at it
against the sun, I noticed the print of the soft pad of the beautiful
beast in the dust that covered the slab.   I examined it from
different angles and there was no doubt in my mind that the
leopard had passed over that slab of smooth rock.   I knew, of course,
that it is the habit of tigers and leopards to stalk along mountain
ridges and the discovery of the footprint on the slab told me nothing
new: the leopard had passed this way and disappeared among the
rocks: to find him without first discovering his tracks was impossible.
Then I directed my gaze towards the beautiful spit at the foot of
Misty Mountain and began to examine its cliffs, crowned with the same

ovely, playful pines as all the other slopes of the southern gorges. From where I was sitting I could see that on that narrow spit, covered with the short grass of which the deer were so fond, a hind was grazing, and beside her, in the shade of a bush, lay some brown, rolled-up object. It was not difficult to guess that that object was a fawn. Suddenly, just where the incoming tide was tossing its white-flecked breakers high up the cliffs as if trying to reach the inaccessible dark-green stone-pines, an eagle rose in the air, soared high over the spit, spied the fawn and dropped down upon it like a stone. But the hind heard the sound of the huge, falling bird and took quick action to meet it: she stood on her hind legs in front of her fawn and tried to strike the eagle with her forelegs, while the eagle, angered by the unexpected opposition, began to attack her, until, at last, the sharp hoof of the hind struck him a well-aimed blow. The mauled eagle regained his balance with some difficulty in the air and flew back to the stone-pine, on the top of which he probably had his nest. It was about noon and it was getting hot: at this time the deer usually leave their open-air grazing grounds and, until the evening, walk back to their permanent coverts, hiding in the deep coombs among the shady trees. So that hind, too, the only one on the spit, raised her fawn and led him away from the Spit of the Eagle's Nest straight to the coomb where our little hut stood.

There was hardly any doubt in my mind that the hind was Hua-lu, and, oh, the conflicting emotions that arose in me suddenly, without any warning, changing swiftly like the sunlight and the shadows upon the rolling waves of the ocean below! But all those feelings were crowded out by a thought which afterwards determined all my activities in that region. "The Spit of the Eagle's Nest," I reflected, "provides no exit for the deer except a very narrow neck of land of about a hundred yards, and should that neck of land be fenced off by a palisade, the deer could only leave the spit by throwing themselves over the sheer cliff into the sea and then swimming for the shore. But that was hardly a safe way of escape for the deer, for below sharp, black rocks appeared and disappeared among the waves and any living creature that fell upon that terrible reef would be instantly dashed to pieces."

This thought just flashed through my mind, but it began to grow on me until I could think of scarcely anything else.

After a rest I decided to walk carefully once again round the whole of the table-land, taking good note of every reddish speck I might see, in case the leopard had thought of something by this time. . . . I could see the hinds escorting their fawns from the open grazing grounds to their permanent haunts in the coombs here

and there on the sides of Misty Mountain, or else simply finding a
temporary shelter for them near their present grazing grounds in the
oak underbrush. Again and again I watched from where I was a
spotted deer becoming entirely invisible as it entered the shade of a
tree, thanks to its protective spots which so much resembled the
dancing leaf-shadows. There, in the shade, they spent their time
feeding on the tender shoots and leaves of the vine or scratching out
with a hoof the ticks that tormented them. I could not see the leopard
anywhere and, in the end, came back to the same smooth slab of
rock and sat down beside it. Having nothing else to do, I again
began to study the print of the leopard's paw and, suddenly, I became
aware of another footprint next to the first one, far more distinctly
outlined in the dust. And that was not all by any means: looking
again at the new footprint against the sun, I discovered two bristles
sticking out of the ground and, picking one of them up, I recognised
a hair from the leopard's paw. While I had been walking round the
plateau, the sun, of course, began to throw its beams at a different
angle and it was possible that at first I had missed seeing the other
footprint, but I could not possibly have failed to notice the bristles, and
therefore I could not help concluding that the leopard had all the
time been stealing after me. That confirmed entirely the stories
I had heard about the leopard and the tiger: it was their usual habit
to get in the rear of the man who was tracking them.

There was no time to lose now. I hurried back to Lu Wen,
anxious to prevent the eagles from discovering the covered-up carcass
of the deer, and was lucky to find him at our hut. He was delighted
to hear my story of the killed stag with such a fine pair of antlers
We went back by a short cut, climbing up the steep side of the gorge
Having reached the top of Misty Mountain, Lu Wen and I went
round the ridge along the whole plateau, trying to walk as softly as
possible and examining every rock with great care. As we came
up opposite the smooth slab of rock, I jumped down from the ridge,
and with the help of a long stick I covered up my tracks from the
leopard, and then I again took a flying leap to the first small bush
where I hid myself to windward. Lu Wen continued his walk along
the ridge, while I propped up my elbows and gun against some rocks
and waited. Before long I saw the black shadow of the crouching
leopard silhouetted against the blue background of the sky: the huge
cat was creeping along without suspecting that I was watching it
behind a rock along the barrel of my gun. Lu Wen, on the other hand,
could hardly have noticed anything even if he had looked back.
When the leopard had crept up to the slab and stood on it, raising
himself so as to have a good look at Lu Wen over the top of the large

stone, I got him well in my sights and prepared to pull the trigger. It seemed to me that the leopard, seeing only one man instead of two, was at a loss to account for it and looked round bewildered as though asking of his surroundings, "Where on earth is the other?" When, having looked round irresolutely, he cast a suspicious glance at my bush, I got the bridge of his nose in my gun-sight and, holding my breath, fired. The leopard just crouched down on the slab of rock, lowered his head between his paws, moved his tail a few times, and looked as if he had crouched to make his fateful spring.

What a beautiful rug we got! But it was not the valuable skin of the leopard that made Lu Wen so happy: in his mysterious medical lore, mixed up as it was with so many superstitious beliefs, it was the heart of the leopard, his liver and even his whiskers that were of even greater importance. Yet he forgot even those when he saw the antlers of the killed deer.

"Plenty, plenty medicine!" he said, cutting the antlers out of the stag's skull together with the frontal bone.

In reply to my question why he did not cut the antlers off at the pedicles, but took them with the frontal bone, he replied, "Me catchee thlee times more medicine that way."

It appeared that the value of the antlers was twice or three times as great if they were cut away with the frontal bone. Those ordinary antlers which were cut off at the pedicles were only used as a medicine, but the antlers with the frontal bone were a priceless possession, a pledge of family bliss and happiness: in the rich Chinese households they were preserved under a bell-glass, and when in the course of time all that was left of the antlers was only their shape, their lovely velvet having crumbled into dust, they would still fill the master of the house with the hope that even in his old age he would keep his youthful virility.

"Such antlers go long, long walk." Lu Wen said, "bling vely much medicine."

Like the greatly prized Ginseng, these "walking" antlers would change hands many times and each time they changed hands, their price would go up considerably until the richest and cleverest "lascal" took them to the most powerful mandarin, who would slip them surreptitiously into the wide sleeve of his robe with his left hand, while performing a highly satisfactory operation with his right hand for the "lascal."

"Are mandarins also 'lascals?'" I asked.

"Mandarins likee long, long walk," Lu Wen replied.

We loaded ourselves with the leopard's skin and the venison, the deer's spotted coat, the priceless new antlers, the leopard's heart, liver and whiskers and, as we descended Misty Mountain and came opposite the Eagle's Nest, I looked down at the spit and I saw there. . . . The thought I had conceived earlier in the day, having obtained such strong support in the precious booty we were now carrying home, assumed a very definite form, for I had been revolving it in my mind, without being conscious of it myself, all the time, and suddenly I felt happy.

What I saw was what Lu Wen, who had lived here for thirty years, had seen hundreds of times: I saw the deer-flower slowly crossing the isthmus to the grazing ground of the Eagle's Nest.

Having pointed out the hind to Lu Wen, I explained to him my simple plan for obtaining a constant supply of a great amount of "medicine" and, greatly delighted, he exclaimed, "All light, all light, captain!"

His exclamation puzzled me and even to this day I have not finally succeeded in finding a satisfactory answer to the question why Lu Wen should have begun to call me captain after I had told him of my little discovery?

VIII

Lu Wen caught a beautiful pheasant and brought the bird for me to see.

"Let's cook it," I said, knowing the lovely dish the white meat of a Mongolian pheasant makes.

Lu Wen replied, "Me likee eat him vely much, but no can chop off head, captain."

I chopped off the pheasant's head. He said, "All light, captain," and began to pluck the bird.

A little later, having put some rice in the pot with the pheasant, the two of us had a delicious meal together.

Now, to chop off a pheasant's head is not exactly an important business, but for all that, thinking over again why Lu Wen should suddenly begin to call me "captain," I could not help associating this rather unimportant affair with the new title conferred upon me: apparently it was the business of captains not only to make discoveries, but also to chop off heads. It seemed that when Lu Wen first came to the jungle, he was not the quiet and wise man he had become during his quests for the Root of Life. Once upon a time he, together with other Chinese trappers, caught the spotted deer, the Manchurian red deer and the mountain goats by means of the terrible Chinese traps: he felled trees and piled them up with their roots close to each other, leaving only here and there sufficient room for the animals to run between the tree trunks; but it was in those free passages that deep pits were dug and covered up with boughs, and the animals fell into them, as often as not breaking their legs. Lu Wen also used to chase the deer over the frozen ground with his little dog, which had so vicious a temper that it used to hang on by its teeth to the deer's side and run alongside until the deer, his feet cut by the frozen snow, was brought to bay. With such fleetfooted small dogs the Chinese did their best to chase the deer over the frozen ground into the sea where they caught them from boats, tying them up with ropes in the water. The captured deer were kept until they had grown new antlers and then, after the precious antlers had been cut off, they were slaughtered for meat. It was difficult to imagine that time when Lu Wen, with the other Chinese trappers, brutally maltreated the rare, dying out animals for the sake of obtaining the delectable antlers for rich people. Yet Lu Wen started his life in the jungle as a trapper of wild animals and he, of course, could distinguish the footprints of different animals much better than I, as well as guess by their footprints what they were up to, and, indeed, I believe that he could even think the way animals thought. I must confess, however, that I was never greatly impressed by the experience gained by such jungle trackers and I certainly never spoke of them in the tones of awe-struck veneration which some people affect when talking of such trackers. What does all the knowledge of such native trackers amount to compared with my own ability to make a chemical test of any substance and decide its composition and calculate the quantity of its component parts to the fourth decimal? More that that: I can concentrate all the powers of my mind upon any field of research, such as chemistry, and in a short time overtake any tracker who has spent all his life in obtaining personal experience in one particular line. No! It was not his astounding knowledge of the life of the jungle that I admired so greatly in Lu Wen, but the feeling of affinity and kinship which he showed to every creature and plant in nature. What I had found so admirable about him was not that the life of the jungle was an open book to him, but that he was able to endow everything in the world with a living spirit. It was obvious that some kind of profound change had taken place in his life, and that that was why he had given up his cruel sports, the savage trapping of animals resulting in the destruction of life and, instead, had devoted himself to the quest for the Root of Life.

There are certain experiences which one must never ask about or talk about, for by themselves they say little. A man discloses his deepest experiences in his work and his friend is able to divine them himself by pondering over his work. I knew that Lu Wen had to support his brother's large family, and very often I could not help

feeling that Lu Wen had been left in the lurch at some family share-out
and gone away into the jungle, feeling nothing but hatred for his
brother.   Perhaps he had spent the first ten years of his life in the
jungle just as a hunter in order to prove to his father, who had thought
him a good-for-nothing wastrel, that he could earn his living by his
own hands better than his brother.   And then in the fullness of time
he had gone back to China with ample proof of his abilities to convince
his father and to show his contempt for his brother, but there was no
one left either to convince or to scorn.   Both his father and his brother
had died in one of those plagues which are so frequent in China and
only the wife of Lu Wen's brother with her numerous children were left
behind.   It was quite likely that the great change in Lu Wen's
character had taken place then.   Before, his whole life was devoted
to the task of proving himself worthy of his father's esteem, and then,
suddenly, there was no one left to prove his worth to.   I heard
many similar stories from the Chinese afterwards.   But even if
I had heard the same story from Lu Wen himself, it would still have
told me less about him than the two tall poplar-trees which Lu Wen
had planted a long time ago with his own hands near his cottage.
How joyfully he welcomed them, always murmuring some Chinese
words to the different creatures which sat waiting in the foliage in
expectation of his arrival!   His favourite crow was not a grey one, as
with us, but a black one.   At the first sight you might take it for a
rook, but on looking closer, you'd remember that a rook has a white
beak, while that bird had a black one.   "So it is a raven!"   But
suddenly a sound would come out of that black crow which was just
like the sound made by our ordinary grey crow.   It was a very
clever crow and sometimes when Lu Wen went away into the jungle,
it would see him off a long way, flying from one tree to another.

Among the birds which lived on the trees were a blue magpie,
a warbler, a kingfisher, several thrushes, a yellow-hammer and a
cuckoo; a quail would come running and whistling in the bushes,
but its call was not the "wet-my-feet" of the quails in our fields, but
more like "lose-your-tea!"   So all the birds looked just like ours and
you could recognise them at once, but soon you would notice that
something or other was the same and yet not quite the same.   Take
the starling, for example: he was black and his beak was yellow and
he also had the same iridescent feathers as our starlings have, and
when he was about to burst out into song he would, just like our
starlings, thrust out his little chest and you would be waiting excitedly
for him to start twittering his spring song, but—nothing happened:
all he did was just to croak hoarsely.   And the cuckoo's call was not
"cuckoo," but a kind of "ke-ke."

Lu Wen talked to all of them every morning and fed them. I was deeply touched by this friendship between Lu Wen and the birds and, indeed, by the feeling of kinship which he showed in relation to every living creature. What I particularly liked about it was that Lu Wen acted as he did without any ulterior motive and that he never attempted to make others do as he did because he considered it right. He never thought of putting himself forward as an example, but everything just seemed to happen as it did because he could not do otherwise. It just happened that he caught a pheasant and, of course, one had to eat it, but how was he to do it if it could be done only by chopping off the pheasant's head? So he asked a man who was more capable of chopping off heads than he was, a *captain*. But, on the other hand, how happy he was that the captain himself was greatly outraged by the wholesale destruction of the beautiful, dying out species of deer and wanted to preserve and breed it!

We set about carrying out my plan and, to begin with, we cut a large number of the bines of the vine, lemon tree and other climbing plants in our coomb, smoked them thoroughly over a fire so that the deer should scent the soot a long way away and, recognising in it some sinister human device, should fear it. We also made a sledge, roomy enough to carry all those stems, which one man could draw. Long before daybreak I was on Misty Mountain and, having waited until the deer-flower had taken her fawn out on the spit, I lit a beacon as a signal to Lu Wen. I then retraced my steps and I had barely gone half way down Misty Mountain when I saw that Lu Wen had taken up his position on the narrow neck of land and the hind-mother had become our prisoner: she would rather have thrown herself over the cliff into the sea on those sharp rocks than have plucked up courage to go straight for a man: she was trapped and from that moment the Spit of the Eagle's Nest became one of the most beautiful small rocky zoos in the world. We worked feverishly until nightfall, stretching the smoke-covered stems of the creepers across the narrow isthmus. Next morning, crouching behind rocks, we waited until the deer began to wander from their grazing grounds to their usual shady haunts in the coombs and we saw how the deer-flower was quietly walking along the deer path on the cliff towards the narrow neck of land. The day before, we, too, had walked along that path to cut down a pine-tree to make little posts for our palisade. Now the hind came upon our tracks and stopped, dilating her nostrils. She scented something on the ground and bent down her head. Presently she raised her head high, caught the smell of the smoky stems in the air, looked for some time in the direction of our hiding place, realised her danger, whistled and ran back, and her fawn went skipping after her into the oak brushwood, without for a moment losing sight of the raised stump of her white tail.

Now I was sure that the hind-mother was Hua-lu: the sun was shining through the little bullet hole in her left ear. We followed her with our eyes for a little time, then, feeling very happy, we left our hiding place and at once set about the construction of the palisade working away at it every day.

So it was that the two of us formed a partnership of our own free will: I, an educated European, who in the eyes of a Chinese was a captain, able to make up his mind quickly about everything, to think of something new and to make unexpected discoveries, and the old seeker of Ginseng, who not only knew the jungle and its wild animals, but who possessed a deep understanding of them and who knew how to encompass everything round them in the jungle by his feeling of kinship. As regards real human culture I recognised him as my superior and I treated him with deference. He, no doubt, looked upon me as an enlightened European and he treated me with that cheerful wonder and warmhearted friendship with which many Chinese treat Europeans as soon as they are sure that the latter do not intend to exploit or cheat them. At the time of course, I did not suspect what the issue of the business we had started would be, nor that it was, like air travel and radio, one of the newest undertakings embarked on by man.

Man understood the taming of wild animals only at the very dawn of civilisation and, having obtained for himself a few species of domestic animals, he for some reason gave up this work and went on living with his domestic animals just as a matter of habit while killing all wild animals. Now we were going back to that neglected work, equipped with the great knowledge humanity had accumulated during all that time. We were different, and we had to carry on the business begun at the dawn of human civilisation by savages in a different way.

IX

Siberia began to breathe in our direction and our sub-tropical region began to clothe itself in Siberian garments. The luminous insects in the mountains had long disappeared and not one was to be seen any more. The young pheasants, now fully grown, had left their fastnesses in the oak underbrush combed back by the typhoons and other impenetrable bushes. The vine leaf grew crimson in the sharp morning frosts, the ash began to turn golden. And, most important of all, the constant mists had disappeared and, while in our country the sun usually is bright in spring, here it is brightest in autumn—and what a sun it was! It shone here just as the sun shines in Italy and, in this light, the Siberian autumn flamed with blossoms much brighter than all the spring flowers of our Western climate. During one of the first September morning frosts the Manchurian red deer began to bellow in the jungle, and one moonlight night Lu Wen and I heard in our little hut the bellowing of the red deer followed by the sharp blows of antlers against antlers. Another time a red deer began to bellow somewhere and something else answered him from the opposite direction, almost like another red deer. Lu Wen, however, noticed a slight difference between the bellowing of the first red deer and the second. I was told a tiger could bellow like a red deer and that he imitated the deer's rutting call. The second, Lu Wen surmised, was either a tiger or a man who was trying to lure the red deer, excited by his pursuit of the hinds, to his hiding place by blowing a special deer horn made out of birch-bark. We began to listen to the bellowing that came from opposite directions, trying to guess whether it was a man or a tiger who was imitating the deer's tortured cry. Soon the animal that bellowed first began to approach nearer and nearer to whatever it was that bellowed after and which remained in one and the same place. The red deer came nearer and nearer—and then everything suddenly grew silent. The Manchurian red deer was now approaching the other creature—man or tiger—silently and only from time to time could we catch the sound of a snapping twig. If it was a tiger, it must be crouching at the verge of a wood, ready to spring on his prey, and if it was a man, he must have already cocked his gun and, imitating the animal, purposely stepped on some twig. The jungle kept its awful silence and gave no answer to the question: man or tiger? Then suddenly the silence was broken by a distinct rifle shot: so it was a man who put an end to the stag's life.

Under the trees, decking themselves out in bright colours before the long spell of winter's sleep, is this agonised bellowing of a tormented animal—that is what love is like among the deer! Once I found in some bushes the skulls of two stags with interlocked antlers. The two giant red deer with their eight-tined interlocked antlers perished in a fight for a hind and some little rogue of a stag tasted love's sweet raptures afterwards—the pity of it! and yet doesn't the same thing happen also among us, among people?

As the days passed, the morning frosts grew keener, the reeds among the rocks became laced with hoar-frost in the mornings and, as the sun rose, the hoar-frost turned into dewdrops which sparkled in the sunshine more brightly than the drops that run off an icicle during a thaw. While the Manchurian red deer pursue the hinds, the spotted deer are getting ready for their time of torment. Many a time had I watched a stag in the jungle patiently rubbing away the remnants of the velvet from its antlers which were now left bare and insensitive. While the Manchurian red deer fills the glades and mountains with his bellowing, the spotted deer is preparing himself for the coming fights and by the time the frost has well nipped the ripening grapes and they have become sweet, the spotted deer starts to bellow.

We had to obtain stags for our enclosure, and Lu Wen and I were also getting ready for the deer's pairing season. We were planning to tame Hua-lu, so that we could let her out during the pairing season and, when the stags started fighting for her, to call her back by the usual call on the deer horn made out of bark in the hope that the stags, maddened by their passion, would run after her. Our trouble was that the grazing ground on the Spit of the Eagle's Nest was this year covered with a rich harvest of just those grasses upon which the spotted deer fed, and Hua-lu was quite happy to graze on the spit and paid no attention to the branches of trees which we had collected and upon which the spotted deer love to browse, nor to the maize and soya bean we had spread on the ground for her. Among the panicles of the mountain reeds, which had turned completely yellow, she found short grasses which we could not even see on the grazing ground which had also turned yellow. She spent her time there either nibbling the green grass with her head bent down to the ground or standing motionless in the shade of a tree and feeding her fawn. Occasionally, she would lie down and do her best to pick out the pernicious ticks from her hide and from the hide of her fawn. Oh, how overjoyed I was one morning when at last I saw that, although she had got scent of me, she did not run away as she used to do before then, but walked along following my scent at a distance as though curious to find out whether I was hiding somewhere near! When at last she did see me, she did not, as deer do, scamper away in a headlong flight, but merely turned round sharply and walked off quietly with her fawn! Another time when she got scent of me, I began to blow my birch-bark horn. She stopped and although she saw me blowing the horn, she remained standing and listened for a long time to the sound of the horn. She was trying to make out what it was all about, but failing, of course, to get at the meaning of it, she at last stamped her foot, whistled and walked away quietly, evidently deciding that it was safer to do what she always had done before. Every day I now blew the horn for her, but all I achieved was that when she heard the sound of the horn, she would stop nibbling the grass and, walking in the direction of the sound, she would see me and stop and listen for a long time: all the time I blew the horn she remained standing and her fawn, having nothing to do, would often begin to suck. But during the first year I never succeeded in making her come up close to me when I blew the horn.

Meanwhile the frosts, which were still very light, dried up and coloured all the leaves. The small-leaved maple blazed a bright-red, the big leaves of the Manchurian nut-trees turned yellow. And the magic change that came over the bank of the Zu-Su where I first saw Hua-lu standing on her hind legs and browsing on the vine-leaves, emerald with the sun shining through them! Where in summer there was a whole green mountain village of trees densely intertwined with the stems of the vine, all the cottages now became red-tinted from the scarlet vine-leaves and the green thicket where I had spent my luckless hour now seemed especially to stand out by its profusion of red and yellow tints. Before it looked as if the vine had completely smothered some tree, but now it could be seen that even beneath the green mantle of vine the tree had sufficient light and was alive. That Manchurian nut-tree now shone golden from beneath the red vine-leaves, and everywhere against a background of red and yellow, here, there and yonder, hung ripe bunches of black Manchurian grapes only just touched by the frost.

One night Lu Wen woke me and asked me to go outside. He pointed at the sky where the Great Bear, leaning against a black mountain, seemed to drag out the missing star in its tail from behind a black crag. How beautiful the stars were at this time! Thousands of them seemed to be showering down from the sky! The air was dry and transparent. Suddenly, there came to us in the stillness of the night from under the Great Bear quite an extraordinary sound: it began with the peculiar whistle so characteristic of the spotted deer, then the shrill whistle quickly grew deeper and deeper until it finished up with a low bellow at the bottom of the scale. On the other side of our coomb, directly opposite, there came in reply the same kind of half whistle-half bellowing, and farther away, on the slopes of Misty Mountain, we could hear the same peculiar mating call of the rutting spotted deer, and farther away again still— hardly audible, sounding more like an echo of the bellowing close at hand, and farther still—like the echo of that echo.

The time we had been waiting for so long had now arrived. The pairing season of the spotted deer had begun.

The bellowing went on until morning and, when day broke, we saw a big antlered deer with a conspicuous black stripe down its spine standing on the slope of the mountain, near a glade. He looked very

E

much like Black Spine who had come to the brook with the other deer when I was having my first bathe in it.

The big antlered animal looked from a distance even more terrifying than he had looked to me close at hand from the stream. He was walking about slowly with his head raised high, constantly looking round him on every side, as if expecting something. Then apparently something took place in the bushes and he rushed away there at full speed. Presently a hind emerged from those bushes, speeding away as fast as she could, while Black Spine went in pursuit of her, up the slope of the mountain to its very top. Just then the first rays of the rising sun came streaming from behind the mountain ridge. The mountain reeds, covered with rime, began to glisten and the glitter of that mountain blinded us. By the time Lu Wen and I reached the top of Misty Mountain, the hind had already hidden herself among a herd of grazing hinds, like a high-spirited girl who during a game manages to hide herself and disappear among a crowd of her girl-friends. But because of that one hind, no deer in the herd was allowed to leave the grazing ground. Black Spine walked round and round the herd very slowly. He seemed to have had a bathe in some muddy pool at night, probably in a vain attempt to cool as much as possible his agonising passion. His belly was contracting spasmodically. He did not nibble the grass. It was quite clear that his passion brought him no joy, that it brought him nothing but torment and that his life now was just one almost unceasing and tortured bellowing. There was no rest for him, not even for one moment. If just one hind took it into her head to leave his harem and go off by herself, he at once went in pursuit of her and returned the runaway to the herd.

Suddenly all the deer turned their heads in one direction, where, from behind a hillock, a pair of antlers shot up into the air. Black Spine pricked up his ears, but the antlers soon appeared to be too trivial to bother about: it seemed that quite an ordinary stag of middling size had picked up the scent of the same fleeing hind. Black Spine did not even trouble to drive him off. All he did was to wrinkle his muzzle and give a snort and the other stag stopped dead in his tracks on the slope of the hill, not daring to advance another step. A stag could get the scent of the hind both in the air and on the ground, and many more stags came from the direction of Misty Mountain along the same path, sniffing her scent and advancing slowly. Then, for a moment, they seemed to bow their heads and next they disappeared altogether behind the last rise and after a few minutes their antlers would suddenly shoot up from behind the hillock and become plainly visible to all the deer. But all those stags were of so little consequence that the wrinkling of Black Spine's nostrils was enough to stop them. There were, however, a few arrogant spirits among them, and to drive them off Black Spine had not only to wrinkle his muzzle, but also to thrust his grey tongue out sideways and advance against them at a trot. A few of the driven-off stags, though, would after a short time begin to move forward again rather slowly. Black Spine soon got tired of driving them away and let them remain near the herd, for the lord and master of the harem realised that there was no harm done and that he had nothing to lose if he permitted the rascals to stand still and merely inhale the scent of the hind.

Some of the stags were quite young with a pair of sharp brow-tines instead of antlers; having nothing to do, these copied the grown-up stags, whistled and growled at each other, butted each other, knocking their heads together for a long time in an attempt to push each other off their places. So a longish period of peace was ushered in, a life of friendly give and take which is usual among the deer, something like the life among people during a period of prolonged peace: the hinds grazed peacefully, concealing in their herd the still reluctant hind which, however, was fast approaching the time when she would yield to the stag's passion; the prickets amused themselves by crossing their brow-tines, like rams, and butting each other, while the grown-up, though still rather young stags stood decorously in a semi-circle on the slope of the mountain, not daring to challenge the will of the all-powerful lord and master of the harem. But quite suddenly the whole herd, scenting something out of the ordinary, turned round to the hillock, behind which all the stags had come following the scent of the hind on heat. Presently they saw a pair of antlers shooting up from behind the hillock—but what antlers! They seemed to grow out of the ground very slowly and the alarmed deer, no doubt, were wondering if there would be an end to them at all? But when after the antlers there appeared the mighty head of the stag and his unconquerable brow, the whole position became clear to everybody: the mightiest lord of the jungle had arrived!

I, too, at once guessed that the powerful stag with the huge antlers was Grey Eye, upon whom I had gazed with such wonder on the first day of my arrival at the coomb of Chiki-Chiki. Even at that time he impressed me as greatly superior to the other stags, even in comparison with Black Spine, but now his neck was terribly distended, the grey, winter coat hung under it like a beard, the blood-filled, sensitive new antlers had been transformed into a most prodigious weapon with brow-tines which were capable of inflicting a mortal wound upon an enemy. Like Black Spine, he was all covered with mud, his belly was filthy, bespattered with mud in a fit of his own lust, and it contracted convulsively—the animal was spoiling for a fight, ready to run any risk so long as he asserted his sole right to the propagation of the species of spotted deer. To sire a new generation of deer he was ready to hazard everything, even his life.

Seeing the herd of hinds, Grey Eye stopped only for a moment, but in that brief space of time he had taken in the whole situation and the rest of the deer, too, knew perfectly well what he intended to do: it was quite probable that the relative strength of the two stags had been measured in combat in former years, or, maybe, one look at the stags was sufficient to tell the other deer which of the two was the stronger. All the stags which stood between Grey Eye and the herd of hinds shied away from him. It was, of course, quite likely that Black Spine and Grey Eye had some old deadly accounts to settle between themselves, or they might have had a gentleman's agreement according to which Black Spine undertook never to cross Grey Eye's path, but that if they did meet, neither should give way to the other, but fight it out between themselves to the death. The stag's antlers are, of course, a terrible weapon, but it is not in them that the main danger lies: there have been cases where a hornless stag has crushed the ribs of one which possessed a pair of excellent antlers. But Grey Eye's antlers were only to be disregarded at a stag's own peril, for they conveyed the impression of tremendous, hidden strength. On the other hand, Black Spine's wicked eyes seemed to harbour some deep-laid plan of trapping his mighty opponent or tricking him in some mean way: "Come life, come death, *you* won't get off so easily—I can tell you that!" Grey Eye, however, did not intend to waste any time and quite openly, lowering his head, went straight for Black Spine, striking his antlers viciously against his enemy's antlers and with his brow delivering a mighty blow against his enemy's brow. Black Spine gave way a little, but Grey Eye's onslaught failed to throw him and he remained standing on his feet, which was the only thing that really mattered, for if he had fallen down, even on his knees, Grey Eye would have freed his antlers and pierced his side and heart with his brow-tines—and that would have been the end. Stags can go on fighting indefinitely with their antlers or butting each other with their foreheads so long as one of them does not weaken and so long as one of them is not thrown to the ground. Everything seemed to point to a long drawn out battle which would tax the strength of the two stags, but, as chance would have it, Black Spine happened to stumble against the stump of a tree, and, getting a firm purchase for his forelegs on that tree-stump, he dealt Grey Eye such a terrific blow with his antlers, catching his enemy off his guard, too, that the lord and master of the jungle fell on his knees. But Black Spine had no time to take advantage of his favourable position. Realising the mortal peril he was in, Grey Eye immediately jumped to his feet and struck his opponent with such force that Black Spine not only fell upon his forelegs, but swayed sideways and was about to fall on his side. It seemed that in another moment Grey Eye would free his antlers and hit out so powerfully against the side of the falling stag that, having struck the ground, Black Spine would not rise again. So it would doubtlessly have happened, had not Grey Eye for some reason fallen together with his overthrown rival, and now both of them were fighting on the ground, their breath rattling in their throats as if they were in their death-throes. It was difficult to make out what had really happened, but Lu Wen had seen it happen before and he was therefore the first to realise what a golden chance we had been offered of capturing two of the mightiest stags for our deer farm, for the two stags had got themselves entangled in their own antlers and we could easily tie them up, if we did so before either of them had freed himself or the two of them had mortally injured each other. Overjoyed, Lu Wen rushed to our hut to fetch some ropes.

What a piece of luck! What a wonderful chance!

However, no undertaking can thrive unless you are lucky—things always happen like that—if you are not, then sooner or later you are sure to run up against some piece of bad luck. . . . Our business prospered from the very first. We succeeded in roping two first-class stags, Grey Eye, the lord of the spotted deer during the rutting season, was in our hands, and Black Spine, his bitterest enemy, was in our hands, too, and, in addition, Lu Wen caught another four stags and two prickets in the trap we had prepared for them on the spit.

X

The hour before dawn has, to my fancy, been given to man as an alternative to that everyday happiness when people, having enjoyed each other's closeness, or, perhaps, having worn each other out by reproaches, jealousy or premonitions of impending disaster, or having spent a sleepless night because of the cries of a sick child—are sound asleep in the early hours of the morning. I, too, am, of course, susceptible to that kind of ordinary interchange of joy and pain; it is in this joy that a home is built, but in the hour before dawn, granted to me instead of happiness, I, together with all the vital forces of nature with which I form one whole, share in that mysterious common work as a result of which happy people, awakening on a sunny morn, often exclaim in a transport of joy, "Oh, what a lovely

day!" And now I, who have been tempted to speculate on the riddles
of human existence in the early hours of the morning, say confidently
that at the root of every true happiness there needs must lie this
hardly perceptible and utterly selfless work of all the united forces of
the world during the hour before dawn.

I always used to get up even before Lu Wen and for some ten
minutes, leaning with my shoulder against anything hard, I waited
for something to happen and, while waiting for some decision, I
would think that there were no days in nature which were absolutely
identical, like two chairs; for the same day happened only once and
then it was gone for ever. So that while in the hour before dawn the
new day, which had never dawned before or ever possessed quite the
same unique qualities, was taking shape, I, too, was meditating
about something that concerned me most on that day and that,
like the dawning day, was still indeterminate and vague; but when
everything within me merged into one harmonious whole and the
day outside took on a definite form—I would go out to work.
However, it sometimes happened that the day would remain
indeterminate and it was quite impossible to make anything of it,
and my thoughts, too, would refuse to merge into one harmonious
whole, and my axe would strike mechanically and with no purpose,
to-day like the day before.

While dusk still covers the earth, the tints of the sky in the
autumn and all through the winter, after the uninterrupted mists of
spring and summer, give it a vivid, tremulous quality that is as rare
as it is wonderful. To judge from the winter sky of these regions with
its bright sun of an Italian splendour, the earth ought to have revealed
itself at dawn as a paradise of blossoming trees and shrubs, but the
Siberian winds had destroyed everything, and the whole glory of the
sun is turned seaward, and the entire sea, the whole boundless ocean, is
one intense blue, and the cliffs on the shore stand out black against
that expanse of blue, and the stone-pines on the cliffs—those dauntless
challengers of the typhoons—are never the same, each tree is quite
unlike the other. Afterwards, when it grows much lighter and a
golden road opens up across the blue sea and stretches away into
infinity, any inconspicuous flower you come across on the ground,
every minute floret or faded speck of colour, is transformed by the
magic of that sun into the most brilliantly hued flower you ever saw.

Of my entire vine-thicket where I once met Hua-lu only a
black tree remains now, a tree round whose boughs the vine-lianas
are twisted in a tangled mass, and in the place of my tent's window,
a vine-stem is hanging lifelessly in the shape of a noose, and inside
that noose the only remaining vine-leaf is dancing in the breeze, a

leaf that would have looked red in any light, but that now looks as red as blood. And yonder the lifeless sward of the yellow grazing ground is strewn with smears of red in the shape of little saucers; those are the remnants of the azalea leaves, stains of colour so vividly red that they look like little pools of the blood of deer: the blood has been spilt on the dead sward and on the dead sward it remains, like little vermilion saucers.

In a little while the whole earth is irradiated with the morning light. In the hollows there appear the hitherto concealed coverts of the deer's grazing grounds, oak bushes with the oak leaves rolled up into little brown trumpets—that is the winter fodder of the spotted deer which have not learnt, as the ordinary reindeer have, to dig up the snow with their hoofs in search of grass. But what would happen if all that lime and oak scrub were to be buried under snow ? How were we going to feed our deer in winter ? The thought was too alarming to let us stand idly leaning against a tree. We picked up our axes to cut down the twigs with their shrivelled and curled-up leaves and bound them into bundles. . . .

Lu Wen had sent out a message into the jungle and Chinese workmen arrived at our hut. On the fenced-off Spit of the Eagle's Nest we built a shed with stalls for the deer, a yard where the captured deer could be let out and a special box for the cutting off of the stags' new antlers. We spent all day at work, and the evenings I spent writing, calculating, thinking out the construction of the box for the cutting of antlers, and there was plenty to think about seeing that we had no spare iron, nor nails, nor wire, to take the place of hooks, hinges and screws.

I observed with astonishment the way the Chinese played cards: if one of them happened to get the lucky card and to win all the money in the pool, he never bothered to show his cards to his friends for them to see the winning card, he just threw his cards among the rest and raked in the money. Nobody dreamt of asking him to show his cards, for to cheat was considered impossible. What an excellent way of playing cards ! Should, however, someone try to cheat, he would not have his ears boxed but he would be killed on the spot, and that was why, fearing death, no Chinese ever dreamt of cheating: well, *that* was not so excellent. . . .

All sorts of unanswerable questions would crowd into my head, problems that seemed to defy all solution. At times I would come to the conclusion that I could not solve them because I had not the books to consult or because there were no educated people about I could ask for advice; but as a matter of fact, as I discovered afterwards, those questions were not to be answered by submitting them for decision to other people, but were best left in abeyance for the time being; they could not be answered by just thinking about them. Those problems could only be solved in the light of experience and in accordance with all the changes that time brought with it.   Where I chiefly differed from the Chinese was that I used to calculate everything, write everything down, give an account of everything to myself, while with them everything was done as an act of faith and they relied upon their memory for everything.   Why was that? Well, there were many such questions, some of them of so urgent a nature that it seemed absolutely necessary for me to find an answer to them, but there was nobody I could consult about it.   I should like to have known exactly the origin of my authority as captain: was it conferred on me because it was, as it were, a fragment of the power exercised by the European captain all over the world, a captain who had now enjoyed for a long time the advantages over all other people of being able to cast up accounts, jot down facts and get things done, or had I become a captain in the eyes of the Chinese simply because, being a white man, they looked upon me as the representative of Captain-Capital? . . .

Hundreds of questions came into my mind and my inability to answer them sometimes increased my feeling of solitude and caused me such acute pain that I was incapable of calculating, planning and thinking out the construction of the antler-cutting box.   At such times Lu Wen always came to my assistance, not directly, but somehow, by the smile with which he was always able to remind me that my Root of Life was not injured, but had only stopped growing for a time: a stag had stepped on its head with a hoof; let a certain number of years pass and the blossom on its stalk was sure to open up!   So long and so persistently did I think of it sometimes that the Root of Life was transformed into a symbol, that it went racing through my blood, that it became the main source of my strength.   Then instead of the great pain, there came a joy as great, and I was overcome by a desire to do something which would make Lu Wen and the Chinese workmen as happy as I was.   I was trying to prove to Lu Wen in the terrible language of "me—you belong" how necessary it was for Oriental peoples to cast up accounts and to put things in writing so as to make them masters in their own countries and become captains themselves.   Lu Wen, who because of the great goodness of his heart understood both birds and beasts, could not understand me.

"You count," he said, pointing to the paper, "you understand it ploper."

"Of course, it has to be done with understanding," said I.

"But me can count, no understand. Me help you and evelything be all light, plenty medicine! You count, we help you."

XI

When the pairing season came to an end and the last impregnated hind went to spend the winter in her native gorge of Misty Mountain, the stags, worn out by their bellowing, their constant pursuit of the hinds, hunger and hatred of each other, now gathered into small herds as if nothing had happened, and went into the mountains to recover in the cedar groves from their terrible sickness. At this time we, too, let our prisoners out of their loose-boxes into the yard and all of them, such bitter enemies not so long ago, began to feed peacefully from the long trough made out of an enormous, hollowed-out tree. Among them was mighty Grey Eye, lord and master of the spotted deer, the surly Black Spine with the sinister secret in his eyes, Dandy, a young three-year-old stag, a dainty-limbed, graceful animal with large brown eyes which are so rare among spotted deer, Blinker, a small-sized but stocky and very good-natured stag who always blinked when one looked into his eyes, Sprawly and Shorthorn who seemed to be brothers: the deer usually have their spots scattered anyhow, but those two had the white dots in regular rows on their hides, a characteristic probably inherited from one and the same hind. The youngsters, the prickets, we for some reason began to call simply Mikes.

The deer enclosure was quite a large yard of an irregular shape, for we had made use of growing trees as poles. We had not felled a single tree in the yard, so as to provide the stags with growing antlers with shade on a hot day. The trees had also been left untouched to enable us, if necessary, to nail stakes to them to form a triangle, the whole yard then assuming the shape of a triangle with its apex towards the narrow corridor with the box-stalls; all we had to do was to drive the deer from the base of the triangle to its apex and they could then easily and without any trouble be made to enter the narrow passage with the stalls: the box for the cutting off of the deer's growing antlers was at the end of that passage. The box had a collapsible bottom, and the stag fell through it and remained suspended, his flanks supported by a special scaffolding made out of planks and his feet dangling in the air. In this way any stag could be caught any time we wanted to cut off his antlers or to weigh him.

The protracted and rather noisy construction of the deer-pen and the antler-cutting box by the Chinese workmen postponed the taming of Hua-lu for a long time. All that time she seemed to spend with her fawn somewhere among the piled-up rocks, hiding herself among

the pines at the very tip of the spit.   I had long since destroyed the
eagle's nest, to make sure that the birds of prey did not alarm the
deer, which, if panicked, could destroy every obstacle in a concerted
rush and regain their liberty.   As soon as the pen on the spit had been
finished and everything became calm again, I took a small trough with
soya beans and a few bundles of oak-twigs to the stone-pines among
the rocks where Hua-lu was hiding.   There was no food for her among
the rocks and Hua-lu got very hungry and, as was to be expected,
finished up all the beans and oak-leaves during the first night.   Then
I moved the small trough nearer to the shed, put more beans in it and
blew my bark horn for a short time.   Soon I saw her head emerge
from behind the rocks and after a while she was in full view of me,
but she would not come nearer, however much I blew my horn, and
she remained standing at a safe distance from me all the time and
listened.   I was beginning to wonder whether she really liked my
blowing, but one day she summoned up enough courage to approach
the trough while I was blowing the horn and, bending down her head,
began to eat; from that day she always fed from the trough and she
did not care whether I blew the horn or just stood still and watched
her.   By little stages I brought her almost up to the gates of the pen
and I even tried to place the trough in the open gates, but however
much I blew my horn, she could not be induced to enter the pen.

Still, I did not have to bother about her reluctance to enter the
deer-pen very much longer.   The time came when any spotted deer
roaming Misty Mountain as free as a bird would have come to us
himself, if he had known the conditions under which our deer lived
and begged us to let him, too, feed from the trough with the beans.
There came a day when winter was quite unexpectedly upon us.
One evening I happened to look up at some cliffs towering over the
spit and shaped like deer and for a long time I was admiring
them, imagining that the sculptured group of deer was just an
accidental play of light and shadow in the mountains: there were
three grown-up stags among the deer, two hinds, one stag with huge
antlers, a pricket and two fawns.   All those heads, held fan-wise in
different positions, stood out against the background of the evening
sky.   Then, suddenly, one of those rocks resembling a deer moved.
But that was not all: a hardly audible whistle reached us on the spit
below.   Then it became clear to me that those were all deer standing
at a great height and above them, on another shoulder of the mountain,
there were more deer, and on the steep declivities of Misty Mountain
more deer were standing. . . .   Wherever I looked there were deer
and in the dusk their shapes seemed to merge with the mountains and
form one whole.

Seeing the deer on the mountain sides, Lu Wen immediately set about repairing the net which held together the rushes on the roof of our hut: he was quite certain that when the deer appeared on the slopes of the mountains at nightfall, there would be stormy weather next day. I, too, had a curious premonition of impending storms and was awaiting the change in the weather with some alarm. It seemed to me rather strange that the last few days had been so like each other, as if they were really only one day, reflected in mirrors; everything had been so unnaturally quiet, frosty, cloudless. A shiver ran down my spine every time I saw the Italian sun of the forty-second parallel shining over an absolutely dead waste-land, all yellow and motionless! A land unlived in by any creature, an unknown world! I had a queer feeling that I had come upon a region of perpetual change, where the spring sun sent the sap coursing through the trees in the daytime and where at night the cheated sap froze in the frost and the whole tree split from top to bottom. For years, sometimes for centuries, mighty trees had gone on living in the lee of the cliff, then the cliff suddenly crumbled, leaving only a trail of rock and sand to mark its place and the typhoon hurled the tree about like a match-stick. And the havoc the floods wrought! And how ridiculous it was that man, the wisest creature on earth, should have to consult the deer about the next day's weather!

Unable to suppress my excitement, I left our hut next morning in the hour before dawn to find out what exactly the deer had been forecasting. But when the change in the weather came, the ground disappeared from under my feet and I felt like a deer in the antler-cutting box. All the countries in the world seemed to have got mixed up, the seasons of the year counted for nothing: it became very warm, summer clouds appeared in the sky, at first very bright, then dark, beautiful, sweet clouds, and a thunderstorm, quite unknown in these regions in summer, a real downpour of rain accompanied by thunder and lightning, broke upon us. And so it went on until the evening.

It seemed the deer had deceived us after all; but no, at nightfall it got cold suddenly, the water froze in the wooden pails, and a blizzard began to rage.

What was happening in the mountains? Sheltered by the high walls of our coomb, we sat quietly before the fire in our little Chinese hut, listening to the howling of the wind and the crashing of falling rocks: something came down with a terrific crash on the sea-shore and we thought of the cliff that used to overhang our footpath. Then, suddenly, an eerie stillness would descend upon our world, as if the monster Typhoon, a dragon of enormous length, had flown over us and at last its tail had passed over: the tail had passed over and a stillness fell. Meanwhile the sea went on hurling pebbles upon the beach with a loud, seemingly subterranean, roar—an endless multitude of rounded, polished stones from the bottom of the ocean, and presently it would take them back, and the shingle seemed to protest, growl, murmur. Ten times the sea had hurled its pebbles upon the beach and ten times it had taken them back again, when suddenly the typhoon returned with a dreadful shriek, in which every other sound was drowned, and it went on flying over us again in the darkness for a long time, until once more we heard the growling and murmuring on the beach: the sea was throwing up its shingle upon the shore and taking it back again and while that was going on the typhoon was veering round. . . .

Were it not for the merciful mountains, our little Chinese hut would by now have soared upwards, taking us with it, like the lightest feather from a pheasant's tail, and all the deer would also have been carried up skywards by the typhoon, and the leopards, and the tigers. But the wild animals had sensed the danger the day before and gone betimes to seek shelter in places well protected from the fury of the wind. There in the deer coverts they were safe without so much as a gentle breeze blowing over them and, having nothing to do, they began to break off branches from the trees as they stood under them. Many a time when I had been out hunting, I had come across those sheltering places and recognised them from afar by the broken branches of the trees and the churned-up ground. We had of course taken into account the dangers from the typhoons and we had built our stalls in such a way that no typhoon could harm our deer. But I trembled at the thought of Hua-lu—the whole of the Spit of the Eagle's Nest was exposed to the wind and there was only one sheltered place where she could have hidden and that was our deer-pen: she could save herself only by seeking shelter there.

The hour before dawn which I spent next day outside our hut helped my eyes to get accustomed gradually to the white snow, but later on my eyes found the glitter of the snow under the glaring Italian sun quite unbearable. The typhoon was still raging, though with diminished fury, and we simply had to reach the deer-pen and save Hua-lu. We followed the path between the little hills, fearing the sudden onslaught of the wind as much as the spring of a crouching leopard during a hunt, and our tracks in the snow looked so ominous that it almost frightened us. Perhaps the famished tiger was also prowling about somewhere and he, too, was leaving his tiger tracks in the snow. Or did he prefer the pangs of hunger to this horror of seeing his own footprints in the snow? It was only in the hollows, of course, that the snow remained lying undisturbed; on the wind-swept crags the yellow reeds continued to sway violently. We found it almost impossible to totter across those wind-swept crags in the face of the blast. Instead we crept over them like tortoises and although the typhoon got some grip on us as we crawled painfully along, it could not tear us from the ground. From the top of the last crag we caught a glimpse of the whole Spit of the Eagle's Nest and we were glad that our deer were safely sheltered in their stalls. Hua-lu was standing with her fawn in a deep hollow opposite the deer-pen—she seemed to be just waiting for someone to open the gates and let her into the yard. Standing in that hollow, she did not show the slightest sign of alarm when we opened the gates and entered the yard. I took the wooden trough, which was already familiar to her, filled it with beans and put it in the middle of the yard. After fastening a rope to the gates so that by pulling it we could close them, Lu Wen and I entered an empty box-stall and, to get some light, opened the sliding window almost noiselessly. Through that opening I directed the sound of my birch-bark horn, while Lu Wen held the rope in his hand, ready to pull it when I gave the signal. At the first sound of the horn, Hua-lu's eyes contracted and became friendly, her ears, usually so rigid, relaxed and seemed to turn in different directions. Stretching out her neck, she began to twitch her nostrils and took a little step forward. I blew the horn again and she took another step, then another and another. But right in front of the gates she stopped and seemed to hesitate. I purposely kept quiet so that she should not get too used to the call. It was, however, the beans which attracted her more than the sound of the horn, for she could see them quite plainly now. After a pause, I blew the horn again and that last call settled the matter: she set off again, went up to the trough and began to eat the beans. It was then only that I gave Lu Wen the pre-arranged signal: he pulled carefully at the rope and the gates closed so gently that even we were completely unaware of it. Hua-lu, however, heard it, turned round and pricked up her ears. But she did not seem in the least perturbed by the fact that the gates were now closed: all she was concerned about was to be allowed to eat the beans in peace. And when she felt reassured about that, she again bent her head down to the trough and began to grasp with her black lips a few of the delicious beans at a time.

XII

Many times during that winter the thought flashed through my mind to go and have a look at my Ginseng. I found it very hard to conceive how this tenderest of sub-tropical plants could possibly survive under the snow. How could this root adapt itself to the complete change from a southern climate to the nipping cold of this terrible climate? I also wanted to see the whole of the Valley of Song under the snow, to listen to its stillness without the birds and the summer musicians—the grasshoppers and the cicadas—but so strenuous was the work of looking after the deer that I could not make the necessary preparations for the journey. We were kept busy feeding the deer and cleaning out the stalls. Not that that rather hard work either tired or bored me. I could never rid myself of the peculiar feeling I had towards Hua-lu, the feeling that she was not only a deer, but also a flower, and a rare flower at that, which was in some way—in a way still incomprehensible to me—connected with the, as yet unrevealed, potentialities of my own personality. And there was, of course, the further consideration that all the deer and the whole of the enterprise upon which we had only just started was my own personal affair, even if I did not expect anything for myself from it and looked upon any profits that it might bring in the future as Lu Wen did, namely, as some medicine for future generations unknown to me. So far as I was concerned, however, that enterprise was by itself the best medicine in the world for me. I sometimes used to watch Hua-lu for hours, as she turned her ears this way and that, and I would follow the direction of her gaze at the time. I looked for a long time until, at last, I saw what she had previously heard. Sometimes an eagle would fly overhead, or a wolf would run past, and then the long tear-glands beneath her eyes would distend and that would make her big eyes look quite enormous. Now Hua-lu not only allowed me to stroke her between the ears, but she let me introduce her to Ly-Bah: the dog was always present in the yard during the deer's feeding time. All the deer soon got used to the dog and paid no heed to him. Hua-lu alone was for a long time shy of him because of her fawn. She realised very well that Ly-Bah would not dare to touch her fawn, but her mother-instinct forced her all the same to look askance at the dog, and at feeding time she did her best to make him keep at a safe distance from her. Our dog, however, was so quick that the hind never succeeded in hitting him with her sharp hoof. One day, however, a flea had bitten Ly-Bah and, following the usual practice of dogs in such a contingency, he suddenly forgot everything in the world and, concentrating all his wrathful spite on that one flea, he wrinkled his nose and began searching for the flea on his stomach with his teeth, his hind legs spread out and sticking up in the air. Hua-lu noticed it, ran up to the dog and lifted a foreleg. . . . All the other deer—Blinker, Sprawly, Shorthorn, Dandy, and even Grey Eye, and yes, even Black Spine—immediately stopped feeding and watched the scene with evident relish.   At that time I had already learnt to recognise their laughter, or rather the way they expressed it, not with their mouths, but with their eyes where something seemed to gleam.   That playful expression was particularly noticeable in Hua-lu's eyes as she raised a foreleg and with evident enjoyment gave Ly-Bah a very soft rap with it.   Oh, what a clamour that dog raised!

It is not the frost that makes winter so terrible a season in this part of the world, but the icy blasts.   The snow never remained for long either on the tops or on the sides of the mountains, for it was swept away by the bitter wind, the typhoon; but in the dells, coombs and gorges and in the mountain valleys there was plenty of snow and it was only thanks to their footprints in the snow that I one day discovered that the wolves were planning an attack on our deer and drove them off with a hail of lead.   Another day the snow revealed to me that a leopardess and two cubs still lived in the Leopard Valley, the leopardess, no doubt, being the mate of the leopard I had killed. Examining the hoar-frost on the top of a tree on another occasion I discovered that a bear was hibernating in its hollow trunk.   It was, as I found out, quite a small bear with a white ring round his neck. On another occasion still I saw the tracks of a tiger in the snow.

As soon as the great colds, accompanied by high winds, began, the deer left the northerly, wind-swept slopes of the mountains and migrated to the mountain sides, which were exposed to the full glare of the sun, where they fed in the oak scrub.   If they had known, like the reindeer, how to dig in the snow with their hoofs and get to the dry grass underneath, only the ice-crusted ground would have been a menace to them.   But these animals, survivals from a less harsh climate, could not, it seemed, adapt themselves thoroughly to the inclement conditions of the present time and when after a heavy snowfall, the bushes disappeared in deep snowdrifts they became helpless creatures unable to fend for themselves.   That was the hardest time of the year for them.   There was perhaps only one week left until spring, but one hind with young did not last so long and perished from starvation.   If she had not been with young, she would certainly have survived.   Such accidents, I later noticed, were quite frequent, old hinds in particular often dying because of their young: by that last fatal effort of theirs the animals seem to enjoin upon all living creatures the need of carrying on with the duty of multiplying their species to the last breath.

When the ice on the wind-swept tops of the cliffs had melted during the first spring mists, and the moss, which deer find so tasty, again appeared on them, a young hind went up to the edge of such a cliff and began to feed upon the moss. She stepped inadvertently upon a big lump of snow which overhung the sea. The lump of snow, undermined by the spring mists, toppled down and but for the ice-crust which still lingered on the side of the cliff, the fleet-footed hind would have succeeded in hoisting herself on to the top of the cliff by her forelegs alone. But now only the scratches made by her forelegs remained on the edge of the cliff: the battered body of the hind lay on the rocks at the verge of the sea, a prey to foxes, badgers, raccoons and, perhaps even the octopus.

Many lives perished during that difficult time of transition from winter to summer. One hind had raised herself on her hind legs to feed on the dry leaves of a young oak-tree. I suppose, owing to the ice-crust beneath the tree, her hard hoofs must have slipped and, in her fall, she must have stuck with her neck in the fork of the oak and I found her strangled like that. Then there was another case of a stag who jumped over an oak bush of several intertwisted, dense trunks. The body of the stag cleared the bush, but his hind legs, just above the hoofs, were caught in the trunks and stuck there as in a vice. Oh, yes, many such fatal accidents happened to them and, as I had noticed, the thing that proved most fatal to the deer was panic. . . .

Spring means rains and mists. The sun shows itself very rarely, for an hour or so, and even then it causes a lot of trouble: the trees, tricked by the warmth, begin to revive, and at night the rising sap freezes and tears the trunk apart.

Invisible in the mist, the snow on the mountains melts and runs down in streams. Invisible in the mist, tall grasses begin to push through the ground. And it is only your ears that tell you of the great migration of birds. One or two weeks pass in the densest mists. We cannot see anything except our little Chinese hut, but the happy day arrives at last: the green buds open up in the sunshine and—until now there was a great silence—the pheasants begin to crow all over the place.

The deer begin to shed their antlers. The big stags as a rule shed their antlers earlier, but then their new antlers also begin to sprout earlier and the rutting season starts with them earlier, too. Lu Wen used to tell me again and again during the winter months about some immortal stag who was said never to shed his antlers. All Lu Wen's legends and fairy-tales were dear to me because they originated from some fundamental truth; when listening to his legends I always tried to penetrate their meaning so as to make them intelligible to my understanding and glean something from them that might be useful to me. This was also the case with the immortal stag. When all the stags had shed their antlers and the calving of the hinds began, I had no time to think of the stag with his perennial bony antlers, but I caught a glimpse of the immortal stag one day from the top of a hill: there he was with his many-branched bony antlers, grazing in lonely majesty on a deer pasture. I had to solve the mystery of the immortal stag and for that reason, although I had decided never to shoot spotted deer, I did not hesitate to kill this one, and, taking careful aim, I fired. It was then that the mystery of the unshed antlers was solved: what had happened was that probably during the stag fights during the pairing season this old stag had lost his sexual organs and the life force which pushed from underneath against the old antlers ceased to flow and new antlers stopped growing, while the old, bony ones remained unchanged. But where change had ceased to exact its tribute from the living body, and in the old everything remained as of old, it was easiest of all to see immortality—and that, perhaps, is the most comprehensible and most truthful image of immortality which everybody can grasp: dead, unchangeable, bony antlers. I, of course, told Lu Wen everything, showed him the bony antlers and the scarred, smooth place on the body of the killed stag. But again quite naturally Lu Wen replied that it was not the same stag, that an immortal remained immortal and could not be killed by a bullet. It was then that the bitter thought flashed through my mind that Lu Wen, with his legends, was just like the stag with the unchanging bony antlers. I felt bitter about it because against my own wish and, as it were, for a reason that did not matter and that was not of the slightest importance, I lost the companionship of that best of men. Our paths diverged at this point and I remained alone, and to be with that best of men was to me henceforth like being among animals: however much you might like them and however much you might get friendly with them, you could not help remaining alone, for you could not share with them your most precious and, perhaps so far as you were concerned, quite superfluous possessions.

Our deer gradually shed their old antlers just as if they had still been at liberty. Grey Eye was the first to shed his, Black Spine followed suit after a short interval, then Blinker, Dandy and the brothers Sprawly and Shorthorn. After he had shed his antlers, Blinker one day came up to me with that peculiar snuffle of his. He lowered his head, as if trying to toss me with his non-existent antlers. I guessed that he wanted me to scratch his knobs, for, I supposed, it must be there that it itched badly. He seemed to like it very much. Next time, as soon as he saw me from a distance, he rushed at me snuffling as usual and nearly knocked me down. I scratched his knobs again and we parted. But the third time, spoilt by my previous treatment of him, he ran up to me looking as if he expected me to obey his orders: scratch me, if you like, but if not, I shall scratch myself! I refused to pander to such insolence, but he, wishing to scratch his knobs against me, butted me with such force that I was not only flung to the ground, but also hurled against the fence. Realising my helplessness, Blinker rushed at me and, if he had butted me once more, I should, of course, not have got up again. But the moment he bent down his head to butt me with it, I realised my danger and immediately caught hold of his right leg above the hoof with my left hand, while hitting him with my right hand in the side with such force that he fell over. And that was not all by any manner of means! I pulled a stake out of the fence and gave him such a good thrashing that after that he became a model of meekness. He went on blinking, whistling and lowering his head for me to scratch his knobs, but I had only to wag a finger at him and he walked away. The other stags all remained wild and did not allow anybody to approach them.

The scales for weighing the deer gave me a lot of trouble, but in the end I succeeded in constructing a pair and attaching them to the antler-cutting box. When the stag entered the box, I pressed a lever and the bottom of the box became a weighing machine. As an experiment I took two stags which were of absolutely the same size: Sprawly and Shorthorn. One of them, Sprawly, that is, I began to fatten like a pig on concentrated fodder, letting him eat as much as he wished. The other one, Shorthorn, who weighed exactly as much as Sprawly, received the normal diet of the other deer. The purpose of my experiment was to find out how much more the new antlers of a fattened stag would weigh and whether in this way it were not possible to obtain a pair of antlers of a weight unheard of before in China. As time passed and the antlers grew, I could plainly see how beautifully the growing antlers of the fattened stag filled with blood, how wonderfully they shone with a translucent, peach-coloured light and how lovely the velvet on them sparkled like threads of silver! Oh, I had thousands of plans in my head! But the most important plan of all, the thing I dreamt of day and night, was to sell a pair of antlers that I had obtained by my own work and to buy with the money yards and yards of wire so that I could cut off from the mainland the whole of Misty Mountain with all its deer and their enemies: the leopards, wolves, raccoons and badgers. My business of selling growing antlers to the Chinese I mentally divided into four sections: first, my tame deer enclosure where the stags whose antlers began to grow would be kept prisoner until the time came for their antlers to be cut, after which they would be let out to roam at will on the slopes of Misty Mountain; secondly, the semi-park on the Spit of the Eagle's Nest; thirdly, the park of Misty Mountain and, fourthly, the jungle adjoining Misty Mountain which was to serve as a regular reserve for wild deer.   I further dreamt that in my business of taming new kinds of wild animals I would, on Lu Wen's recommendation, surround myself with Chinese like him and contrive it so that they, while remaining inwardly independent, should themselves become "captains" like Europeans and be able to stand up for themselves.

XIII

The humid heat of summer.   At night lights are flitting about everywhere.   In the morning large spiders weave their webs round bushes and grasses; you walk in the jungle with a stick, clearing away the spider-webs in front of you.   If the sun happens to break through the clouds even for one hour, you gladly get reconciled to weeks and weeks of misty weather.   Then every spider-web, which in that damp climate is always covered with tiny drops which seem to cling to one another, is transformed into a diamond tissue of exceeding beauty.   It was during such an hour of sunshine that a hind came up to the rock where I was resting—the gentle wind blowing in my direction deceived her—and I, lying on the top of the rock, could observe the great event in a deer's life.   The fawn was born spotted like his mother, and those spots among the dancing leaf-shadows hid both mother and fawn so well that one could have passed close by without noticing either of them.   After the calving, the fawn could not stand on his feet, so the hind lay down on the ground and spent a long time trying to push her udder near his head and teaching him how to suck.   It took the fawn a long time to realise what his mother wanted him to do, but as soon as he did realise it, he began to feed. When she thought that he was sufficiently strong, she stood up and he, too, stood up and tried to suck her standing, but he was still too weak and he swayed on his thin legs and lay down again.   The hind also lay down, but she no longer tried to push her udder towards him, for now he knew himself what to do.   It was then that I was overcome by a desire to cough: however much I tried to suppress it, however much I tried to keep my lips tightly closed, she heard my suppressed cough, her eyes met mine and in the twinkling of an eye, without even a whistle, she bounded to her feet and vanished.   The mother's panic communicated itself to the fawn, but he could not, of course, run and, instead, he clung so closely to the ground that it seemed to me that without knowing in the first place that he was there, it would have been quite impossible to see him.   Wishing to conceal himself to sink into the ground, to disappear utterly from the sight of his enemy, he seemed to put his faith in the inflexibility of his little body, and when I picked him up, he remained in the same position, and I put him back on the sward like a lifeless thing. I was sorry to leave him there, but Lu Wen and I had no cow. Lu Wen did not drink milk. He used to say, "If I were to drink milk, I'd have to look on the cow as my mother." But that incident gave me a valuable idea for our business: in future when we got some cows, I should take Ly-Bah with me for a walk in the jungle during the calving season when we were sure to come across such fawns, abandoned by their mothers and stiff with fright; the deer reared from such fawns would surely become domestic animals.

While the hinds were calving, the antlers of our stags were growing bigger and bigger and, as time passed, both the hinds and the stags seemed equally preoccupied: the hind expended all her care upon her fawn, while the stag expended all his care upon his sensitive, exceedingly tender new antlers, which the slightest blow might transform into a bleeding, pulpy mass. Grey Eye was perceptibly ahead in the growth of his antlers and one morning Lu Wen, having spent an hour in examining his antlers, said, "Soon you and me must cut."

So we immediately began to make ready for that big and risky operation: Grey Eye's antlers, according to Lu Wen, were worth no less than one thousand yen! But the main thing that worried us was not the medicine, but the deer himself: for a frightened deer paid no heed to any obstacles, he might not only turn his antlers into a red, pulpy mass, but he was quite capable of breaking his legs in an attempt to regain his freedom. We had no one to tell us what to do. In the old days Lu Wen himself used to cut off the growing antlers of a stag by a method that was both barbarous and risky: the Chinese simply bound the stag and threw him on the ground. As we were undertaking a highly hazardous business, we thought it best to let all the deer out into the yard, leaving only Grey Eye in the box-stall. If the stag were now to be let out of his stall, there was only one way of escape for him—the way to the antler-cutting box; for the other exit from the shed was barred by a movable screen suspended from the ceiling. The screen had a tiny hole in it and Lu Wen, who was standing behind it, saw me open Grey Eye's stall and let the stag out. As soon as I had done that, I hurried to the other end of the passage where I, like Lu Wen, hid behind a screen. I, too, was peeping through a hole, my hand resting on a lever: as soon as Grey Eye entered the antler-cutting box, I had only to press down the lever for the stag to fall through the bottom of the box, while the side planks, covered with soft matting, would press hard against the sides of the stag and prevent him from falling through the trap-door. But it was still a far cry to that. On leaving the stall, Grey Eye stopped in the semi-darkness of the passage, where he remained standing motionless, uncertain what to do since his usual exit was now barred by the moving screen, and he was loath to go the other way which he did not know. What was he to do ? To help him make up his mind, Lu Wen began to push the screen gently forward. The stag was still at a loss what to do: should he face the unknown dangers or should he make a rush against the screen ? He could easily smash it, perhaps smash himself, too. The screen moved nearer and nearer, from behind it came the familiar, kindly voice: "Mike, Mike!" Lu Wen called every deer without distinction Mike.

Grey Eye overcame his fears and decided to move carefully in the direction where he scented all sorts of perils for himself. He took a few steps and stopped. Lu Wen moved the screen forward a little, and the stag took a few more steps towards the antler-cutting box and so he got nearer and nearer to the place where the floor was suddenly to give way under him. What I feared most was that he should guess the presence of a cunning trap just before entering the antler-cutting box. There was one way in which he could still frustrate our scheme: he had only to lie down on the floor and then we should have been quite helpless, for we could not possibly take him by force, since he had only to leap forward and everything would be lost. It was dead quiet in the shed, only the rope on the pulleys could be heard creaking very softly. The moment came when the stag had either to lie down or to risk it. His front hoofs were now on the trap-door, the screen moved forward and was close to him. Grey Eye entered the antler-cutting box and I immediately pressed the lever. Something went down with a crash and Lu Wen at once opened the door in the screen and rushed into the box where he jumped on to the back of the stag to prevent any mishap during the antler-cutting operation. It was only then that I went outside, lifted the top of the box and lashed Grey Eye's head to the crossbar between the sides of the box.

The operation of cutting off the growing antlers of a stag is a very painful one. The blood spurts out in fountains under the hands of the man who is cutting off the antlers at their base, but any pain there is lasts only for a second. A young stag usually screams his head off, his eyes rolling in terror, but an old, proud stag often shows no sign of fear or pain. Such a stag was Grey Eye: in that most terrible position when his legs were dangling helplessly in the air, when to a wild stag it must seem that everything is lost, when, moreover, his flanks were held fast by something, one man was sitting on his back, while another was cutting off the pride and joy of his life, the new antlers, which to a stag must seem like killing a child before the eyes of his mother—in such a situation Grey Eye not only did not utter a sound, but he did not show the slightest sign of pain or alarm. Personally, I keep this example of fortitude shown by the lord and master of the spotted deer as an ideal before me: I have seen it myself and I know it to be true that there are no humiliating situations provided you do not humiliate yourself.

Having cut off Grey Eye's antlers, I untied his head. Lu Wen jumped off his back, I pressed the lever which released the side planks and the stag fell to the bottom of the pit from where, having obtained a support for his feet, he shot out like a bullet into the yard. Hardly ten minutes later, no longer than it took us to fill the big feeding trough with beans, Grey Eye had completely recovered from his painful operation and, a hornless stag now, was chewing the soya beans together with the other deer. I felt like jumping for joy at the successful completion of so difficult a business and I could not help embracing Lu Wen, who—dear old fellow!—wept for joy.

But just as we were celebrating our first success, a terrible calamity befell us in the shape of a little, striped rodent which looked very much like a squirrel. It was a chipmunk. There were so many chipmunks about the place that it never occurred to me to pay any particular attention to one of them that day in, day out, used to gather the soya beans under the trough in our yard. But on the morning on which complete disaster overtook our enterprise it so happened that a bean was lying by one of Hua-lu's hoofs. The chipmunk tried to get it, but just at that moment Hua-lu changed the position of one of her hoofs and, without being aware of it, trod on the chipmunk's tail. The rodent with the sharp teeth at once retaliated by driving his teeth into Hua-lu's leg. Hua-lu gave a frightened start, glanced at her leg and heaven alone knows what terrible thing she imagined was clinging to it. What happened a moment later was what usually happens in a packed theatre when someone shouts, "Fire!" and the people, just like wild beasts, are seized by panic and, without a thought for anybody but themselves, rush to the exits. In the same way the panic which seized upon Hua-lu, when she saw a little devil with a bushy tail clinging to her leg, communicated itself to the rest of the deer and all of them—each weighing at least twenty stone—hurled themselves against the fence and by their combined weight, the whole force of their twenty stone having gone into their legs, they smashed the fence into fragments and regained their freedom. The loud noise of the collapsing fence, the scratches, the pain inflicted by the blow against the fence—all that must have been felt by Hua-lu as merely the natural consequence of the presence of the little devil on her leg. She tore along, her white stump of a tail waving like mad, showing the way to the rest; and all the deer were tearing along after her, every deer in front pointing the way to the next deer that followed him with his tail, and behind all of them there rushed, whipping them on, the invisible striped devil—the chipmunk.

I lost my senses completely, and what man would not! I rushed into the mountains in search of the deer, as if there were the ghost of a chance of catching panic-stricken wild animals! I, of course, could find no trace of them, however far I roamed in search of them through the jungle, but towards evening, in the gloaming, I caught a glimpse of all of them on the top of a cliff. Turning my head, I saw more deer on another cliff, there were deer everywhere, on the steep sides of our coomb, on the slopes of the mountains, hundreds and hundreds of deer, everywhere! I nearly went off my head that night and it was in vain that kind-hearted Lu Wen tried to comfort me.

XIV

I had an unfailing remedy for every kind of misfortune and depression: I used to leave the Chinese hut in the hour before dawn and, leaning against a wall, concentrate all my thoughts upon one single thing, namely, that my Root of Life was growing and that I must give it time to mature. For that reason I must not give way to despair if any misfortune befell me, but always accept it as something inevitable and think, think, think of the time when, sooner or later, the moment of attainment would come. I believe that by such an exercise I have greatly developed my will-power and that by thus fortifying my resolution I have become immune from any consequences that shameful weakness might bring in the trail of any disaster. But now at the first serious shock of my life, my well-thought-out plan, which I had had little chance of testing by experience, proved an utter failure and I was so upset that I forgot all about my Ginseng.

I spent my time sitting with Ly-Bah on the ruins of our deer-pen and, from time to time, I would blow my deer horn. It occurred to me that had I been even a little superstitious, had I been inclined to explain the simple and intelligible, but hardly bearable, events of my life as due to some inexplicable causes of a supernatural kind, I could not have helped thinking of Hua-lu as some enchantress who had obtained an uncanny hold over me by her beauty; for did I not see with my own eyes how she had transformed herself into a beautiful woman and, when I had fallen in love with her, had she not vanished suddenly? And when by my own almost superhuman effort I had succeeded in widening the enchanted circle round me, calling to my aid the whole of my masculine, creative force, did not that same Hua-lu smash it all up into fragments? How on earth did it all happen? Why, a striped little devil appeared suddenly out of the blue—a chipmunk! Thus from earliest times that protective crust of superstition grows like another skin on to man: witches and devils give place to inanimate objects, to man's environment, to all sorts of big and small objects, only children, only children remain alive. . . .

Many such thoughts passed through my mind, oppressed with melancholy as life's wave seemed to ebb. But a new, more vital wave was not far away. Ly-Bah had for some time been casting strange glances at something behind me, trying to attract my attention and at the same time conveying by the look he gave me that I need not be alarmed as something very ordinary was happening behind my back; yet there could be no doubt that something was happening there, that something was not as it had been a short time ago. However, for some reason I paid no attention to Ly-Bah's queer behaviour and continued to be preoccupied with my melancholy thoughts until I became conscious of a curious rustling sound behind me. It was only then that I looked round and . . . there, close to me, stood Hua-lu with her fawn, eating the soya beans spilt on the ground during the deer's stampede. Oh, the joy of seeing her again! But that was not all. A chipmunk, and not one chipmunk, either, but five little striped devils were also very busy with the soya beans. . . . How many times had I experienced it in my life! Just as I was beginning to fall back upon some far-fetched interpretation, to summon the mysterious and remote forces to help me to understand and to relieve my troubles, life itself stood suddenly revealed before me and offered me, her own favourite, such a present out of her inexhaustible store that I went wild with joy, I felt like screaming madly with happiness, my heart rejoiced, my tail wagged delightedly! I shall never forget the moment of intense joy when the sun pierced through the bank of mist and the spider-webs, covered with dewdrops, sparkled with thousands of diamonds and priceless gems. And the countless flowers around me! How beautiful they were! The azalea bush yonder smothered in ropes of pearl, and the scarlet Siberian lily and the other lilies wearing diamonds for caps, and there the little builder had caught up with his silver thread that whitest and tenderest of flowers, the edelweiss, engaging it also among his fairy workmen for the building of morning joy. Such an abundance of precious stones one can find only in Arabian fairy-tales, but even the wonderful Arabian imagination could not create so rich and so happy a caliph as I!

What a depth of virgin soil, what an inexhaustible creative force there is in man, and how many millions of unhappy people come and go without obtaining a proper understanding of their Ginseng, without being able to discover in their own hearts the source of strength, courage, joy and happiness! Look, how many deer I had had and what beautiful deer they were! Think how Grey Eye behaved under the knife! But had I ever been so happy when I possessed them all as I was now when only Hua-lu came back? It might be said that as soon as I saw Hua-lu I realised that with her help I should be able to catch hundreds of deer and that that was why I felt so happy. Not at all! I was happy because, having lost the deer, I began to understand how much I had put into that work, and now that Hua-lu was here again I could once more resume the wonderful task I had set myself to accomplish. Soon Lu Wen and I were happily engaged in re-erecting the fence and this time we made sure that the deer would never be able either to jump over it or break it down with all their combined weight. Now it dawned on me gradually that Hua-lu's return from the jungle in reply to the sound of my horn meant more to the ultimate success of my undertaking than the possession of all the lost stags, for henceforth I was free to make daily experiments without any risk whatsoever: every morning I let Hua-lu out to roam at will in the mountains and in the evening I called her back by sounding my horn. By giving her and her fawn some special delicacy I had prepared for them, every time they came back to the deer-pen, I finally brought it about that she rushed back to the feeding enclosure at any hour of the day as soon as I blew my horn.

So the days passed and the pairing season of the spotted deer was drawing near. One day by sheer chance I hit upon the idea of the best way not only of getting back my lost deer, but capturing new ones. A herd of hinds happened to come to the little hill opposite the Spit of the Eagle's Nest and for some reason or other Sprawly, whose large antlers were just shedding the velvet, was with them. It was very early in the autumn and even the Manchurian red deer had not yet begun to bellow, but, of course, among animals, as among men, there are freaks. Most likely the stag I had fed so well as an experiment had begun to pursue the hinds long before the pairing season, and he had probably also been paying his unwelcome attentions to the hinds a long time before they were on heat. Watching Sprawly from under cover, I waited patiently until he got behind the hill, then I opened the gates, tried out the rope with which I could close them from a safe distance, and let Hua-lu out of the deer-pen. She ran up gaily to the other hinds, but Sprawly soon noticed her and made straight for her. The two met like old friends, having probably got to know each other well during the period of their enforced captivity, so unusual for wild deer. At any rate, there they stood side by side, but Hua-lu, of course, let Sprawly sniff her only up to a certain limit and no sooner had the fattened stag overstepped that limit than she left him and hid herself in the herd of hinds. After about an hour she must have forgotten all about Sprawly and left the herd. But the moment she detached herself from the other hinds, he began pestering her again with his unwelcome attentions and all she could do was to hide herself in the herd again.

I decided that now was the time for my experiment and, lying behind a rock to windward and tightening the end of the rope in my hand, I began to blow my horn. Hua-lu immediately left the herd and, in answer to my call, ran straight back to the pen. Sprawly, I was glad to see, ran after her as fast as he could and not only did he not hesitate when running through the gates, but he did not even think it necessary to turn round when they closed behind him, nor did he show any signs of panic at my appearance.

How impatiently was I now waiting for the beginning of the pairing season of the spotted deer! The vine-leaves were getting redder every day, here and there in the coombs the maple leaves blazed like flames and then, after a small typhoon, the frost was born in the stillness of a starry night and on the same September night, exactly as a year ago, on the same side of the same mountain, the first Manchurian red deer began to bellow.

Two more weeks passed, each day bringing with it changes that were visible to the eye. The grapes ripened. On the yellow deer pastures the dead azalea leaves lay flat on the ground, like little red saucers, and the whole grazing ground looked as if it were covered with the blood of deer after their mating fights. Then once more in the mysterious stillness of the night, just when the black mountain range was cut in two by the Great Bear, the first spotted deer raised his agonised cry and another deer, like an echo, answered him, and the echo called forth more and more distant echoes. The thing that worried me most now was that I might miss the day when Hua-lu, like every other hind, began to leave in her tracks that mysterious scent which greatly excited the stags: scenting it in the wind from afar or just in front of them on the ground, they stopped grazing, followed it in search of the hind and began to roar. As soon as they scent it, the stags are ready to engage in a mortal combat for the possession of the hind, but the hind herself is not really on heat yet and all she cares about is to have a romp and nothing else. The nimble-footed hind will be the first to have a game with an inexperienced and rather slow-witted stag and when he, his passion aroused, rushes at her, she will speed away as though trying to make him believe that this bridal flight is the best and the only precious thing in a hind. Now that Sprawly had been caught again and was living in captivity I could with certainty tell the day when Hua-lu had reached the stage where she was ready to engage in the first frolics of the mating game, but was not yet ready to yield to the rutting stags, bespattered with mud by their own lust.

The expected evening came at last and I recognised the first signs. Leading Hua-lu by a rope, I took her very slowly round Misty Mountain, along the well-known deer path. The moon was shining brightly that night, the roaring of the stags filled the air and, occasionally, the dry sound of the blows of bony antlers could be heard from a distance. For some reason the deer seem to lose their fears on a moonlight night and I could often see quite close to me a pair of antlers or the white stump of a tail. Sometimes a stag would begin to bellow so near that it was no longer one drawn-out roar, as it seems to be from a distance, but a concatenation of different sounds, all of them, though, like the most distant bellowing of stags, expressing suffering: an agonised growl, a moan, a cry. Deep inside me I felt, like Hua-lu, a curious loathing for that passionate roar of the stags which close at hand sounded so utterly horrible, but among those coarse sounds there was one note that was different: it was a note of ingenuous, almost childlike complaint, a tenderly submissive whimper for sympathy. As a human being I could not help fancying that Hua-lu was so fascinated by the roaring of the stags only because of that plaintive note of entreaty for sympathy with their suffering, and that it was that that made her willing to gambol and run about with any stag. She would frequently stop during our walk round Misty Mountain, listen, give a shudder and, of course, left her trails everywhere.

A gentle breeze blew across Misty Mountain and every time a stag caught the scent of Hua-lu, he stopped bellowing and followed her scent on the wind; but besides the odour he yearned for, he also caught the smell of the animal he dreaded more than any living creature—man! and he stopped in great perplexity, forgetting even to roar. Oh, yes, they possess a power of smell which man has completely lost! I could guess by that plaintive note that in their scent, as with us in the case of flowers, they, too, recognised an image of beauty which, perhaps for one moment only, had nothing to do with passion, but when afterwards passion reasserted itself and found nothing for itself in mere beauty, then it was transformed into a roar, as with us a glimpse of beauty is often transformed into music. . . .

So, no doubt, many stags, scenting Hua-lu in the soft wind which blew all over Misty Mountain, stopped their bellowing, followed her scent on the wind and, stumbling across the terrible trail of man, stopped in their tracks and stood still for a long time, not knowing in their confusion what to do; but after a while they continued their pursuit in spite of the man's scent, moving along Hua-lu's trail carefully, marking every sign she left behind her in the air and on the ground.

XV

At sunrise it became frosty. I brought Hua-lu back to the deer-pen, saw to the gates which were now to serve as a trap and, concealing myself behind a rock to windward, began to await events among the low hills which stretched in a chain one behind the other up to the foot of Misty Mountain.

The air had a slight nip in it, and was quite transparent. The sea, of an intense blue, surrounded Misty Mountain on three sides, while the mountain reeds, covered with the white lace of rime, looked more and more beautiful against the blue background of the Pacific. By and by, as it grew lighter, the scene became so beautiful that a sharp pain went through me and it seemed to me that were my pain to grow just a little more intense I, too, like the deer, would raise my head and begin to roar. But why is it that when everything around me is so beautiful, such a terrible pain shoots through me? Is it because, like the deer, I expect something pleasant to happen to me at the sight of such beauty and, failing to get satisfaction, my disappointment is so keen that it is transformed into physical pain and I am ready to burst out roaring just like a deer?

When the sun rose and the whole world began to sparkle, stags appeared here and there on the sloping deer paths of Misty Mountain, far off at first, looking small like flies, then growing bigger and bigger, disappearing altogether for a time in the valleys on the sides of the mountain among the coomb. In a short time, they began to show themselves from behind the first low hill, the second, the third, and when a stag came to the last hill, he seemed to grow out of it with his antlers—it looked as if a pair of antlers were shooting up from the ground.

A solitary stone-pine grew on the hillock opposite Misty Mountain, a tree hardened by its constant battles against the typhoons, twisted into knots, and each knot—the scar left by a typhoon—stretched out a conquering branch with long, dark-green needles: its trunk was all twisted, but it was for all that a victorious trunk, tall and unconquerable, and its shadow over the yellow pasture with the blood-red stains of dead azaleas stretched up to a small hollow with dark-green grass and oak underwood. This hollow was like a small coomb: it got deeper and deeper until it reached the sea and a tiny stream meandered at the bottom of it, appearing and disappearing among the rocks. It was in that little coomb that a small herd of hinds and prickets was grazing now and there were also two stags there, two very well-behaved stags, which neither molested the hinds, nor nibbled the grass, nor raised their heads and roared, but just stood there motionless like a pair of monks, engrossed in their own meditations. A majestic stag of enormous size, but without antlers, suddenly appeared from behind the low hill and went straight to the stone-pine which cast its long shadow over the hollow with the grazing deer. Strange, indeed, did that stag look with his majestic air of lord and master of the deer and yet with only two knobs instead of antlers! It was Grey Eye who, of course, had come down the mountains on the trail of Hua-lu. From the top of the hillock with the stone-pine he now looked straight at the open gates of the deer-pen. I made up my mind to get him as I had got Sprawly and I quietly opened the gates wide, fastened the rope to them, gave a few parting pats to Hua-lu and let her out. She ran out gaily and, seeing the herd in the small coomb, she was about to join the other hinds, setting off in that direction at a gentle trot, without hurrying. But Grey Eye, realising what a difficult job it would be to get her away from the herd once she joined it, immediately set off at a run to intercept her and, cutting across her path, he succeeded in stopping her. It was not so long ago that I had seen that stag looking so beautiful, but now he looked bedraggled, covered with mud, and the muscles of his belly contracted convulsively; his neck, distended from constant roaring, looked enormous and his eyes were bloodshot. Hua-lu tried to escape from that terrible monster by running towards the tree, but he immediately went in pursuit of her, and both of them disappeared behind the hillock. I seized my horn and began to blow. Hua-lu heard it apparently and turned back, for I caught sight of her again at the very entrance to the coomb where the small herd was grazing and the two black monks were still standing motionless. If the coomb with its thick undergrowth had not stopped her, Hua-lu would quite certainly have rushed through the gates, bringing the stag after her, but she lingered just for a moment in the bushes and Grey Eye overtook her there. . . .

. . . Had he, I wonder, as we humans have, some impersonal image of beauty at that moment, an image created for him by the special power of smell which only deer possess? No! I was quite certain of it now: there was no trace of any such image left in him it was not beauty he saw before him, but a means of satisfying his lust, of giving him joy, of making life pleasant to him. He rose in the air on his hind legs like a bull and then, suddenly, there was nothing in the air any more! Oh, yes, that sort of thing happens very often just another moment and . . . but there is nothing there! Hua-lu did the only thing she could do to save herself: she lay down on the ground. That meant the end of everything, of beauty as well as of pleasure. Grey Eye, seeing that there really was nothing more there threw back his head and let out a shrill whistle and the whistle gradually began to swell out into deeper and deeper notes until it became a roar, and there he stood roaring in deeper and deeper accents, raising his voice again and again and again. In the interval between the sharp whistle and the bellowing sound there was one plaintive note—a note all stags have—with which he expressed either his disappointment at being cheated of his joy or his appeal to Hua-lu to take pity on him, and it was that note that supplied me with the key to the understanding of the music of the stags. But I could not help reflecting that my own great sorrow was also due, like the stag's to my inability to draw the line between beauty and pleasure and that was why the feeling of beauty gave me such exquisite pain.

If I had studied the pairing of deer scientifically and had set about my studies in the correct way, I should have begun by refusing to seek to understand the deer by analysing my own feelings. But had I not myself suffered here in the jungle just like any other animal? I was sorry for them, I sympathised with them as if they were my own kith and kin: there Hua-lu lay, going through an experience that every hind went through during the pairing season while he stood over her, deeply, painfully humiliated, looking so terribly emaciated, bespattered with mud, a bedraggled lord and master of the jungle with two bony protuberances instead of a pair of majestic antlers. It was so clear, so obvious that the only way of self-preservation was to fight! Now all questions boiled down to one single question: either I or you, either I kill, or I die myself. . .

The herd of hinds came out of the coomb and surrounded their sister Hua-lu, as if they understood and sympathised with her. But the master of the harem, Grey Eye, remained standing there in the expectation of the fulfilment of his joy and, in the meantime, he looked for somebody to fight with, he wished to pit his strength against some other stag as soon as possible. The two monks, one with six-tined and the other with four-tined antlers, were also standing there as though rooted to the ground, not daring to move a step forward

Or did they realise that with their antlers alone they could do nothing ? Or, on seeing their lord and master without horns, could they not even now summon enough courage to challenge him ? Or had they noticed that Black Spine, Shorthorn, Dandy and many more stags were hurrying along the deer paths down the mountain sides ? For some reason Black Spine stopped on the hillock with the solitary stone-pine and refused to take another step: as always there was something secretive about him, as though he were hatching some devilish plot. Between Black Spine and the hillock on which Grey Eye stood ready to engage in a life-and-death combat, eight different stags I had never seen before grouped themselves on the rising ground. Perhaps Black Spine's plan was to let the eight stags have their fight with Grey Eye first and to fall upon the tired lord of the jungle after he had defeated the eight of them in turn and then finish him off without much trouble.

Grey Eye first wrinkled his muzzle and snorted contemptuously in the direction of the first stag on the slope. Quite often that is sufficient to make an opponent take to his heels. But the stag paid no attention to the warning of the hornless deer. Grey Eye thrust out his tongue sideways. The stag not only stood his ground, but in his arrogance he himself wrinkled his nose. . . . It was only now that the lord of the jungle moved towards him, but even then the unknown stag refused to run away. On the contrary, he lowered his antlers and himself moved forward a little. He must have been a very young and arrogant stag and did not know what a blow from Grey Eye meant. One single blow with Grey Eye's knobs was enough to bring him to his knees. Grey Eye then did what all stags do in such a situation: he inflicted such a terrific blow in the flank of his opponent against his heart, that he broke the stag's ribs with his knobs and the fragments of the ribs pierced a vital spot under the left shoulder bone. The reckless stag would never get up on his feet again. Grey Eye next wrinkled his nose in the direction of the second stag and that one ran away with his tongue lolling out of his mouth; he made a rush at the third stag, and that one, too, took to his heels, followed by the rest. Only Black Spine remained now and when Grey Eye wrinkled his nose at *him*, Black Spine replied by wrinkling his muzzle in his turn and immediately advanced against Grey Eye.

Not far from the solitary tree on the hillock another tree once stood, but only a small stump remained of it now. The two enemies met at that stump, intending, no doubt, to make use of it for gaining additional support for their forelegs. Both braced themselves against it at the same time and began to butt each other, each doing his utmost to overpower his rival. They kept on describing circles round the tree-stump for a long time, but neither, it seemed, could get the better of the other and, as the fight went on, I could see that they had dug a deep ditch with their hoofs round the tree-stump. Suddenly, as the two big stags hit out anew against each other with their foreheads, the tree-stump went flying from under their feet, coming down a long way from the place of combat, and both the stags fell into the ditch, one on top of the other. At that moment Hua-lu quite unexpectedly rushed out from behind a bush and, pursued by Dandy, fled as fast as she could. I immediately blew my horn and she came running straight in my direction with Dandy at her heels. Grey Eye and Black Spine also saw Dandy pursuing the hind and they rushed after him, and after them came the rest of the stags and the herd of hinds and they all passed close by me, jostling each other as they ran through the gates. When they had all rushed past to the very end of the spit, I had time not only to shut the gates, but also to carry out a rough examination of the fence and even to strengthen it in one or two places.

I arrived at the pine-covered rocks when the fight between Grey Eye and Black Spine was drawing to a close, but neither by my presence nor by firing shots in the air could I save those two fine stags. Grey Eye and Black Spine were fighting at the very edge of the sheer cliff above the reef and, no doubt, the fight would have been over long since had Grey Eye had antlers. But, having no antlers, and unable to parry the blows of his opponent, he had received several wounds on his unprotected neck and when, suffering from much loss of blood, he collapsed on his forelegs, a stream of blood began also to pour out of his mouth. Black Spine hit him in the side, but at the last moment Grey Eye suddenly raised himself from the ground and, summoning the last of his strength, delivered such a mighty blow that Black Spine lost his foothold and went over the cliff, tumbling down like a rubber ball from rock to rock until he got smashed up upon the reef. Grey Eye had just time to look down from the top of the cliff and, perhaps, even to see the white crests of the waves which broke continuously over the reef covered with a reddish foam. Then he, too, lurched and fell over.

Here and there among the cliffs I could hear the dry blows of antlers against antlers, the groans of mortally wounded stags, the noise of falling rocks. All these deer were now mine.

XVI

Ten years had passed since with the help of the tamed Hua-lu I had captured many stags and began to build up a large business for the sale of new antlers. My friend did not come back, and I alone did all the work. Another year passed. I was still alone, and I knew no rest. And one more year. . . . It sometimes happens that after the passing of a certain period of expectancy you begin to think of someone dear to you, living a long way from you, as if he or she were dead. Then when both you and your friend have changed irrecognisably you suddenly meet. What a frightful meeting it is! You start and you go pale as you begin to recognise that long-lost friend of yours by his features, so mercilessly changed with the passage of time, and, finally, you recognise him by the voice. Gradually, as you plunge deeper and deeper into the past, you begin unconsciously and step by step to forgive someone for something which, if you were asked, you could not tell yourself what it was, you begin to feel so light-hearted, so gay, and then, at last, the long-wished-for meeting takes place: under the influence of the return of joy in life the two friends become as young in their own eyes as they have ever been. It is in this way that I interpret the power of the Root of Life Ginseng. It also happens, however, that the upsurge of the vital forces of the root is so great that you discover your beloved friend, whom you have lost for ever, in another person and you begin to love that new person as you did the one you have lost. That, too, I consider to be the action of the Root of Life Ginseng. Any other understanding of the mysterious root I hold to be either superstition or just purely a medicinal matter.

So it was, as time passed—one year, two years—and my friend did not come, that I began to forget and, at last, completely forgot that somewhere in the jungle my own Root of Life went on growing and growing. All around me everything had changed: the little village on the bank of the Zu-Su had grown into a small town, the few hundred original settlers had now grown to many thousands. I often travel now on important business to Moscow and to Shanghai, and in the streets of those large cities the thought of my Ginseng comes to me more often than in the jungle. Together with the other people who are engaged in the building up of a new civilisation I feel that the Root of Life has come from the primeval jungle to our own civilised world of creative endeavour, and that the seekers of the Root of Life in our new jungle of art, science and utilitarian endeavour are nearer to their goal than the seekers of the root of the plant, which is a survival from past ages, in the primeval jungle. I find my work very absorbing and that, of course, saves me from fits of depression. But soon the time arrives when I am no longer a solitary man.

We meet and for a long time we cannot find the right words to say to each other. Yonder was the tree on which she had once sat and gathered the wonderful basket-like shells of sea-urchins, hung on

F

the boughs of the tree by the waves and by the typhoons. The Zu-Su had since deposited so much sand on that tree that it was only by certain hardly perceptible signs that one recognised the place where I had seen the deer-flower change into woman. We stood in silence there, on the sea-shore, near the foam-flecked waves breaking upon the rocks, listening to the measured beatings of universal time and, together with the sea-urchins, the sea-shells and the sea-stars, aware of the brief register of our own human pendulum.

How quickly the mountains crumble away! There was a cliff not far from where we stood which used to overhang the shore. Beneath it the spotted deer, the Manchurian red deer and the raccoons used to walk to the sea-shore, to the edge of the salt water, and we, too, had one day walked along that common path arm-in-arm. But the typhoon had brought down that cliff and the path now runs round the edge of the crumbled stone. On the spot where Lu Wen's little Chinese hut with its paper windows once stood, now stands a research laboratory—a huge building with wide Italian windows. Of the entire deer-farm with its galvanised wire-netting stretching for several kilometres and cutting off the whole of Misty Mountain, there now remains only a few aging stags, but Hua-lu is still alive and wanders all over the place just like a domestic animal.

We paid a visit to Lu Wen's grave under an enormous cedar. The Chinese had cut a small shrine in the trunk of the cedar where they still perform their rites and burn their joss-sticks. It was there while telling the story of the life of the man who was one of my dearest friends that I suddenly remembered my own root Ginseng which was growing somewhere near the Valley of Song. Why not go there now out of curiosity and have a look at Ginseng? And so the two of us went to look for the root which had once before been found.

I had, to be sure, long forgotten the guide-posts left by Lu Wen, but I knew that the way to the Valley of Song led through the Sevencrested Gorge by way of the Third Bear Valley. So we passed through the gorge and climbed up the side of the valley to the top. In the Valley of Song everything was as before: the same huge, wide-spaced trees with large, sunny glades and the singing birds. But when we left the Valley of Song and went down the ancient terrace into the dense wood with the shade-loving grasses, I lost my way. We walked up and down a long time in the hope of finding the place where Lu Wen and I had sat in silence for so long.

Many a time I have found it much easier to discover a forgotten place at night than in the daytime and, what is even more remarkable, a question which I had put to myself at the time would suddenly rise up in my mind, and it was only then that I would realise, by the particularly strong smell of some mushrooms, that the question had arisen just because of that peculiar smell and that the place I was seeking must be somewhere near. It was only then that I would look round more closely and—remember where the place was. So it was now when we at last came gropingly to the right place and our quiet talk stopped, that I suddenly heard the voice from the brook calling out, "Speak, speak, speak!"

And then all the musicians, all the living creatures of the Valley of Song, struck up their instruments and raised their voices in song, and the whole living silence opened up and called to us, "Speak, speak, speak!"

After that I saw the trunk of the crab-tree over which Lu Wen and I had once crossed to the other side of the brook, and I remembered everything to the smallest detail.

We stopped on the same spot where Lu Wen and I had once knelt—Lu Wen was praying, I thought—and we began carefully to part the shade-loving grasses. We were so excited and we worked with such a will that a certain reserve which still existed in our relations disappeared completely and we were drawn rapidly to each other and—suddenly—we saw Ginseng!

I spent a long time making out of cedar bark the same kind of little box I had seen so many years ago in Lu Wen's cottage in the hands of the Manchus. When the box was finished, we strengthened it with strips of bast. We then dug out the root very carefully so as not to damage a single fibre. It looked very like the other root which the Manchus had showed me: it was shaped like a naked man, it had hands and feet, and the hands had little fibres like fingers, and it had a neck and a head, and the head had a pigtail. We filled the box with earth, the same earth in which the root grew, put the root in with great care and went back to the place where Lu Wen and I had once sat, listening to the living stillness, each thinking his own thoughts. But now we could not sit so long in silence, each aloof from the other, for the brook began to call, "Speak, speak, speak!"

The musicians of the Valley of Song struck up, and we talked happily to each other and to good effect.

I'd rather not say it, but having begun, I'd better make a clean breast of everything. It was not the same woman who came to me, but I say: the strength of the Root of Life is such that in her I found my very being. I came to love this other woman as I loved the one I had yearned for in my youth. It is in this, I think, yes, it is in this that the vital force of the Root of Life lies—to come out of oneself and find oneself in another human being.

Now I have found something which for ever fascinates me, a work created by myself, a work which makes me feel as if we, armed with knowledge and with an acute desire for love, were going back to the task which occupied our savage ancestors at the dawn of civilisation: the taming of wild animals. I am now looking for any opportunity that would enable me to combine the methods of modern science with that feeling of common kinship with all living creatures which I have inherited from Lu Wen. So this is the fascinating work I am now engaged on. I have a dear friend, my wife, and dear children. If I look at the way other people live, I can justly regard myself as one of the happiest men in the world. But once more I say: if we are to talk frankly, then let us make a clean breast of it! There is one trifling event in my life which, if looked at objectively, exerts no influence whatever on the general run of my life, but this trifling circumstance, it sometimes seems to me, forms the same kind of starting-point with me for the creative force of life as the change of antlers with a deer. Every year and always during that misty spring when the deer throw off their old, ossified antlers, some kind of renewal takes place within me just as in the deer. For several days I find it difficult to work either in the laboratory or the library, and I can find neither rest nor peace in my happy home. A kind of blind force drives me out of my home, seized by a sharp pain and in the throes of an acute depression: I wander about in the woods and the mountains and, in the end, always find myself on the top of the cliff, from whose innumerable crevices, as from some tear-glands, water drips continuously, gathering into larger and larger drops, so that it looks as if that rock were always weeping. It is not a human being, it is a stone; I know full well that a stone cannot feel, and yet I seem to be one with it, indeed my heart becomes so inseparable a part of it that I can hear something inside that rock beating, and then I remember my past and I become as I was in my youth. Before my eyes, as I sit in the vine-smothered tent, Hua-lu is about to push her little hoofs through the tangle of vine lianas. My past comes back to me with all its poignant raptures and it is then, as if I had not learnt anything by experience, that I say aloud to my real friend, to the rock whose heart beats in unison with mine, "Hunter on the hill, oh, hunter on the hill, why did you not then grasp her by her hoofs?"

I seem during those wasted days to divest myself of everything I have ever created, just like a stag shedding his antlers, and afterwards I go back to my home, to the laboratory, and start to work again.

It is thus that I, together with all the other workers, obscure and famous, enter the twilight hour before sunrise, the hour of the creation of a new and better life for all the peoples of the earth.

NATURE'S CALENDAR

*The seasons of the year are full of unpredictable surprises;
but, to my fancy, there is nothing essentially more real in
the whole world than they; spring, summer, autumn, winter.*

LUMINOUS DAYS OF EARLY SPRING

Spring's First Radiance

In the morning it was twenty degrees below zero, but by the middle
of the day it began to drip from the roof. The whole of this day,
from morning till evening, radiated brightness like a crystal. The
firs, still wearing their mantles of snow, stood motionless, as though
made of alabaster, and all day long the tints changed from pink to
blue. A wisp of the pale moon hung a long time in the sky, while
below, along the line of the horizon, the soft colours of early spring
were mingled.

Everything was beautiful on this first day of spring's pellucid
light and we spent it in hunting. Regardless of the hard frost, the
hares crouched close to the ground, not in the swamps, where they
usually crouch on a frosty day, but in the fields, in the bushes and in
the glades near the verge of woods.

The Road at the End of March

In the daytime all spring birds come flying to the spring road to
feed; at night, in order not to sink up to the ears in the granular
snow, the beasts of the field and the forest also pass along the same
road. And for many more days man will travel on sleighs along this
reddish road, over the dung which prevents the snow from melting.

Little by little the road becomes a dam for the spring brooks
rushing towards it. Yonder, on one side of the road, the little streams
have mingled to form a whole lake. This lake presses furiously
against the dam, but cannot burst through it. A man and his little
boy are driving in a sledge along the road. Just then a new stream
comes rushing into the lake and the dam can hold out no longer
against this added pressure and it breaks at one point, a noisy torrent
of water swirling across the road in front of the two travellers in the
sledge.

A RUBY EYE

The gloom of dusk is settling on the frosty silence. Deep shadows hover over the bushes of the naked woods, as if the woods themselves were gathering up their thoughts for the night. Athwart the darkness of the bushes the sun looks with a ruby eye—and this red eye is not bigger than a man's eye.

BLUE SHADOWS

Silence falls again over fields and woods, a bright, frosty silence. Yesterday's snow lies on top of the old, frozen snow like a powder full of glittering gems. The crust of snow does not give anywhere; in the fields, in the sunshine, it holds even more firmly than in the shade. Every little bush of dead wormwood and agrimony, every blade of grass, every seeded spikelet is reflected, as in a mirror, in this glittering expanse of freshly fallen snow, and they all see themselves blue and beautiful.

SPRING FROST

Frost and a northerly gale played havoc with the sun's business last night and what a terrible mess they left behind them! Even the blue violets were smothered in crystals of snow and broke in one's hand, and it seemed the sun itself was ashamed to get up this morning to see everything in such utter confusion.

It was not easy to put things right, but the sun cannot be put to shame in spring and already at eight o'clock in the morning ichneumon-flies were skipping about over the big roadside puddle, which was exposed to the rays of the sun.

THE BIRTH OF SOUND

After the thaw—a sunny morning. The snow has sagged, beneath the firs and pines it looks as if the ground had been strewn with sand: those are the dead, brownish needles reappearing from their different layers and, as the snow melts, forming a dense coating of needles. The same thing is happening under the agrimony bushes: they have been pulled about mercilessly by goldfinches and tits in winter and now everything lies under them in one layer.

In the towns there is water everywhere, in the woods—snow; the country roads are a well defined brownish tint in an expanse of white. On the margins of woods, beneath the trees, are little circles: here in the sun spring has already come in all her glory. From noon until four o'clock the rays of the sun seem to set the snow itself on fire: from under the snow the small branches and the little twigs of the fir-trees begin to leap upwards and, when spring comes all at once, the warmth in the woods is, for an hour or two, so overwhelming that a whole wood is set in motion—you can see with your own eyes how the wood is rising.

Streams are running in the ditches along the roads, but in the woods all is still quiet, save that here and there there are intense flashes of light. The first drops are born in the glades, at the verge of the wood, and it is they that give birth to the first sound.

THE FIRST STREAMS

I heard a light whirring of wings accompanied by what sounded like the sharp call of a woodpigeon and I rushed to my dog to make sure whether the woodcocks had really arrived. But Kent was running along quietly. I went back to admire the floodwaters and again, as I walked, I heard the same sharp cooing of a woodpigeon. And again and again. . . .

At last it occurred to me that I ought to stop moving when I heard that sound again. Gradually, however, the sound became continuous and I realised that somewhere beneath the snow a little stream was singing.

This filled me with such delight that I gave up the chase and went to listen to the streams. I was soon amazed to find that I could distinguish their different natures by their voices.

THE HOTTEST HOUR

The snow is melting in the fields, but in the woods it still lies untouched, closely packed hummocks of snow on the ground and on the boughs of trees, and the trees themselves are prisoners of the snow. The thin tree-trunks had been weighed down to the ground and they had got frozen in and now they are waiting impatiently for the hour of their liberation.

At last the hottest hour comes, the happiest hour for the motionless trees and the most terrible hour for the beasts and birds.

The hottest hour comes and the snow begins to melt imperceptibly; then, in the great silence of the wood, a little fir branch suddenly begins to move and to sway. As it happens, beneath the fir-tree, covered by its broad branches, a hare is asleep. He wakes up in alarm and listens: surely, a branch cannot move by itself?

The hare is frightened, and there, under his very eyes, another branch begins to stir, and a third one, and all, freed from the snow, suddenly leap into the air. The startled hare starts running, but after a little while he sits down again, his little body stiff as a post, and listens: where does danger threaten, where must he run to?

But no sooner does he stand on his hind legs than he sees a whole birch-tree leap from the ground into the air under his very nose, straighten itself and begin to sway to and fro! And next to it a fir branch springs to life! And off they go! Everywhere firs are leaping into the air, the whole wood, breaking loose from the imprisoning clutches of the snow, begins to stir, the whole wood is in motion!

The terror-stricken hare runs madly from one end of the wood to the other, and every kind of beast is on its feet, and the birds fly away from the wood.

A MAN'S TRACKS

On the sunny verge of the wood the footprints of a man who has passed this way in winter show no signs of yielding to the sun. While the snow has melted on the entire glade and the earth shows up black on it and the dead leaves are dry to the touch, the spreading, gigantic tracks remain embedded in white lumps of snow a foot and a half high—clear evidence that a man has passed there in winter.

I noticed, however, that on a nearby mound the pads of a hare had sunk together with the melting snow and spread over the black earth in circles as large as a cap.

SPRING WATERS

The snow is still deep in places, but it is so granular that even the hare falls through it to the firm earth below and brushes the snow up with its belly.

All the birches are weeping happy tears in the rain; the raindrops, flashing, fly downwards and are extinguished in the snow, and that is why the snow little by little grows granular.

The road is covered with the last crunching remnants of ice, bits of broken crockery we call them. And that yellow bed of ice in which the spring torrent went swirling along, has also melted away and turned into soft mud: a hare who had crossed the little stream at night, left its prints on the yellow bed under the water.

THE BROOK AND THE PATH

The snow has melted on the footpath which runs along a pine wood and the footpath is dry now. Beside it, a brook is rushing along noisily: thus both of them, the path and the brook, run side by side along the verge of the wood, disappearing in the distance; but on the other side of the brook, on a northerly slope, the melting snow still lies on the ground among the firs and the pines.

LUMINOUS DROPS OF MELTING SNOW

Sun and wind. Spring snow. The tits and the crossbills are singing their love songs. The crust of frozen snow is shivered by the skis, and flies tinkling all over the place, like glass. Against the dark background of a pine-wood the young birches grow rose-tinted in the sun. The sunshine creates something like a glacier on the iron roof, water runs down the roof in a continuous stream and this makes the glacier recede. The strip of warm iron yawns wider and wider between the glacier and the edge of the roof.

A thin stream of water, falling from the iron roof, lights on a cold icicle hanging in the shade, in the frost. The water, as it comes in touch with the icicle, freezes and so the top of the icicle grows thicker and thicker in the morning.

When the sun, having come round the roof, glances at the icicle, the frost disappears and the stream from the glacier, running down the icicle, begins to drip in golden drops, and so everywhere in town golden drops are dripping down from the roofs until the evening.

THE WOODCOCK

Spring progresses, but it does so slowly. In the pond, which is still not entirely free from ice, frogs have appeared and are croaking. The nut-trees are in flower, but their catkins are not yet broadcasting the yellow pollen. When a bird brushes against a twig as it flies by, no yellow smoke rises from the twig.

The last patches of snow have disappeared in the woods. The dead leaves on the ground, free at last from the weight of snow, look as if they had been firmly pressed: they have gone brown. A short distance from me I saw a bird with big, expressive black eyes and a long bill, as long as half the length of a pencil, the colour of last year's leaves. I sat motionless and when the woodcock was quite sure that I was not alive, he stood on his feet and, brandishing his pencil, struck the hot, rotted leaves with it.

I could not see what it was he got from under the leaves. All I saw was that one small, round aspen leaf remained attached to his bill after he had pushed it through the dead leaves into the earth and taken it out again. Then as he went on striking the ground, another leaf was added to the first, and another. When I moved at last and he took wing, flying along the verge of the wood quite near to me, I had time to count: there were seven aspen leaves on the woodcock's bill.

BIRCH SAP

Showers interspersed with sunshine. I was photographing a brook and when, having got my feet wet, I was about to sit down on an ant-hill, as I am in the habit of doing in winter, I noticed that the ants had already crawled out and were sitting close to each other in one dense mass, waiting for something; or were they merely shaking off their winter's slumbers before starting on their summer's tasks ?

A few days ago, before a hard frost, it was also very warm and I wondered why no ants were to be seen and why the sap in the birches did not rise. Afterwards a hard frost set in—eighteen degrees below zero. Now everything was clear to me: the birches and the ants knew that there was to be a keen frost, and they knew it because of the icy ground. Now, however, the ground has melted and the sap in the birch-trees has risen.

A HARE'S FUR

Snow is always welcomed as a great joy. The white fur of the hare, shed in the spring fights during the moulting season, lies thickly on the black earth. There were so many hares last winter that you see the tufts of the white hare's fur everywhere on the ground on top of the coating of dead aspen leaves.

The grass had grown green again and it was bent as it pushed through the dead aspen leaves among the trunks of aspens, between the long, yellow stalks and spikelets of the mat grass, and it was that first green road that the moulting hare, still white, but his fur hanging in tufts, had taken.

WARM SHOWERS

The lime-tree outside my window has large green buds and on each bud there is a luminous drop of water, as big as the bud itself. The drop rolls from bud to bud and down a thin twig where it mingles with a drop from another bud and then falls to the ground. Higher up the tree, along the bark of a large branch, a whole stream is running down invisibly, like a river along its bed, spreading out on the small boughs and twigs and taking the place of the fallen drops. So the whole tree is full of raindrops and the whole tree is dripping.

SPRING CLEANING

A few more days, a week perhaps, and nature will begin to cover up with flowers, grasses, sprouting green mosses and thin, young shoots the vast rubbish heaps in the woods. It is the most touching sight in the world—the way nature carefully tidies up its dry, dead bones: once, in the spring, it hides it from our sight with flowers, another time, in the autumn—with snow.

The bird-cherry buds were to-day transformed into green spears. The catkins on the nut-trees are broadcasting their pollen and a puff of smoke rises beneath every flitting bird in the nut-tree. The golden catkins are still raising clouds of dust, they are still alive, but their time has passed: it is the minute blue flowers, scattered in thousands and thousands of little stars beneath the trees, which now reign supreme and charm the whole world with their beauty.

The ice has melted, only the dung now remains on the road that runs through the wood and, as though scenting it, millions of seeds from fir and pine cones have drifted on to that dung.

COMMON PATHS

The pollen from the blossoming plants has covered the little stream in the wood so thickly that neither the tall trees growing on its banks, nor the clouds in the sky are any longer reflected in it. The gnarled tree-trunk which spans the stream from bank to bank and which served as a bridge in spring, now towers so high that if you were to fall off it, you would get badly hurt. But nobody wants it any more, for the stream can be crossed now quite simply over the pebbles. The squirrel, though, still finds it useful: there he is walking along the tree-trunk, carrying something big in his mouth. Now and again he stops, does something to that long thing in his mouth, perhaps nibbles at it, and then continues on his way.

SPRING'S MOVEMENT

After the fir and the pine, the aspen begins its sowing: all the glades are thickly covered with its catkins.

I watch the green blades of grass pushing through last year's straw and hay. Green carpets are being woven in the fields and the hum of insects is getting louder and louder.

THE POLLEN OF ASPEN

To-day I have been photographing the catkins of the aspen, which are dispersing their pollen. Bees, too, are rushing about: you can hardly tell which is bee and which is pollen; is it the plant's seed that flies past to grow again in the earth, or is it a bee which flies in search of food?

It is so still that during the night the flying pollen of the aspen has descended upon the roads, the backwaters of river and lake, and everything is covered, as if with snow. I remembered one aspen grove where the pollen lay so thick upon the ground that I set fire to it. The flame darted over it in an instant and everything became black.

The aspen pollen is in itself a whole phenological period of spring. At this time the nightingales sing as well as the cuckoos and the orioles, but the golden-crested wrens are also singing, although their singing season only starts in summer. I always feel a little heavy at heart and also somewhat moved at the time the aspen begins to shed its pollen: what a waste of nature's bounty, a waste of seeds even greater than the waste of eggs at the time of the spawning of fish!

While the old aspens are shedding their pollen, the young ones change from their brown, baby clothes into their green dresses and, like village girls during a fête, display both their old and their new costumes.

Ploughing has begun. In some places tractors are used, in others ploughs drawn by horses.

After the rain the hot sun has transformed the woods into hot-houses, filled with the stifling scent of growth and decay: the growth of birch-tree buds and young grass and the decay of last year's leaves. The smell of decay is different, but it, too, had a fragrance of its own. Patches of dead grass and stubble, mounds covered with yellow fibres of plants—everywhere green grass grows. The catkins on the birches have also turned green. From the aspens the catkin-seeds fall in a shower and they swing about everywhere.

A thick spike of last year's mat grass rose high over the ground yonder, swaying in the wind—how many times did it scare away both hare and bird? But now an aspen catkin has lighted on it and broken it for ever and the new green grass will soon cover it up, but not yet. . . . The dead, yellow stalk will take a long time to dress, it will be a long time before the green body of the new spring grows round it.

A wind rose and still more aspen catkins began to float in the air. The whole earth has been sealed up with these aspen worms. Millions and millions of seeds—and only a few of them will take root, yet in spite of that the young aspen saplings will shoot up so densely that a hare will find his path barred by them and will have to go round them.

The wind has been broadcasting aspens for three days, but the earth unceasingly demands more and more seeds. Soon a fight will start between the aspen saplings: with their roots they will fight for earth and with their branches for light. The young aspen wood soon begins to thin out and when the trees reach a man's height, the hare starts to pay them visits and feed on their bark. When the light-loving aspen wood rises still higher, fir trees will begin to grow in its shade, at first clinging shyly to the young aspen trunks, but gradually they will overtake the aspens and in the end they will smother by their dark shadows the light-loving trees with their perpetually trembling leaves. . . .

When the whole aspen wood is dead and, instead of the gentle rustle of leaves, the wind raises a howl in the wild fir-tree forest on a winter's day, one aspen will be found to have survived somewhere in a corner of a glade. It will be full of holes and knots, woodpeckers will tap at its trunk, starlings will nest in the holes made by the woodpeckers as well as wood pigeons and tits, a squirrel or a marten, may make its home in one of them, and when the tree falls down, the hares will come to feed on its bark in winter, foxes will come after the hares—a whole club of the beasts of the forest will be here. . . .

BEFORE EVENING

The day was warm on account of the hot winds and in the strong currents of air at nightfall a new phase of spring began. Almost at the same moment the early willow began to blossom, the thrush burst into song and the ponds became alive with frogs, the evening air being filled with their voices.

Shrews went out chasing insects before evening and in their element—the aspen foliage—they were as inaccessible to us as fish in water.

A TARDY STREAM

It is warm in the woods. The grass shows up a bright green among the brown bushes. What delightful paths! What a delicious stillness in the air, as if nature had fallen into a trance! The cuckoo began to call on the first of May and now it has become very vocal. A black grouse is muttering at sunset. The stars, like the buds of the pussy-willow, swell in the transparent clouds. The morel mushroom is growing. The young birch-trees loom white in the darkness. The aspen trees have divested themselves of their grey catkins. Only the spring stream is late, it has not retired yet between its banks and still flows rippling over the green sward, and the sap from a broken branch of a birch is dripping into the stream.

THE DISSATISFIED FROG

Even the water was dancing—so great was the joy of the frogs! Later on they came out of the water and went wandering all over the earth: wherever you stepped in the evening, there was a frog.

This warm night the frogs croaked softly, and even those of them who had some reason for being dissatisfied with their fate joined in the croaking: on such a night even a dissatisfied frog felt happy and, forgetting its worries, it began to croak like the rest.

THE FIRST CRAWFISH

It thundered and rained, but the sun shone brightly through the pelting rain and the broad band of a rainbow spanned the heavens from end to end. It was the time when the bird-cherry began to blossom and the wild currant bush burst into green bud over the surface of the water.

It was then also that the first crawfish put its head out of some cranny among the stones on the bottom of the river and moved its feelers.

THE BIRD-CHERRY BLOOMS NO MORE

Flakes of white blossom lie scattered on the burdocks, the nettles and every kind of green grass: the bird-cherry has ceased to bloom. Instead, the elder tree is in flower and beneath it—the wild strawberry. A few buds of the lily-of-the-valley have also opened up, the brownish leaves of the aspen have turned a delightful green, the sprouting oats stands in rows of little soldiers in the black field. In the swamps the flags are long and thick and they throw a green shadow into the dark pools, water boatmen go scurrying over the surface of the black water, blue dragon-flies go fluttering from one island of sedge to another.

I am walking along a well-trodden path between thickets of nettles. The smell of nettles is so overpowering that my whole body begins to itch. With a cry of alarm thrushes drive a predatory crow farther and farther away from their nests where they have already hatched out their eggs.

Everything is so fascinating, every trifle in the life of the innumerable performers of life's bridal dance on earth.

WOODLAND VERGES

THE WILLOW HERB

Summer has come and in the coolness of the woods the butterfly orchis, so white that it seems to be fashioned out of porcelain, fills the air with its exquisite perfume, and by a stump of a tree, in the full glare of the sun, there rises to its full, splendid height the beauty of our woods—the rose-bay willow herb.

The Sunny Verge of the Wood

Whether at the dawn of a new day or at the dawn of a new year—it really makes no difference—the verge of a wood is the refuge for every kind of living thing.

The sun rises and wherever its ray falls, everything awakens from sleep, although down yonder, in the deep, dark recesses of the gullies, sleep goes on undisturbed until at least seven o'clock.

At the very edge of the wood's verge the flax is over an inch tall and a horsetail is growing in the middle of the flax. What an oriental wonder—a horsetail, sparkling with dew and standing, like a minaret, in the rays of the rising sun!

Dragon-Flies

When the mare's-tail became dry, the dragon-flies grew extremely wary and they seemed to fear the shade more than anything else.

Two red dragon-flies hung motionless on a blue bell-shaped flower; I put them paired and still united on the sand in the hot sunshine. They began to stir, as they were brought back to life by the sun, and in the first instant of revival each was only thinking of itself: what either of them wanted most was to free itself. When they did disengage themselves, they flew away, each a different way, each by itself.

Red Cones

The dew is cool and a fresh breeze tempers the heat of summer. It is only because of that that it is still possible to take a walk in the woods; otherwise there would have been countless numbers of horse-flies in the daytime and in the evenings—millions of gnats. For now is really the time when the horses, maddened by the flies, race blindly to the fields with their carts.

I take a walk in the woods on a fresh sunny morning. The people, working in the fields, are having a quiet rest. The woodland grasses are drenched in cold dew, the insects are asleep, many flowers have not opened up yet. Only the leaves of the aspens are astir, their smooth upper sides already dry, while to their lower sides the velvety dew still clings in little, transparent droplets.

"Good morning, my sweet little firs, how are you? have you any news? any news?"

They reply that everything is all right, thank you, and that their young red cones have now grown to half their usual size.

That is true enough and can be easily proved: for the old empty cones hang next to the young ones on the trees.

I emerge from the chasms of firs to the sunny verge of the wood. On my way I come across a lily-of-the-valley in a dark corner of the wood. It still preserves its shape, but it has gone quite yellow, poor thing, and smells no more.

THE HUMBLE-BEE AND THE STALK

What a slender stalk the bistort snake-root has and how bowed down it is by its thick flower!

But when a big, heavy-weight humble-bee sits down on this flower, which is itself so thick and heavy, its stalk will droop and bend. The humble-bee, alarmed, sets up an angry buzzing and does its best to settle on the flower. The stalk still bends and the humble-bee goes on buzzing angrily, until, bent to the limit, the stalk resigns itself to its fate. Then the humble-bee buries its head deep inside the flower and falls silent.

MY MUSHROOM

In a wood where mushrooms grow one dell stretches out a hand to another across the undergrowth, and when you pass through the bushes, your own mushroom greets you in the dell. You need not waste your time looking for it: your mushroom always looks at you first!

THE BUTTERFLY-ORCHIS

To my own sense of smell, our butterfly-orchis has a somewhat depraved odour, especially towards the end, when all the signs of spring have disappeared and summer begins. It seems to be aware of its own shortcoming and it is ashamed to exhale its fragrance in sunlight.

I have often observed that when the butterfly-orchis—the Beauty of the Night, as we call it—loses its first freshness and its white colour begins to fade and it even grows a little yellow, then—during those last days of its beauty—it also loses all shame and begins to exhale its scent even in the sun. It is then that you can safely say that the spring of that year has gone for ever, never again to return.

A SILVERY MORNING

Look how full of life the wood is! The dew has not dried yet and the grass and the leaves still sparkle and everything is clothed in silver.

There are many black tree-stumps among the green ferns, every-where there is cow-wheat, mezereon, periwinkles. . . . Each bush is covered with small pink flowers and there is a hum under the trees and in the bushes and in the grass, butterflies go fluttering among the pink and blue flowers, bees dart in every direction, beetles drone, deep-voiced humble-bees buzz. There is a great festival in the bush. No one there hears the dull beatings of my heart, which pounds away like a sledgehammer, for only I can see from the way my dog behaves that some big bird is sitting underneath the bush.

Like a black cloud, a black grouse issues with a startling whir from under the bush: the glade re-echoes with the noise of its wings and the whole wood suddenly begins to boom all around me.

It is at that moment that it seems as if your heart stops beating, as if something has torn itself away and flown off. I can see the bird clearly in the sights of my gun, but I whisper to myself, "Wait! It won't get away!"

Afterwards everything just happens automatically, and although I cannot see anything for the smoke, I know very well that behind one of the mounds the red wattle of the wounded bird is leaping up and down—one minute it shows itself, another minute it is gone.

The wood is full of life! A black grouse sits under every bush and it will always be like that: for now the key has been found to all the bushes, tree-stumps, burrows, ditches and marsh mounds.

So much time has passed and yet the morning is still silvery. My dog has entered the water and has come out all silvery. Not far away a she-bear crossed the brook with her cub over some large stones laid across it; the old, old bear went across without mishap, but the clumsy baby-bear fell in and when he jumped out again, he, too, was all silvery, and he ran after his mother: puff-puff-puff! A young elk pricked up his pink ears in the brake and there he, too, stood all silvery! The meadow by the stream was alive with bees, just like one big honeycomb.

A WHITE RAINBOW

Has anyone seen a white rainbow? You can see it in the marshes early on a fine morning, but only when the mists are rising from the ground shortly before dawn and the sun, as it shows itself, pierces through them. Then all the mists gather into one very dense arch, very white, sometimes rose-tinted, sometimes tinted a creamy colour.

I adore a white rainbow. It is to me like a young mother with her breasts full of milk. This morning the white rainbow reclined with one of its ends upon a wooded coomb and, arching over our hill, it descended with the other end into our marshy valley.

The rye is turning brown. The flowers in the meadows are gorgeously bright this year because of the constant rains. In the wet alder-bushes, growing at the edge of the marsh, which drenched me as I passed through them, I soon found my footpath to the marshes.

HARVEST TIME

The woodpecker's song has not many trills now. He has no time for warbling now that he has to hollow out nests all day long, tapping away with his own head as with a heavy hammer and chipping away with his own beak as with a chisel.

A WILD PANSY

A butterfly, all black save for a white thin edging to its wings, alights and becomes a triangle. But among these small butterflies there is a blue one, one with which we are all very familiar. This butterfly, when it lights upon a blade of grass, becomes a flower. You pass by and it will never enter your head that it is a butterfly at all—it is a flower, nothing but a flower: a wild pansy!

A BALL ON THE RIVER

The yellow water lilies have been open since sunrise, the white ones open up at about ten o'clock. When all the white water lilies have unfolded their petals, a ball starts on the river.

JAM

At about ten o'clock in the morning I came back to the same cool, sleepy meadow across which I had walked early this morning. In the hot blaze of the sun everything hummed among the flowers, everything exuded a sweet, delicious smell, something was brewing there, as though every flower and bee had joined together and were making jam.

THE WIND IN THE WOODS

It is windy, cool and clear in the woods. The trees rustle and through this rustle one can clearly hear the bright summer song of the wren.

The noise in the wood comes only from the tops of the tall trees. In the dress circle—in the young aspen copse—the delicately-shaped little round leaves are merely trembling, one leaf bumping so gently against its fellow leaf that the noise made by those constant collisions is hardly audible. Below, on the sward, the silence is complete and in that silence the busy to-and-fro of the humble-bee can be heard.

DEAD TREES

The dead bodies of trees are quite unlike the evil smelling dead bodies of animals. A birch-tree is lying on the ground yonder, covered up with bistort snake-root and by the sharp-toothed stalks of cow-wheat. Old age made the bark on the dead birch-tree curl up into little funnels and in each funnel some creature is quite sure to live.

DROUGHT

The great drought has dried everything up. The brook is bone dry, but the bridges of trees which had once been washed away by floods still remain, and the sportsman's path to the haunts of the wild duck still runs along the bank. On the sand are the fresh prints of birds and little animals who come here to water for old times' sake. They find drinking water, though, in little pools somewhere in the woods.

THE DECLINE OF THE YEAR

To everyone else it is only the beginning of summer now, but to those who observe minutely life's movement in nature it is the decline of the year: the days are already growing shorter and once the rye is in blossom one can count on the fingers the days that still remain before it will be time to harvest it.

In the oblique rays of the morning sun the whiteness of the birches on the verge of the wood is whiter than marble columns. There, under those birches, the buck-thorn's unusual flowers are still in bloom; I am afraid the mountain-ash will have very few berries this year, but the raspberries have fruited well and the currants, too, have big, green berries.

Every day the call of the cuckoo grows more and more infrequent and the replete summer silence grows greater and greater, interrupted only now and again by the calls exchanged between the parent birds and their fledglings. Only on the rarest occasions do you now hear the drumming trill of the woodpecker. When it comes from somewhere near, you cannot help giving a start and thinking, "Is there no one else left in the woods?" The general noises of meadow and copse have died down. The thrush, it is true, still sings sweetly, but he is singing all alone. . . . Perhaps his little song sounds more sweetly now, for, after all, the best time is still to come—isn't it the beginning of summer? But no! the year is already on the decline.

AUTUMN DEW

The Young Aspens are Cold

On a sunny day in autumn the young, many-hued aspens crowded closely together on the verge of a fir-wood, as though they had felt cold there—in the wood—and they had come out to warm themselves on the wood's verge, just as in our villages people come out and sit down in the sun on the mounds of earth outside their cottages.

Autumn

In the villages the air is full of the smell of drying crops. At sunrise the flails on the threshing floors are beating a gay tattoo.

The mushroom is indefatigably pushing through the ground. . . .

On Wisdom

Words of wisdom, like autumn leaves, fall without any effort.

Autumn Dewdrops

There is a smell of autumn in the air. Flies knock against the ceiling. Sparrows gather in flocks. Rooks forgather in families to feed on the roads. Dewdrops are cold, grey. Some dewdrop will glitter the livelong day in the bosom of a leaf.

The Fall of Leaves

A hare comes out of a dense thicket of young fir-trees and, on seeing a wide glade, stops under a birch-tree. He dare not cross to the other side and he goes round the entire glade from birch to birch. Now he stops and listens. He who has reason to be afraid of something in the woods, had better not walk through it while the leaves are falling and whispering. The hare listens: it seems to him all the time as if somebody were whispering and stealing after him. No doubt even the timorous hare can pluck up courage not to look round, but then something else might happen: you have overcome your fears, you have not allowed yourself to be deceived by the falling leaves and just then someone takes advantage of it and, making use of the constant rustling set up by the falling leaves, he pounces on you from behind and catches you between his teeth.

AUTUMN

When I arrived here the rye was only just beginning to turn yellow. Now when I am going back people are already eating the rye and the new green corn is pushing through the ground. Then the trees in the woodlands blended into one green mass, now every single tree stands out by itself. Such is autumn always. It does not undress the multitude of trees all at once, but it gives every tree a chance to live its own individual life a little time and to display itself apart from the rest. We, too, I reflected, assume a special grace in the autumn of our lives and we become conscious of it as a personal contribution to the creative purpose of the world.

DEW

Mists rise from the fields, the meadows and the water and melt away in the azure of the sky, but in the woods the mists linger a long time. The sun rises higher and higher, the sunbeams penetrate through the woodland mists into the depths of the thicket and it is possible to gaze straight at them, there in the thicket, and even count and photograph them.

The green paths in the woods and across the glades seem to smoke, the mist rises everywhere, water gathers on the leaves, on the needles of the firs, on the spider-webs, the telegraph wires. As the sun rises still higher and the air becomes warmer, the drops on the telegraph wires begin to merge and to thin out. The same thing, no doubt, also takes place on the trees: there, too, the drops merge.

When, at last, the sun begins to get really warm, big, prismatic drops gather on the telegraph wires and begin to fall on the ground. The same thing happens in the woods, whether on fir or pine or deciduous tree—it is not like rain, but just as if happy tears had been shed. The aspens, in particular, seem to be trembling with joy every time a drop, falling from above, makes the leaf upon which it alights swing to and fro, and so lower and lower the whole aspen glitters and trembles in the dead calm of the wood from the falling, luminous drops.

At this time a few taut spider-webs got dry and the spiders began to draw in their signalling threads. A woodpecker started his tap-tapping on a fir-tree, a thrush began to peck the berries of the mountain-ash.

A WINDY DAY

This fresh autumn breeze knows how to whisper tenderly to the sportsman, and the sportsmen themselves often begin chatting to one another from an excess of joyous expectations. One either talks, or one is silent: both talk and silence come easy to the sportsman. It sometimes happens that a sportsman who has been talking excitedly, sees something flashing by in the air and falls silent as he follows it with his eyes. Then he asks, "What was it I was telling you about?" He cannot remember, but it doesn't matter: he can start telling another story.

It is like that that the hunting wind in the autumn always whispers something, and without finishing one tale, starts on another; now the mutter of a young black grouse can be heard, it stops, and the voices of cranes are borne upon the wind.

THE BEGINNING OF AUTUMN

At sunrise in the wood to-day a birch, richly festooned with leaves, stepped out of the wood on to a glade, as though dressed in a crinoline; another one, more timid, was shedding leaf after leaf on a dark fir. Afterwards, as the light grew stronger, every tree appeared to me in a different way. This always happens at the beginning of autumn when, after the rich abundance of summer in which all of them share, each in its own way begins to go through the experience of the fall of the leaves.

Is it not the same with men? In joy they all look alike and only in times of sorrow, as the struggle for a better life begins, does every man reveal his own individual traits of character. Regarded from the human point of view, the woods in autumn present to us the birth of personality.

But how else are we to look at it? And who will give shelter to the orphan—to that poor, torn off leaf which is now fluttering in the air?

This comparison which flashed through my mind put me in a very happy mood, and pulling myself together, I looked round with a keen feeling of kinship towards nature. Here is a mound combed clean by the feet of black grouse; before, you would always find in a hole on this mound the feather of a black grouse or a capercaillie and, if it was speckled, you knew that it was a hen that had been digging there, if black—a cock. Now yellow leaves and not birds' feathers lie in the holes of the combed mounds. And yonder is a very old russula fungus, as big as a plate and all red, its edges turned up with age; this plate is full of water and a tiny yellow birch leaf is swimming about in it.

THE SPROUTING CORN

A divided sky with clouds going in different directions brought on a downpour of rain. For the next two days it rained without intermission, and when the rain stopped, the sky was still overcast, but the clouds looked frosty. In the morning, however, the sun was shining and, paying no heed to nature's conspiracy against me, I hurried out to have some sport with my camera. The winter rye was pushing through the earth, its blades drawn up in rows like soldiers on parade. Each of these soldiers was clad in red to the ground, his bayonet was green, and on each bayonet was a drop of water as big as a cranberry, flashing in the sun, either blinding, like the sun itself, or iridescent, like a gem.

When I looked into the view-finder of the camera, I saw a picture of an army in red shirts and green rifles, each soldier irradiated by his own sun, and my heart leapt with joy. Paying no heed to the mud, I lay prone on the ground and tried to snap the sprouting corn from every possible angle.

AUTUMN SUNRISE

There are autumn blow-balls which are smaller than the summer ones and much sturdier than they, and there is not one, but sometimes as many as ten flower-heads on one stalk. I photographed them, and I also took a photograph of the white sun, which dived into the clouds, now showing itself like a white circle, now disappearing altogether.

One must never miss the opportunity of taking a snap of a bright beam of light in the woods. Happy is the man who can obtain a picture on which a sunbeam tells the fairy-tale of a dewdrop!

And so all that dewy morn my heart leapt with joy and human sorrow came not near me. Why indeed should I weep or mourn so early in the day when those who are habitually given to grieving are still asleep in their beds ? By the time they wake up and start moping, the dew will have dried up and then I shall have plenty of time to worry over their sorrows.

Mopers of the whole world, said I, do not begrudge me these moments of joy.

A PARACHUTE

In the great silence of the woods a yellow leaf fluttered gently down from a birch hemmed in by tall firs. When it fell the air was so still that even an aspen leaf forbore to tremble. The fall of the leaf seems to have attracted the attention of the whole wood, and all the firs, birches and pines with all their leaves, twigs and needles, and even the bush and the grass beneath the bush marvelled and kept on asking: how could a leaf be shaken off the tree and move about in such a dead calm?

Obeying the general entreaty to find out whether the leaf had moved of its own accord, I went up to it and then I knew. No! the leaf did not shift by itself: it was a spider, desiring to descend, that cumbered it and made it its parachute.

LATE AUTUMN

Autumn lingers on like a narrow road with sharp bends. One day—frost, another—rain and, suddenly, snow, as in winter—a white snowstorm with a howling wind and, after that, again the sun, again it is warm and again green vegetation appears. Afar, at the very end of the glade, a little birch stands with sweet, golden leaves, looking as if she has fallen into a trance from which she cannot awaken. The wind cannot tear her last remaining leaves off: he had torn all he could.

The last days of autumn come when the berries of the mountain-ash grow crinkly and become, as they say, "sweet." At this time the last days of autumn are so like the first days of early spring that you cannot tell the difference between an autumn day and a spring day except, perhaps, by falling back on your inmost feelings, for in autumn you are thinking, "Let me only live through another winter and then, oh, how I shall rejoice at one more spring!"

It is at such a time that the thought comes to you that it needs must be like that: it is necessary to toil and moil and suffer privations, for after that you have a right to enjoy some cheer. I remembered the fable of "The Grasshopper and the Ant" and the ant's stern speech.

Now in early spring, on just such a day, you expect happiness whether you deserve it or not: when spring comes, you come to life again and away you go like the grasshopper without a thought for the ant.

THE GLIDING BROOK

Here is the clearing where a few days ago I gathered white mush-rooms. Now it is all white, each tree-stump is covered with a white table-cloth, and even the red mountain-ash is covered with a dusting of rime. The clearing is bounded by two streams, and the large, slow stream has frozen over, but the little swift brook still goes rippling along.

THE FIRST FROST

The night passed under a large, clear moon and at dawn the first frost settled upon the earth. Everything looked grey, but the puddles did not freeze over. Then the sun appeared and the temperature rose, and what a delicious dew gathered on the trees and the grass, what lovely patterns gleamed on the branches of the firs as they peeped out of the dark wood! Most beautiful of all was the queen-pine, which glistened from top to bottom. My young dog's heart leapt with joy.

THE EYES OF THE EARTH

From dawn to eve rain, wind and cold. I have often heard women who have lost their dear ones say that a man's eyes seem to die first, sometimes even before he loses consciousness; sometimes the dying man says, "Why can't I see you, darling?"—that means that the eyes have died and next, perhaps, it will be the tongue's turn to fail.

The lake at my feet is just like that. According to popular fancy, lakes are the eyes of the earth, and here I have no doubt at all—these eyes do die before everything else and they feel how the light is dying. While in the woods the fight for light is only just beginning, a fight accompanied by such exquisite glimpses of beauty when the tops of some trees are ablaze and seem to be lit by a fire of their own, the water on the lake looks dead and the breath of a grave in which only cold fish can live comes from it.

The rains have utterly exhausted the farmers. The swifts have gone long since. The swallows gather in flocks in the fields. We have had two days of frost. The limes have all turned yellow, from top to bottom. The potatoes have gone black. The long evenings are upon us. . . .

THE DEAD LAKE

All is quiet in the golden woods. It is as warm as in summer, spider-webs lie on the fields, the dry leaves rustle loudly under one's feet, the birds fly high out of the range of the gun, a hare raises a cloud of dust on the road.

I left home early and walked for miles trying to get rid of my headache, but in the end I only succeeded in exhausting myself so completely that I lost all ability to think. All I could do was to follow the movements of my dog, keep my gun in readiness and now and again glance at the needle of my compass. In the end I found myself so far away from my home that I could not tell whether the needle of my compass any longer pointed in that direction and so I entered a world which was totally strange to me. For hours I seemed to be pushing my way through the densest underwood, and suddenly there lay before me, in the heart of the golden woods, a completely circular, dead lake. I sat down on its shore and gazed for a long time at those closed eyes of the earth.

In the evening there came a sudden change in the weather: in the woods, behind the wall of trees, a huge *samovar* seemed to start boiling: that was the rain and the wind undressing the trees. According to all my signs and observations, the geese ought to be flying to-night.

THE FIRST FALL OF SNOW

It was a still, moonlight night with a touch of frost in the air and in the early hours of daybreak the first snow fell. Squirrels scampered up the naked trees. In the distance I thought I heard the call of the black grouse. I was about to steal after it, but then I suddenly realised that it was not the call of the grouse at all, but the noise of carts on the distant road which was brought to me by the wind.

The day was changeable, occasionally the sun would shine brightly, occasionally it would snow. At ten o'clock in the morning there was still a coating of ice on the marshes, there were white table-cloths on the tree-stumps and on the white ground aspen leaves lay like little blood-red saucers. A jack snipe rose in a swamp and disappeared in a whirl of snowflakes.

The wild geese were feeding. I stood motionless in the twilight with my face turned towards the setting sun. I could hear the cries of the geese which were flying over my head, a small flock of teal flashed past and a few larger ducks. Every time the birds appeared I felt so excited that I lost the thread of my thoughts and later picked it up only with difficulty. I was thinking how beautifully everything was thought out: our lives had been so arranged that none of us could live very long and none of us could possibly succeed in grabbing everything for himself without leaving anything for anybody else, and that that was why the world appeared so infinite in its variety to every one of us.

GEESE-SWANS

The night was clear, with a moon and stars. A hard frost. In the morning everything looked white. The wild geese were feeding in the stubble-fields, their usual feeding-grounds. A new gaggle arrived and the augmented flock, about two hundred birds in all, began to fly from the lake to the fields. Until noon the black grouse were in the trees where they went on muttering. Then the sky became overcast and it became freezing cold.

After lunch the sun reappeared and it continued fine until evening. I could not help feeling glad at the preservation from the general havoc of our two lovely, golden-leaved birches. The wind blew from the northward, however, and the lake looked fierce and black. A whole flock of geese arrived. I was told that the geese do not stay long with us. When the lake had frozen over so hard that there only remained a small sheet of unfrozen water in the middle of it, I could hear at night, in the darkness and the silence, low voices coming from somewhere in the centre of the lake. I often thought that they must belong to people, but no! those were swans talking to each other on the small unfrozen sheet of water.

In the evening I stole up to the geese through a ravine and I could have wrought real havoc among them with my gun, but I tired myself out in climbing up the steep side of the ravine and my heart was pounding, or did I just want to play the fool for a bit? Anyway, there was a tree-stump near the top of the ravine and I sat down on it, so that I had only to raise my head to see the stubble-field with the geese, the nearest bird being only about ten yards from me. I held my gun in readiness and it seemed to me that even if they should suddenly rise from the ground, they would not be able to fly away before suffering terrible losses. I lit a cigarette, blew out the smoke very carefully and dispersed it just as it came out of my lips with my hand. But behind that little field there was another ravine and, taking advantage of the dusk just as I was doing, a fox was stealing up to the geese. I had no time to raise my gun before the whole gaggle of geese rose in the air and was beyond range. It was a good thing that I had guessed about the presence of the fox and had not raised my head at once. He was following the scent of the geese like a dog, coming nearer and nearer to me. I settled myself comfortably, got a firm purchase for my elbows, judged the distance with my eyes, whistled softly like a mouse—and the fox looked up in my direction. I whistled again and he came straight for me. . . .

A MAN'S SHADOW

A morning moon. The west was hidden by a pall of darkness. At long last, however, a strip of light peeped out as from beneath a blanket, but the blue glades near the moon were still there.

The lake looked as though covered with ice-floes, so strangely and angrily did the mists disintegrate. The village cocks crowed and the swans trumpeted.

I am a bad musician, but it seems to me that the upper register of a swan's cry resembles the cry of the cranes, the same cry with which a crane welcomes the light of day in the marshes, while the lower register of the swan's call is like the cry of the goose—a low gabble.

I don't know whether it was due to the moon or to the sunrise, but I soon noticed some rooks on the blue glades of the sky and very soon it appeared that the whole sky was full of rooks and jackdaws: the rooks were flying round in circles before their departure and the jackdaws, as usual, were there to see them off. Where was I to find out why the jackdaws always saw off the rooks ? Time was when I thought that everything in the world was known already and that only I, miserable ignoramus that I was, knew nothing, and then I discovered that scientists very often do not know the simplest things about living nature.

However, once I realised that, I began in such cases to invent my own reasons. So that so far as the habits of jackdaws are concerned, it is my opinion that the soul of a bird is like a wave: in their mind some ripple or other is transmitted from generation to generation, just as the impulse imparted to a wave by a stone thrown into the water is transmitted from one wave to another. So to this day the jackdaws go on repeating the same thing from one generation to another: they gather to fly off with the rooks, but having seen the rooks off, they come back.

But perhaps the explanation is even simpler than that: it was only recently that we learnt that some of our species of crows are migratory birds. Why, therefore, should not some of our jackdaws also fly away with the rooks ?

The morning wind blew down the little fir-tree I had put up in the middle of the stubble-field so that I could steal up to the geese. I went to put it up again, but just as I had done it, the geese arrived. I went on creeping round the fir-tree very cautiously, hiding from the geese, which, however, were describing circles (the fir-tree must have aroused their suspicions) and flew off farther afield and came down to feed near the village of Dubovitzy. I began to steal up to them from behind a large willow copse in the middle of the field. The stubble was covered with white hoar-frost and my shadow crept before me across the field. I did not notice it for a long time, but suddenly I realised with a shock that my shadow, which looked so huge and terrifying, was getting near the geese themselves. Man's terrible shadow on the white hoar-frost gave an involuntary start, a tumult arose among the geese and in a moment all of them raised a loud clamour, the cry of each goose being as loud as a human "hurrah!" and they rushed straight towards the copse behind which

I was hiding. I had just enough time to jump inside it and to push my double-barrelled gun through an opening between the branches, aiming straight at their long necks.

THE BADGER

This time last year the ground was already white, but this year autumn overstayed its time and white hares, visible for miles, ran over the black earth and crouched on it. It was for them that the times were hard now! I had an idea that the badgers were still abroad, for they had nothing to be afraid of so long as the ground was free of snow. How fat they must be now! I decided to try to lie in wait for one at his burrow. At this sombre season of the year you cannot at once attain to that stillness in a pine-wood in which our indoor notions of dreary and gay seasons cease to have any meaning and everything is in constant motion and in that ceaseless motion finds its meaning and consolation. The high bank where the badgers live is so steep that in climbing it one cannot help leaving the print of one's five fingers next to the print of the badger's paw. I sat down by the trunk of an old fir and kept an eye on the main burrow through the spreading, lowest branch of the tree. A squirrel, which was busy covering its nest with moss for the winter, dropped some dirt, and then that stillness began to which a hunter can go on listening for hours, sitting near a badger's burrow, without getting bored.

Beneath that overcast sky, propped up by the tall firs, it was impossible to get the slightest indication of the movement of the sun, but in his dark burrow the badger knows very well when the sun is setting and a little time later he is ready to leave it, exercising the utmost care, and go on his nocturnal search for prey. Quite often, having poked out his head, the badger will give a snort and withdraw it quickly into the hole and then he will dart out of it with extraordinary agility: the sportsman has hardly time to blink. It is much better to lie in wait for a badger before sunrise when he usually returns to his burrow, for then he goes straight to it, creating an awful din as he moves through the dead leaves. But, according to the season, the badger should really be hibernating now. He does not usually leave his burrow every day and it is really a waste of time to sit up a whole night by his burrow and then have to sleep most of the next day.

It is not as if you were sitting in an arm-chair. My legs were beginning to go dead, but suddenly the badger poked his nose out and I felt better than if I had been sitting in an armchair. After half an hour he poked his nose out again, then changed his mind and disappeared for good in his burrow. . . .

He did not come out after all. Before I had time to reach the woodman's lodge, white flakes began to fall. Was it possible that the badger had scented it only by poking his nose out of his burrow?

THE POWER OF BEAUTY

The painter Boris Ivanovich stole up close to the swans under the cover of a mist and began to take aim, but thinking that he might kill more of them by firing small shot at their heads, he threw open the breech-bolt, took out the grape-shot and loaded his gun with duck-shot. He was just about to pull the trigger when he was overcome by a queer feeling that he was not about to shoot at a swan, but at a man. Putting down the gun, he stood there a long time admiring the birds, then he began to move backwards quietly and soon he had moved away so far that the swans never suspected the terrible danger they had been in.

I have often heard people say that a swan is a bad-tempered bird and that it does not suffer any geese or ducks to be near it and often kills them. Is it true, I wonder? However, even if it is true, it does not interfere with one's poetic conception of a princess transformed into a swan: so great is the power of beauty.

MIST

A starry and an exceedingly warm night. In the hour before dawn I went out on the veranda and all I heard was one single drop falling from the roof on to the ground. At the first gleam of light the mists began to rise and roll over the ground and I found myself suddenly on the shore of a boundless ocean.

The most precious and the most mysterious hour is the hour between the appearance of the first gleam of light and the sunrise, when the dim outlines of completely leafless trees begin to loom out of the darkness: the branches of the birches sloping downwards and the branches of the maples and aspens sloping upwards. I was the witness of the birth of Jack Frost and I saw him dry and whitewash the dead, brown grass and glaze over the puddles with the thinnest crust of ice.

At sunrise I saw in the clouds the formation of the other shore, which hung high in the air. Then at length, in the rays of the sun, the lake appeared out of the mist. In the translucent mist everything looked greatly magnified; the long row of wild duck was the first line of an advancing army and a group of swans seemed like a white-walled, fairyland city rising from the water. A black grouse, flying from his sleeping-grounds, loomed ahead, not going that way by accident, but on some important business assignment, no doubt, for from the other side another black grouse came flying in the same direction, and a third, and a fourth. . . . When I came to the marsh beside the lake a large pack had congregated there already, a few black grouse sitting on a tree, but most of them running about from one mound to another, skipping about and uttering that curious whirring sound, just as in spring.

It was only by the sprouting bright-green winter corn that one could distinguish this day from a day in early spring and, perhaps, also by looking into your own heart: the sparkling wine of spring did not run through your veins and gladness did not pierce through you like a knife. Now your joys are calm joys, a feeling resembling the feeling you experience after the disappearance of pain: you are glad the pain has gone, but you cannot help thinking sadly—why, it is not the pain that has gone, but life itself. . . .

During all this long prelude to winter the lake was pitch black and every day the ring of ice enclosed the black water in its narrowing white shores. Now the ring of ice was shattered and the water, regaining its freedom, rejoiced and sparkled. Torrents came rushing down the hills, as noisily as in springtime. But when the sky became overcast, I realised that it was only thanks to the sun that the water and the line of ducks and the city of swans became visible. The mist covered everything up again, even the lake vanished from sight, but, for some reason, the outline of the other shore remained suspended high in the air.

Cow-Wheat

Late autumn is sometimes indistinguishable from early spring: in early spring the ground is still covered with white snow, in late autumn the earth is still black. However, in spring there is a smell of earth in the air from the thawed patches among the snow, while in autumn there is a smell of snow in the air. It is always like that: we get used to the snow in winter and that is why we notice the smell of earth, while in summer we get so used to the smell of earth that in late autumn the air seems to us to be full of the smell of snow.

It is very seldom now that the sun peeps through the clouds for an hour or so, but when it does—what joy indescribable! It is then that a score or so of frozen leaves on a willow, which have escaped destruction by the gales, fill our hearts with delight and so does a little blue flower under our feet.

Bending down to such a blue flower I was surprised to recognise the only surviving blue partner of John and Mary—the so familiar cow-wheat.

To tell the truth, John isn't a real flower. It is composed of many minute, curled-up leaves and because the colour of those leaves is violet it is called a flower. The real flower with its stamens and pistils is only the yellow Mary. It is from Mary that the seeds had dropped into this autumnal earth so as to cover it once more with Johns and Marys in the new year. Mary's business is a much more difficult one and that was, no doubt, why she had dropped off earlier than John.

But I am pleased that John has survived the frosts and looks bluer than ever. Casting a farewell glance on this blue flower of late autumn, I say softly, "John, John, where's your Mary now, John?"

ANCHAR

I like hounds, but I hate to have to yell at them in the woods, encourage them with cries to hunt down the game, crawl through bushes and myself, as it were, become a dog. My usual practice is to let my dog follow the scent while I boil up some water for tea. I am never in a hurry even if my dog has started a hare. I just go on drinking my tea and listening and when I realise that the actual chase has begun, I intercept the hare, take up my position and—hey, presto!—the thing's done.

That's the way I like to hunt.

I had such a dog once—Anchar. I myself buried him in Alexeyev Lane, just where the woodland dell leads to the timber felling ground. His grave is in that same woodland dell and over the grave a wood-sprite stands sentinel.

I did not rear Anchar. One day a poor peasant brought me a hound: it was a big, fine-looking dog with rings round its eyes.

I asked, "Has it been stolen?"

"Yes, sir," said he, "it was stolen. Only it was a long time ago, sir. My son-in-law pinched him from some kennels when he was only a puppy. A thoroughbred, sir."

"I can see his breed myself," I said. "How good is he in the field?"

"First class, sir."

So off we went to try out the dog.

As soon as we left the village and got to the first boundary between two fields, we let him go and off he raced—all we could see was the green trail he left on the greyish, dew-besprinkled grass.

When we got to the woods, the peasant said to me, "I'm feeling a bit cold, sir. Let's gather a few sticks and light a fire."

'That's very extraordinary,' I thought to myself. 'I wonder if he's pulling my leg.'

But no! he was not pulling my leg. He started gathering sticks, lit a fire and sat down to warm himself by it.

"But what about your dog?" I asked.

"You're young and I'm old, sir," he said. "You never seen a dog like him. Take my tip, sir, and don't you worry about that dog. He knows what he's about, it's his business to search for game. As for us, sir, let's have some tea!"

And he just grinned at me.

We had a cup of tea each.

Crash!

I nearly jumped out of my skin, but the old peasant laughed and quietly went on pouring himself out another cup of tea.

"Let's hear what he's got there, sir," he said.

We listened. The dog was barking hoarsely, the chase was proceeding furiously, though with intervals.

The peasant guessed at once. "Chasing a fox, sir," he said.

We drank another cup of tea and by the time we had finished, the dog must have chased the fox for about three miles. Then, suddenly, he seemed to have lost the scent. The peasant pointed in that direction and asked, "Is that where your cows are grazing, sir?"

And, true enough, that was where the cows from the village of Karachun were grazing.

"I'm afraid, sir, the fox has led him across the cows' trail. It'll take him some time to get on the right scent again. Let's have another cup of tea, sir."

But the fox was not given much time for a rest: the dog again got on his scent and began to run in small circles—the fox had his earth quite near, it seemed. But as soon as the dog began to run in small circles, the peasant stopped drinking his tea, poured some water on the burning sticks, scattered them with his feet and said, "We'd better hurry up now, sir."

So off we went to cut off the fox's way of retreat in the glade where his earth was. No sooner did we take up our places than we saw the dog practically hanging on the fox's tail. For a moment the fox disappeared behind a bush and waved his tail in the direction of the marsh in an attempt to throw the dog off the right trail, but Anchar would not be deceived. One more bound and he grabbed the fox by the neck. The fox had just time to utter one agonised howl and it was all over. The fox lay dead on the ground and Anchar lay down beside it, licking a paw.

The dog was called, rather stupidly I thought, Gonchar, but in my excitement I shouted "Anchar!" and so that name stuck to him: Anchar!

G

Do you know how the sun greets the hunter on a morning in winter?

Just imagine a morning when the frost lies on the grass and a mist covers the earth before sunrise. The sun rises and, in slow stages, the mist lifts and disperses and what was mist a short time ago becomes a blue haze among the green firs and the silver birches, and so, as the sun rises higher and higher, blue and golden vistas open up before you and the whole world is a-glitter in the sunshine. That is how the harsh October day opens up to you and that is how a sportsman's heart opens up: you have a sniff of the frost, you give a sneeze and murmur "Bless you!" and every man you meet is your friend.

"Dear friend," I said to the peasant, "what's your trouble? Why should you want to give away such a dog to a stranger for money?"

"I'm leaving my dog in good hands, sir," the peasant replied. "As for my trouble, it is the usual peasant's trouble, sir. My cow caught a cold when grazing in the winter fields, swelled up and gave up the ghost. I have to buy another cow now, for a peasant can't do without a cow, can he, sir?"

"Well, of course, I see that and I'm very sorry for you. What do you want for your dog?"

"I want one of your cows, sir. You have two, haven't you? Well, won't you give me your brindled one?"

So I gave him one of my cows for his dog.

Oh, what a lovely autumn I had! I did not have to yell in the woods, I did not have to shout at the top of my voice at Anchar to hunt down the game, I did not have to crawl through brambles and get scratched. I just walked quietly along the woodland paths and enjoyed myself watching the trees turning more and more golden as the days passed. One day I'd go shooting the hazel-grouse and all I had to do was to follow their runs and imitate their calls and they'd be coming to me themselves. So as autumn progressed and all the leaves had turned yellow, the sun rose one cold, frosty morning and warmed the earth and by midday all the trees had been bared of their leaves. The hazel-hen stopped coming to my call. The rains came, the dead leaves were rotting, the saddest month of the year arrived—November.

I dislike going on a hunt in the woods with a whole crowd of people. I like to walk through the woods quietly, stopping for a while now and again and holding my breath, for then every little creature of the wood takes me for one of his own kind and I love to watch every manifestation of life in a wood, joying in each and every one of them and killing only those I am permitted to kill. That is why I cannot bear to see hordes of people invading the woods, raising an infernal din and shooting everything they come across. But if occasionally a good friend of mine, a man whom I know to be a real sportsman, asks me to take him out for a day's shooting, I'm only too pleased to accompany him. That is, to be sure, quite a different kind of pleasure, but it is something that I enjoy very much, for I always enjoy the company of a good man.

So when one day at the beginning of November I received a letter from a sportsman friend of mine in Moscow asking me to take him out for a day's shooting, I gladly gave him my consent. As a matter of fact, you all know that sportsman friend of mine, so I need not tell you his name. Anyway, I wrote back to him at once and he arrived on the night of the seventh of November.

It just would happen, of course, that before his arrival there was a lovely nip in the air and the ground had frozen over beautifully, but that when he arrived on the night of the seventh of November, a thaw set in, the ground became muddy and a cold drizzle fell. I could not sleep a wink that night, for I kept on worrying, fearing that the rain might interfere with our sport by washing away the nocturnal trails of bird and beast. About midnight, however, I was glad to see a clear, starry sky and, at the first peep of dawn, there were hundreds of trails of hares on the ground.

We got up before dawn with the morning star, had our tea and talked until the first light appeared through the window. Then left with Anchar to hunt the grey hare.

The winter corn fields this autumn began at the very edge of the village. The corn had come up beautifully, thick, juicy, green—it looked good enough to eat! The grey hare had fed so well on that fine winter corn that—believe it or not—the fat hung like a bunch of grapes inside him, and I myself got almost a pound of it from one hare. Anchar quickly got on the scent of one hare, went round in a wide circle, found the right trail in the lush corn and made straight for the place where the hare was crouching. In the woods the rain-drops were still falling from the trees at the time and there was a constant murmuring going on there. The grey hare is afraid of that noise, so our hare ran out of the wood and crouched among the tree-stumps on the timber felling ground just opposite Alexeyev Lane. As I expected, Anchar soon raced across the field with the sprouting corn to the timber felling ground and from there he hurried quickly to the piece of adjoining wasteland, the little woodland dell: the hares invariably make straight for that dell from the timber felling site. The first thing I did was to station my friend at one side of the ravine, then I went myself to take up my place at the other side of it. He could not see me from where he stood, but I could see him clearly.

A plan is, of course, necessary even in hunting, but things do not always work out according to plan. We stood waiting for hours and still there was neither Anchar nor the hare to be seen anywhere. Indeed, Anchar seemed to have sunk through the ground.

"Sergey!" I shouted.

Oh dear, I did not want to tell you the name of my sportsman friend, for, as I said, all of you know him well. However, we have hundreds of Sergeys.

"Sergey," I shouted, "blow your horn for Anchar, will you?"

I had given him my hunting horn, for he is a great one for blowing a horn.

Sergey was about to blow his horn when Anchar came running towards us along the bottom of the woodland dell. I immediately guessed from the way he ran that he was still following the same trail and I supposed that a fox or an owl must have run across the hare's trail in the cornfield and that the hare must have already reached the little valley and Anchar was now about to hunt him down. But when he came alongside my friend, I saw Sergey put up his gun and take aim. . . .

Nothing would have happened if I had only remembered at that moment that I myself had once taken aim from the same spot at the head of a man and had nearly killed him: the man was walking at the bottom of the deep dell and he was wearing a cap made of the fur of a hare and I could only see his cap and was just about to pull the trigger when his head popped up. If I had remembered that incident, I should have realised that from the top of the ravine only the coat of an animal could be seen and I should have shouted to him and he would have stopped in time. But I thought that my friend was just playing a joke on me—that is a regular habit of city sportsmen who in this respect are just like restive horses.

I thought he was joking when, suddenly, bang! All was quiet after the echo of that shot had died away, the smoke settled in the valley and hid everything from my view.

I felt stunned and it was only then that I remembered how I had nearly fired at a man's head from that spot.

The blue smoke covered the green dell. I was waiting, waiting, minutes passing like years, and there was no sign of Anchar, no sign of my dog! Anchar did not emerge from the smoke and when the smoke had dispersed, I saw my Anchar lying dead on the grass. Yes, there he lay dead on the green grass as though on a bed.

Heavy autumn drops were falling from the large trees on to the little trees, from the little trees on to the bushes, from the bushes on to the grass, and from the grass on to mother earth: a sad murmuring went on in the woods, a murmuring that died down only close to the earth—the earth was quietly drinking up all the tears. . . .

But I gazed at the world with dry eyes. . . .

"Well," I thought to myself, "worse things happen. Why, even a man is sometimes killed by accident!"

I am a hardened man, tough to the core, and I soon overcame my sorrow and was already beginning to think what to say to my friend to make him feel better, how to treat him so that he should not feel terribly upset, for, of course, I knew perfectly well that my friend was feeling as bad as I, and was it not the duty of sportsmen to help one another to banish sorrow with joy? In the village of Tsyganova we should find plenty of vodka in every cottage and I resolved that we should go at once to Tsyganova to drown our sorrow. While I was revolving this thought in my mind, I looked at my friend and I could not help feeling rather surprised at him: he had gone down to the bottom of the dell, had a look at the dead Anchar, returned to his place and stood there, as if still waiting for the chase to proceed.

What was the idea?

"Hoy!" I cried.

He answered.

"What were you shooting at?"

He was silent.

"What," I shouted again, "were you shooting at?"

He replied, "At an owl!"

My heart sank.

"Killed it?"

"Missed."

I sat down on a stone and everything became as clear as daylight to me.

"Sergey!" I shouted.

"Eh?"

"Blow your horn for Anchar!"

And—would you believe it?—Sergey took hold of the horn and—did not blow. He took one step in my direction—he was evidently feeling ashamed of himself, then another and . . . fell into thought.

"Come on," I shouted, "blow the horn, will you?"

He got hold of the horn again.

"Hurry up!"

He put the horn to his lips.

"Come on!"

And he started to blow. . . .

So there I sat on the stone, listening to my friend blowing the horn and my head was full of all sorts of silly thoughts: I saw a crow chasing a hawk and I thought, why the hell did not the hawk turn round on the crow and just give him one—one blow with his beak would be enough. With such thoughts in your head you can sit on a stone for ever. But there was another question that kept on recurring to me: why, oh, why, must a man resort to deceit? Death was the end of everything, everything came to an end so simply, so why did they all have to blow their horns? The dog had been killed, there could be no question of carrying on with the hunt, and it was he himself who had shot the dog and he knew me well, he knew that I was a man and not just a clod of earth, that I would never blame him or utter a single word of reproach to him. . . .

Who did he think he was deceiving?

"Look here," I said, "you just follow this path, it will bring you to Tsyganova, we'll have a drink there. Go there and keep on blowing your horn, while I shall take a walk through the woods and see whether Anchar replies to the sound of the horn!"

"Won't you take the horn and blow it yourself?" he asked.

"No, thank you, old man," said I. "I don't like blowing the horn, my ears keep on ringing for a long time afterwards and I can't hear anything. You see, I must be able to hear the slightest noise."

He looked a little put out and he asked me hesitantly, "And which way are you going?"

I pointed to the place where Anchar was lying.

"Well," I thought to myself, "I've caught you now, my lad. You will have to confess now."

But not a bit of it. He merely said, "I shouldn't advise you to go that way, old chap. There aren't any trees there and he couldn't possibly hang himself on a bush."

"All right," I said, "I'll go the other way, but remember, go on blowing the horn all the way to the village."

When I told him that I would walk the other way, he cheered up and away he went, blowing his horn and for the next two and a half miles—that chap certainly loved to blow the horn!—he went on blowing without stopping for a minute.

"No, sir," I said to myself after he had gone, "all sorts of miracles happen to the living, but to the dead no miracle can happen any more. That is why a real sportsman always looks you straight in the eye and says 'Let's have a drink: the thing's done with!' "

Who *was* he deceiving?

I always carry a little axe in my belt in case it might come in useful and I cut off the top of a dead tree with it, hewed some wood in the shape of a spade and dug a hole in the soft ground. I put Anchar in the hole, made a little mound over his grave, cut some turf and put it around. On a burnt-out patch of woodland there was a burnt stump of a tree which was somewhat in the shape of a little devil: the old women of our village were terrified of it in the dusk and called it a wood-sprite. I went there and dragged that burnt tree-stump to Anchar's grave and put it there as a kind of memorial.

I stood over Anchar's grave for some time, looking at the little devil, while Sergey, I could hear, was still busy blowing his horn.

"Who are you deceiving, Sergey?"

A cold drizzle fell. From the tall trees heavy raindrops were falling on the little trees, and from the little trees on to the bushes, and from the bushes on to the grass, and from the grass on to the wet earth. The whole wood murmured softly and it seemed to say: "Mice, mice, mice. . . ." But mother earth was quietly drinking up all the tears. . . .

It seemed to me as if all the roads in the world were meeting at one point and at their meeting-place stood the little wood-sprite on a dog's grave and looked at me with such awe. . . .

"Listen to me, little devil," said I, "listen. . . ."

And I made a speech at the graveside, but what I said in my speech, I shall reveal to no one.

I felt much easier in my mind after that. When I came to Tsyganova, I said to Sergey, "All right, Sergey, you can stop blowing your horn now. All's over. I know everything. Who did you think you were deceiving?"

He got white in the face.

We had a drink together and spent the night in Tsyganova. You all know this sportsman, don't you? Each of us can remember meeting such a Sergey.

THE FIRST SNOWFALL

ON THE CAPTAIN'S BRIDGE

It is shortly before sunrise that the frost is sometimes engendered and the direction of the wind is determined: if, therefore, you want to know what sort of day it will be, you must not fail to leave your house to observe the weather in the hour before dawn. From my house to the sheer bank of the lake is only a matter of some twenty yards and it was there that I stood observing a thin twig of an aspen wander across the disc of the moon. Soon another twig takes its place, then another still; this aspen thicket is, as it were, the coat of the earth in which I have hidden myself, and those little twigs—a leaf here and there—passing across the face of the moon revealed to me our planet's motion: a favourite experiment of mine and, perhaps, the only one which permits the eye to see this motion.

It is so easy on this high bank at the crack of dawn to rid yourself of the preconceived notion you have carried with you since the days of your childhood of life on a fixed plane, and to feel that you are a passenger on board a big ship, at a point where a certain longitude crosses a certain latitude.

Yes, now I am only a passenger, but after a long, long time this intellect of mine, transmitted thousands and thousands of years hence to some other man, will steer this ship from the dying sun to some other and hotter luminary. . . .

A strong wind rose suddenly, swayed the aspens and brought confusion into the visible motion of our planet. But whether my eye sees it or not, the earth goes on moving at a great speed in space. The wind strengthened, the trees began to knock against each other with their ice-encrusted boughs. At dawn the temperature falls by half a degree every ten minutes and quite soon it became impossible to remain on the bridge of the future captain of the earth: with a strong wind the temperature falls to fifteen degrees below zero. The sky was blood-red at sunrise.

I ran back home for five minutes to put the *samovar* on the table and when I returned the red strip had gone from the horizon, the sun was overcast and over the surface of the lake a gale was raising a dust of drifting snow, exposing the dark ice in places.

Before the drifting snow could cover up the tracks left by the wild animals at night, I hurried off to see if the wolf which had been lying in wait for my dog was still about and I soon found the prints of his familiar paws in the bushes. A fox had also been there. Stop! There was no help for it: the hands of a watch will sooner catch each other than the hand holding the black barrel of a gun aimed at the reddish side of a fox will falter or waver.

You can hunt according to the rules or you can hunt trusting entirely to your luck. Mostly I go hunting according to the rules, but I live trusting to my luck. I just cannot manage to settle down, and besides, it is such a pity to waste time on trifles: life is too short! Still, would any reasonable man so far forget himself as to omit to lay up a good store of logs to carry him through the winter, or allow his cash-box to get so depleted as to have only sixteen copecks left in it? But it is not the first year that I have left everything to chance and the thing I learnt all during that time was that a man should so order his life that his good luck does not give out, but goes on repeating itself: always welcome good luck with a cheerful countenance, dear friend! I know very well that it is not always easy to be cheerful when one's heart is oppressed with care, but what is one to do when one cannot live according to rules? So as my last bundle of fuel had been consumed, I went out hunting and I came back home with a fox. Someone saw me with the fox and the news reached the "furriers." I had barely time to take the fox's skin off when a furrier arrived and gave me enough money for about twenty-one cubic feet of logs. I dispatched a message with him to a friend of mine, uncle Mikhey, an old hunter, to bring me the dry logs as soon as possible.

A blizzard raged all night and my house was turned into an icebox. I went out to make my weather observations in the hour before dawn and came back almost immediately—there was nothing to observe: the wind howled and the snow covered earth and sky in a whirling mass of flakes. In one minute I was chilled to the marrow.... marrow....

Meanwhile, just at that very moment, uncle Mikhey was probably putting on his outdoor clothes after an ample breakfast and going off in his sledge to the woods for my logs. He would never have got the chance of obtaining twenty-one cubic feet of wood with one shot, for he lived according to the rules; he was not absent-minded, he had got his supply of logs in summer. Having got his dry logs, he sold them and did his best to keep his cottage warm with damp logs, and that was why his cottage was always so cold. The only warm place in it was on top of the stove, but there was only room there for the women and children, so uncle Mikhey slept inside the oven. But that was where I drew the line, for I could not understand the sort of life according to rules where one had to sleep inside the oven and so I lived trusting to good luck, trying as much as possible not to be a nuisance to other people....

At dawn the gale had blown itself out. It was still windy, though, and my nose felt a bit pinched. My skis sank an inch in the snow. I looked at my house from the side and got quite a shock: it was not a house at all, but just a kind of Nansen "Fram" in the Arctic, covered with snow, icebound, and around it a white, drifting, powdery ocean of snow. There was no other house for miles around, no trace of a man and even the track of wild beasts had been covered up. To-day I could hardly expect the old lady to bring me my milk from the village. Old uncle Mikhey, too, I shouldn't wonder, would feel sorry for his horse, if not for himself. What was I to do? I dressed, fastened my belt round my sheepskin, picked up an axe and off I went to the woods—to drag back a few damp sticks myself.

The juniper bushes were covered with irregular, dune-like snow-drifts. I fell through one of them up to my neck and floundered about in it till my hands went numb with cold. While I tried to get out of the snowdrift the whole world became suddenly one large expanse of white and it seemed to me as if the snow reached up to the very sky. I had the sensation as though a white hunter was pinioning me with a huge coil of rope and so helpless did I feel that I could not help asking myself why he should be wasting all his energies. If one is alone with nature one cannot escape the moment of sheer panic at a time when one's hands grow limp and lifeless: if, at such a time of great difficulty, one finds oneself in water, it seems easier to drown than to attempt to save oneself and if one has fallen through a snowdrift, it seems that it is much pleasanter to freeze to death than make an effort to move. . . .

In a snowstorm all objects become strangely magnified. The undergrowth looked to me like the wall of a tall wood and quite unexpectedly a wild beast jumped out of it, half the height of the wood and with ears several yards long. The beast made straight for me, so that I even raised my hands to defend myself, but I must have looked even more enormous to the hare than he appeared to me, for he swerved away from me instantly. After him there came what must have frightened away the hare, a kind of huge tower, and from that tower uncle Mikhey appeared and said in his ordinary voice apropos of the hare, "If only I had a stick in my hand I should have killed that squint-eyed devil!"

He, I expect, would have killed more of them with a stick than with a gun.

"What about the logs, uncle Mikhey?"

"Had to dump them in a field."

He could not get through to my house, so he just unloaded them in a field near it.

We transferred the logs to my house on a sledge and immediately set all the stoves in my house roaring. My "Fram" belched smoke from all the chimneys, but the smoke disappeared at once, like the smoke from a cigarette, merging into the white expanse of earth and sky.

LACE ARCHES

The ground is covered with a fresh blanket of newly fallen snow. It is very quiet in the woods and so warm that at the slightest rise in temperature the snow would begin to melt. The trees are smothered in snow; the firs hang down their huge, heavy paws, the birches bend gracefully and some of them even touch the ground with their tops—these have been transformed into arches of lace.

A fir will never bend however heavy the load of snow it has to bear: it will sooner break than bend! But the slightest sprinkling of snow and the birch bends down. The fir towers majestically, defying the sky with its straight, tall trunk, but the birch weeps.

In the snowy stillness of the woods the snow figures are so expressive that I can't help getting the most curious feeling—why, I ask myself, don't they say anything to each other? Can it be that they have noticed me and are just waiting?

When it started to snow again, it seemed to me that it was not the gentle patter of the snowflakes that I heard, but the whispering of those strange snow figures among themselves.

SNOW STARDUST

Last evening tiny flakes of snow were falling out of a clear sky. They seemed to be dropping from the stars and, in the electric light, they even twinkled like stars. By the next morning this produced a delicate blanket of powdered snow: one puff and it was gone. But even that was enough to show off the prints of the hare's pad.

Off we went and we roused many hares.

SNOW FIGURES

As they fell, the flakes of snow knew not what they were doing and because of that figures were fashioned on every bough. The bodies of these figures were whiter than any marble and there is not in the world a freer line than that of the haphazard configuration of snow-flakes. There was no plan in that architecture of the woods, no utilitarian design: it was of no earthly use for anything.

There are days in the woods when the little snow figures on the trees begin to drop, although there is not a breath of wind about; they fall of their own weight as soon as a thaw sets in. On one large branch a night-watchman was sitting up in his sheepskin and dozing, when suddenly Hercules fell on top of him and turned him into a heap of crumbly snow; as he fell a fir-tree leapt up into the air and from underneath the fir-tree a hare jumped out. Afterwards, witches, wolves, grannies with their grandchildren began to topple from the trees and there were only small holes left of them in the snow, just as if mountain-ash berries had fallen through, and above them, the branches on which they had been sitting waved a farewell greeting to them.

So everywhere on a windless day the trees in the woods waved their branches, and it looked as if they were doing it on purpose, bidding a last farewell to the little snow figures.

SNOWBALLS

A new fall of crisp, white snow. I went out with my camera and began to take snaps of the snow figures in the woods. A small twig held in its tiny fingers an enormous snowball. About midday the figures began to tumble off the trees, knocking against each other as they fell: the trees were having a game of snowballs. One such ball hit a hare who set off at a hop, leaving a lovely trail. My dog Trubach immediately followed it up.

A BULLFINCH ON THE SNOW

Every trunk of a tree, every branch gets thinner and thinner the higher it is, and on the top of each tree is a tiny spray. That is why after a heavy snowfall an alder bends in an arch over a lane in a young wood, from one side of the lane to the other. At such a time it is impossible to walk along the broad lane without stooping. One really should go down on all fours and run like a hare.

High up on a fir-tree two branches stood out against the sky from the habitual gloom of the fir-wood and, covered with rime, formed two white crosses and because of that the whole fir-tree looked like Notre Dame de Paris. Next to it, against the dark background of the firs, a little birch, laced with snow, flaunted her beauties, and on top of it a red bullfinch thrust out his little chest.

THE BIRTH OF THE MOON

A clear sky. A gorgeous sunrise in perfect silence. A hard frost—twelve degrees below zero. Trubach is chasing a hare on a white path, relying on his scent alone.

It was altogether a golden day in the woods and in the evening the sunset flamed bright over half the sky. It was a northerly sunset, all translucent crimson, like a glass ball on a Christmas tree or like the specially transparent paper inside a Christmas cracker through which everything looks cherry-tinted. But the living sky had many other tints besides scarlet: there was an arrowy strip of intense blue in the middle of it, resting like a Zeppelin on top of the red, and many more delicately tinted broad bands drawn along its border.

The full splendour of the sunset lasted for about a quarter of an hour. The new moon hung in a pool of azure facing the red, as if seeing it for the first time and lost in admiration of its beauty.

I was standing on a wild patch of woodland where the trees had been recently felled and it seemed to me as if each mutilated tree-trunk stared at the sunset. While standing there I was trying hard to recall the day of my childhood when I first beheld such beauty and for ever after remained nature's prisoner.

A Hunt to the Death

Many a time in winter did I lose my way in the woods. I saw the gipsies of the frost! Even to-day when, at dusk, I glance at the grey strip of the forest from afar, I cannot help feeling ill at ease. But if there should be a light frost after a fresh fall of snow in the morning, I walk off into the woods long before sunrise and it is there that I celebrate my Christmas, so beautiful a Christmas that, to my fancy, no one has ever celebrated anything compared with it.

To-day, however, I was not given much time to pay my meed of admiration to the huge piles of snowy palaces and to listen to the hushed silence of the woods. My foxhound Solovey gave the signal: like Solovey-the-Robber he hissed, snarled and, finally, barked so loud that he at once filled the silence with the music of the chase. He always follows the fresh scent of a fox with such a concatenation of strange cries.

While he pursued the fox, I hastened to the glade with the three firs, for there the fox usually passed in his flight, and I stopped under the green tent of a fir, looking through the openings between the branches. Now Solovey hunted out the fox, now he pressed his pursuit home, nearer and nearer. . . .

The fox jumped out of the dense fir undergrowth on the glade rather far from where I was standing, a red blotch on the white surface of the snow. He looked so like a dog that I could not help wondering what he wanted such a lovely and seemingly useless tail for. I thought I saw a grin on that furious face of his, I caught a glimpse of his bushy tail and—my beauty was gone!

Solovey rushed out on the glade after the fox, looking as red as a fox, but terrible in his strength and mad with rage. One day, seeing on the snow the trail of the beautiful, cunning animal, Solovey went stark, raving mad and ever since, when pursuing the fox, he is transformed from a mild-tempered domestic animal into a wild, terrifying, stubborn beast and it is quite useless to try to call him back: he heeds neither horn nor shots, he just runs, barking for all he is worth, determined to get the fox or die in the attempt. His madness is so infectious that I have many a time only regained my senses in an unknown, dark, snow-covered wood, fifteen miles from the start of the chase.

The trail of the dog and the fox emerged from the underwood in different parts of the glade; while in the dense underwood, Solovey followed the fox's scent in the air, but now, seeing the animal's tracks on the snow, the dog cut across the entire glade and got right on the fox's track near the little fir where I had seen the bushy tail vanish.

There was still the hope that it was a local fox and that he would return and start running about in small circles. But Solovey's barking soon got fainter and fainter and then he could be heard no more: it was therefore not a local fox and I was pretty certain that he had run off to his native haunts and would not return.

It was now that my own pursuit started: I had to follow the trails of the two animals as fast as I could until I heard Solovey's barking again. Their tracks mostly skirted woodland glades; the fox's tracks always went in a semi-circle, while my dog invariably cut across in a straight line, thus shortening the distance between himself and his prey. I tried to follow the straight tracks and, where possible, took a short cut myself. All I could see were the tracks in the snow and all I could think about was that I, too, like Solovey, had become a raving maniac for the day and was ready for anything.

Suddenly my path was crossed by a multitude of different tracks, mostly of hares; the fox had immediately taken advantage of it and tried to throw Solovey off his scent by following the hares' tracks. He probably also intended to force Solovey to follow the hares' scent and give up the chase for him. So it fell out. There was the fresh hare's trail and so recent was it that I expected any moment to catch a glimpse of a white hare disappearing behind a bush and looking back now and again with those black buttons of eyes of his. Solovey, on reaching this place, had been rushing about rather aimlessly, it seemed. Was it possible that he had relinquished the chase of the fox and had run off after some poor little hare?

The fox's solitary trail diverged from the trails of the hares and ran straight in the direction of a swamp, skirting it along a copse of young aspens, and just there—hullo!—Solovey's prints on the snow! My dog's large tracks came out of a coppice, got mixed up again with the tracks of the wild animals and then disappeared in the woods on a life and death chase.

As I was walking along, I seemed to hear Solovey's bark. I stopped for a moment, but I could hear nothing, so I decided that my ears had deceived me. It was silent in the woods and yet it seemed to me all the time that I could hear the whistling of hazel-grouse. The tracks in the meantime brought me out into a field. They looked blue in the sunshine and all across the field there stretched the blue-tinted trail of the animals.

The nimble fox had dived under the lowest board of a fence and dashed off; Solovey had tried to do the same, but could not. He had tried to jump over the fence: I could see on the top board two large gaps in the snow made by his huge paws. Now I realised that I had heard Solovey's bark as I was walking through the woods: when he had fallen off the fence he must have uttered a howl of disappointment and then run round to find a way through the fence. Where he got through, I could not see. All I discovered was that their tracks again met at the edge of a wide strip of burnt-out woodland and that they disappeared together in that vast patch of wild country.

A burnt-out patch of woodland is about the worst thing to come across during a chase. It was just there that the peaty earth had once smouldered, throwing up huge, bear-shaped mounds, and the trees collapsed one on top of the other and so they remained lying in unshapely tiers, while underneath new shoots had sprouted. Not only a man, but even a dog would find it quite impossible to get through there.

The fox went there on purpose to play a trick on the dog and he did not stay there long, either. He dived under the tree-trunks, leaving a gap behind, but Solovey jumped over the heap of piled-up trees, sweeping the snow away and cutting across the trail of a polecat on the tree-trunk. Then both fox and dog fell through a snowdrift, both of them deceived by the soft snow, into a deep hole; the fox was the first to jump out on to the second tier of the fallen fir-trees and he crawled over the third, running half way across the tree-trunk; the dog, on the other hand, after following close on the fox's trail, fell into another deep hole. I could hear the tapping of a woodcutter's axe—somewhere near a man was cutting up trees into logs and he must have had a fine view of the chase and must have seen how the fox and the dog leapt up on those fallen tree-trunks and came down on the other side. No man could follow that trail of the animals, so I described a wide circle round the edge of the burnt-up patch of woodland, fuming all the time at not being able to go the same way as they.

I had scarcely time to follow up my dog's and the fox's tracks to where they had left the burnt-out wood, for I suddenly heard a furious, drawn-out, plaintive barking from the direction of a State-owned wood. By that time I had got out of breath with running and I felt as hot in the frost as if I were at the equator. But all my efforts were in vain. Solovey had got over his difficulty himself and he was again out of hearing. I was very curious, however, to find out the cause of his prolonged and plaintive howls. That was one of those things which I always felt I must probe to the bottom.

A wide road ran through the State-owned wood. What happened was that Solovey had run out of the wood and followed the fox's trail on the road. Then he stopped, for the fresh trail had been obliterated by a sledge which had gone right over it. Perhaps it was the same sledge which was coming back now: a gaily painted sledge with

wedding guests, red-nosed and with beards covered with rime.   Were
they going for drinks ?

I had no doubts now: Solovey had run out of the wood on to the
road hot on the trail of the fox.   But the road is different from the
woods: in the woods he knows everything much better than man
does, for he has inherited that knowledge from his ancestors the
wolves.   The road has been built long afterwards—and can a man
be expected to teach him as much about the things that happen in a
forest as the wolves did ?   A dog cannot grasp the meaning of that
straight human line, and the endlessness of those straight lines made
by man frightens him.   At first Solovey tried to run in the same
direction as the sledge in which the wedding guests had gone for
drinks, all the time keeping a sharp look-out for any trail that might
diverge from the road.   So it was that he ran for a long time in the
wrong direction and the endlessness of the road at last terrified him
and he sat down and began to howl: he was calling for man to come
and solve the mystery of the road for him.   While I was trying to
find my way out of the burnt wood, he went on howling.   Then I could
only suppose that he started to run blindly in the opposite direction
and he soon discovered at the very edge of the road the unobliterated
trail of the fox.   That made him pluck up courage.   Further along
the road the fox for some reason tried to turn aside, but he changed
his mind and turned back, leaving a small semi-circular trail in the
snow.   Solovey, too, ran round that trail, but further on everything
was obliterated: the wedding guests had come back with their
drinks and had driven over Solovey's tracks.

I might never have discovered where the fox had jumped off the
road into a bush, had not Solovey fallen into it with all his weight and
crushed it.   Further on, across a glade with felled timber, I again
saw the life and death trail of the two animals as they rushed headlong
one after the other, knocking off the white caps from the tree-trunks.
They did not run along a straight line long—wild animals dislike
straight lines—and once again they cut across virgin soil, from glade
to glade, from one part of the woods to another.

I noticed with joy that in one place the fox, tired out with the
chase, snatched a moment to rest and left an unmistakable mark
of a fox there.

If anybody were to ask me now where exactly I caught up with
them, I should not for the life of me be able to tell him, nor could I find
the place again myself, or get anywhere near it.   The chase in small
circles at last began.   It went through a tall pine-wood, at the end
of which I came to a dense underwood with wide clearings.   In the
clearings the tracks of dog and fox criss-crossed each other, sometimes

several times on the same glade. There I could again hear the chase at close quarters: the fox was now going round and round in circles. It was then that my pursuit based on mere guesswork came to an end. I was no longer a tracker. I myself became an actor in the third and most terrible act of the life and death drama in which the two animals were the protagonists.

The barrels of my gun were covered thickly with snow. I wiped the snow off with a finger and from the way it froze to the barrels I could guess that the temperature was falling very fast. From behind a little fir I at length saw the fox stealing quietly through the fir undergrowth in the oblique rays of the sun. The snow began to crunch loudly under my feet, but I was no longer afraid of that: the fox had no strength left in him to start on another wild chase. I had no doubt that I would get him here while he was running in small circles.

The fox apparently decided to risk getting out of the undergrowth and he ran across the glade straight to the little fir behind which I had hidden. His tongue lolled sideways from his mouth, but his eyes were still full of terrible hatred which was only partly hidden in that curious grin which a hunted fox seems to have on his face. My hands were burnt on the steel barrels of my gun, but even if they froze to them, the fox would not escape instantaneous death! But Solovey, shortening his run, suddenly caught sight of the fox in the glade and rushed upon him. The fox met him, sitting on his haunches, and turned his sharp teeth and his grinning mouth at Solovey's terrible, gaping mouth. Solovey had many times been caught between the sharp teeth of a fox and every time he had lain sick for weeks afterwards. He could not attack the fox from the front: the fox could be seized only when he started to run and he could still mislead the dog by a wave of his lovely tail in the wrong direction and once more dive into the dense fir undergrowth. In a little while it would be dark and the fox would escape.

Solovey raised a bloodcurdling howl. They were now breathing into each other's gaping mouths. Both of them were covered with sweat, ice and hoar-frost, their breaths froze immediately and settled on their coats in white crystals.

I found it hard to steal behind the fox on the crunching snow: how sharp the frost must be! But the fox no longer paid any attention to any noise: through that grin of his his teeth were bared more and more. Solovey must not suspect my presence, either, for the moment he caught sight of me, he'd throw himself upon the fox, and what if the fox were all the time waiting for the chance of biting through the dog's throat?

I watched them unobserved from behind a fir-branch. There were only a few yards between me and them.

On the tall pines the last rays of the sun lingered for only a moment, the red trunks flared up, then the light of Christmas went out and nobody said in a gentle voice, "Peace be unto you, sweet animals of the forest!"

There was a sudden loud report, as if Jack Frost himself had cracked an enormous nut, the noise was just as loud as a shot in a wood.

Everything got mixed up all at once, the fox's beautiful brush flashed in the air and Solovey rushed off a long way in the wrong direction. But after Jack Frost came the same kind of loud report, though not a rounded one, but a straight one with an echo: I had fired my gun at the fox.

The fox pretended to be dead, but I could see his ears pressed close to the ground. Solovey rushed upon him. The fox drove his teeth into the dog's cheek, but I pulled him away with the help of a dead branch and Solovey drove his teeth into the fox's back. I put a felt boot on the fox's neck and drove a Finnish knife into his heart. The fox was dead, but his teeth still hung on to my felt boot. I had to unlock them with the barrel of my gun.

After recovering from the mad passions of the chase, I usually feel ashamed, even while I am swinging the limp body of a hare over my back. But even in death that beautiful fox did not rob me of the taste for hunting and, had I permitted it, Solovey would have gone on for a long time pulling the dead fox about.

So we were benighted in the woods.

FOX'S BREAD

A BROOD of mallards was hatched out on a mound under a willow-tree in a swamp. Soon their mother took them along the cowpath to the lake. I saw them coming from a distance, hid myself behind a tree and the little ducklings went past close to my feet. I took three of them to be reared at my house and the remaining sixteen went on after their mother along the cowpath.

After a time my black ducklings grew into grey ones and later on one of them became a lovely, multicoloured drake and the other two were ducks which we christened Dussya and Mussya. We clipped their wings so that they should not fly away and they lived in our yard together with the rest of our domestic fowl: we had hens as well as geese.

With the coming of the new spring we made mounds of all sorts of rubbish in our cellar for our wild birds, to look like the mounds in a swamp, and on the mounds—nests. Dussya laid sixteen eggs in her nest and settled down to hatch them out. Mussya laid eighteen eggs, but refused to sit on them. However much we tried, the silly duck would not undertake the responsibilities of motherhood. So we put on the duck's eggs our grand black hen—the Queen of Spades.

In due course our ducklings were hatched out and we kept them for a time in our kitchen, in the warmth, cut up hardboiled eggs for them and looked after them.

After a few days the weather became very fine and warm. Dussya took her black ducklings to the pond and the Queen of Spades took hers to the kitchen garden in search of worms.

"Swiss-swiss," said the ducklings in the pond.

"Quack-quack," the duck replied.

"Swiss-swiss," said the ducklings in the kitchen garden.

"Cluck-cluck," the hen replied.

The ducklings, of course, could not understand what "cluck-cluck" meant, but they knew very well the meaning of the noises in the pond.

"Swiss-swiss" means, "Come along, girls and boys, stick together!" And "quack-quack" means, "Come on ducks, come on drakes, swim faster!"

And of course all the ducklings in the kitchen garden looked in the direction of the pond.

"Stick together!" And off they ran.

"Cluck-cluck!" the grand looking hen called after them.

"Swim, swim!" said the duck in the pond.

And the ducks on the bank began to swim.

"Cluck-cluck!" the Queen of Spades went on calling to them from the bank.

But they just went on swimming. So after whistling to each other for some time, they finally joined forces and Dussya was very pleased to accept the new ducklings as members of her own family: after all, seeing that Mussya was her sister, they were all her nephews and nieces.

The combined large duck family swam about on the pond the whole day and the whole of that day the Queen of Spades, looking very bedraggled and angry, clucked at the top of her voice, muttered to herself and went on digging up hundreds of worms on the bank, such lovely fat worms they were, too!

"Just rubbish, my dear," the duck said contemptuously to her from the pond.

In the evening the duck took all her ducklings home and led them in a long file under the very nose of the grand hen: they just walked past the Queen of Spades, all of the same dark colour and all with the same duck bills, and not one of them even glanced at their foster mother.

We put them all in a big basket and left them for the night in the warm kitchen near the stove.

In the morning, while we were still asleep, Dussya managed to scramble out of the basket and walked about the floor quacking, telling the ducklings to come out. The ducklings replied to her from the basket in thirty voices. The walls of our house, made of resounding pine logs, re-echoed with the whistling of the ducklings and the quacking of the duck, and yet, in all that hubbub, we could distinctly hear the voice of one duckling.

"Do you hear?" I asked my children.

They listened.

"We hear!" they shouted.

So off we all went to the kitchen.

Well, it seemed that Dussya was not alone on the floor in the kitchen. Besides her one duckling was running about, a duckling that seemed to be highly excited and that whistled uninterruptedly. This duckling, like the rest, was only as big as a tiny cucumber. How could such a giant have climbed up the side of a basket over a foot high?

As we were trying to puzzle out that problem, another one occurred to us, namely, had the duckling himself found a way of getting out of the basket after his mother, or had she accidentally brushed against him with a wing and tossed him out? I tied a ribbon round the duckling's leg and then put him back with the other ducklings.

Next morning we rushed into the kitchen as soon as we heard the noise made by the ducks. There on the floor was the duckling with the ribbon tied round his leg, running about at the side of the duck.

All the ducklings imprisoned in the basket were whistling their heads off, trying to get out, but could do nothing, but that one had found some way of getting out.

I said, "He must have thought of something, invented some special way of getting out."

"A clever duckling!" my little son, Lyova, shouted.

I made up my mind to find out how that "clever" duckling had solved what to him must have been one of the most difficult problems: to scale a sheer wall on his little webbed feet.

Next morning I got up before daybreak when my own children and the ducklings were still sound asleep. I sat down in the kitchen near the electric switch so that I could switch on the light immediately and see what was happening inside the basket.

Soon the light of day began to glimmer faintly through the window.

"Quack-quack," said the duck.

"Swiss-swiss," replied one solitary voice.

Then everything was silent. My children were asleep and the ducklings were asleep.

The factory siren sounded. It got lighter.

"Quack-quack," said Dussya.

There was no reply. I knew then that the "clever one" was too busy to reply because he was at that very moment solving his difficult problem.

I switched on the light.

Well, now I knew. The duck had not got up yet and her head was on level with the top of the basket. All the ducklings were still asleep under their mother, only one, the one with the ribbon tied round his leg, had crept from underneath and was crawling up on his mother's back, holding on to her feathers as if they were little bricks.

When Dussya got up, she raised him to the level of the basket. He then ran along her back, like a little mouse, until he reached the edge of the basket and then—flop!—down he came. After him the duck also tumbled down on the floor and the usual hubbub began, hissing and a clamour enough to raise the whole house.

Two days later three ducklings were on the floor of the kitchen in the morning, then five and so on until the moment Dussya raised her head all the ducklings got on her back and down they flopped on the floor.

But the first duckling who had paved the way for the rest, my children went on calling "Clever."

FOX'S BREAD

One day I spent the whole day in the woods and came back home at nightfall with a bulging bag. Taking the bag off my shoulder, I began emptying it on the table.

"What's this?" little Zeena asked me.

"This is a black grouse," I replied, and I told her all about the black grouse, how he lived in the woods, what funny whirring noises he made in spring, how he pecked the buds of birch-trees, gathered berries in the autumn in the marshes and kept himself warm under the snow in winter. I also told her about the hazel-grouse, showed her that she was a grey bird with a little crest and I imitated the whistling of the hazel-grouse on my little pipe and let her have a whistle, too. Then I emptied out on the table hundreds of mushrooms, red, white and black. I further brought with me the blood-red rock raspberry, blue bilberries and red cranberries. I also had in my pocket a fragrant little ball of pine resin and I gave it to the little girl to smell, telling her that trees healed themselves with that resin.

"Who heals them in the forest?" asked little Zeena.

"Why," I said, "they heal themselves. Suppose a hunter comes to the forest and wants to have a rest. Well, he drives his axe into a tree, hangs his bag on the axe and lies down under the tree. After he has had his sleep and feels rested, he takes his axe out, puts his bag over the shoulder and away he goes. But the hole made by the axe in the tree is filled with this sweet-smelling resin and the tree's wound heals up."

I also brought specially for little Zeena all sorts of wonderful herbs and grasses, a blade from one, a root from another and a flower from a third: the spotted orchis, the great valerian, the great tooth-wort and hare-lettuce. As I took out the hare-lettuce from my bag, Zeena noticed a piece of black bread under it. This always happens with me: every time I forgot to take bread with me to the woods, I get hungry, and when I do take it, I forget to eat it and bring it back. But when little Zeena saw the piece of black bread under the hare-lettuce, she just opened her eyes wide and asked, "And where did you get that bread? Did you also get it in the wood, daddy?"

"Well," I said, "there's nothing extraordinary in it, is there? Didn't I get the lettuce there, too?"

"But it's a hare's lettuce!"

"Well, and this bread is a fox's bread. Just taste it!"

She took a nibble at the bread and then began to eat it.

"Why, daddy," she exclaimed, "this fox's bread tastes just lovely!"

Little Zeena ate up my piece of bread and now every time I come back from hunting, I bring a piece of fox's bread for my little daughter who eats it up although ordinarily she is so fussy about her food that she does not touch even white bread.

"Fox's bread tastes so lovely, daddy," she says, "much better than our bread!"

AN OLD WOMAN'S HEAVEN

An old woman was walking alone on a road. Suddenly she felt dizzy: she was ill.

"Well," she said to herself, "it seems I can do nothing about it. I suppose it means that my time has come."

She looked round to see where she could lie down and die in comfort.

"Can't go on living for ever," she said to herself. "Must make way for the young ones."

She saw a pleasant meadow of sweet grass with a clean, sandy path running across it. On the path were the prints of bare, human feet, which showed that somebody had recently walked across the meadow, in the middle of which was an old woodpile, covered with moss and overgrown with tall grasses. The old woman liked the look of that old, crumbling woodpile.

"Can't live for ever," she repeated and she lay down on top of the dead twigs with her legs stretched out across the path: if some good people should pass that way, they would see her legs and give her a decent burial.

Towards evening we were coming back from hunting along the same path and, seeing a pair of human legs we stopped. On the woodpile sparrows were talking to each other. It is wonderful to see sparrows gather in little flocks at sunset under the sky and, just like a crowd of friends, unable to stop talking. "Cheers!" they were saying, as though each of them were rejoicing in being alive and telling the glad tidings to the rest.

Suddenly all the sparrows rose in the air with a flutter of wings and flew away. It was then that we saw an old woman's head where the sparrows had been sitting and chirruping.

We quickly boiled a kettle, made tea and offered a piping hot cup of tea to the old woman, who sat up and began to look cheerfully about her. She told us how she was getting ready to die on the pile of firewood.

"You see, my dears," she said, "my head began to spin and I thought to myself, 'You're not going to live for ever, are you? Time to make way for you, my dears, the young ones.' So I lay down on this soft woodpile, right in the middle of this sweet grass. It was so lovely here that I felt as if I was in heaven. I really thought that my time on earth had come to an end. Then the sweet little birds came. I thought they must surely be the birds of paradise, such lovely cocks and hens they were, so kind and affectionate. I've never seen such sweet birds on earth, and what's more, I understood everything they were saying to each other. 'Cheers,' said one, 'I'm so glad to be alive!' and the other replied, 'Cheers, cheers, cheers! I'm glad to be alive, too!' And all of them went on repeating to each other how happy they were to be alive.

" 'Here in heaven,' I thought to myself, 'even ordinary birds know how sweet it is to be alive in the world, but on earth people are always complaining that they find life so hard!'

"Just then a cock-sparrow, such a cheeky little chap, sat down on a twig right over my mouth, twittered, 'Here's one for you, granny,' and—it doesn't take a bird long, does it?—dripped into my mouth. Well, then I knew that I was not in heaven, but that I am still on earth."

"But," we laughed, "you don't think birds don't drip in heaven, do you?"

"No, my dears," the old woman replied, "the moral of my story is not that birds do not drip in heaven, but that we on earth should not lie about with our mouths open."

LEMON

It happened on a collective farm. A Chinese acquaintance of the manager of the farm brought him a present. The manager, Trofim Mikhailovich, waved him away as soon as he mentioned the present. The offended Chinese bowed and wanted to go, but Trofim Mikhailovich felt sorry and stopped him.

"What kind of a present did you bring?" he asked.

"Me want give you my little dog," replied the Chinese. "The littlest dog in the world."

At the mention of the dog Trofim Mikhailovich looked even more embarrassed. The manager's house was at the time full of animals: there was the curly-haired scottie Nellie, the Anglo-Russian bloodhound Trubach, the black cat Mishka, a very independent creature, a tame rook as well as a tame hedgehog and a fine young ram—Boris.

All those animals were kept in the house for the manager's little boy Shura. The manager's wife, Yelena Vassilyevna, was very fond of animals and she rather spoilt her son. Trofim Mikhailovich felt naturally very embarrassed when he heard about the new dog.

"Hush!" he said softly, putting a finger to his lips.

But it was too late. Yelena Vassilyevna had already caught the words about the smallest dog in the world and she entered her husband's office.

"Can I see it, please?" she asked.

"The dog's here," replied the Chinese.

"Won't you please bring it?"

"But the dog's here," the Chinese repeated. "No want bring."

With a kindly smile he produced from the inside of his padded coat such a little dog that I never saw the like of it in my life and I doubt very much whether any man in Moscow had ever seen so small a dog. It could have been covered with my felt hat, picked up in it and carried away. It had a reddish coat with very short hair, looking almost naked, and it kept on shivering like a very thin steel spring. But for all its tiny size, it had a pair of huge, black, shining eyes, bulging like the eyes of an ant.

"What a dear little dog!" Yelena Vassilyevna exclaimed.

"Take it!" said the Chinese, flattered by the praise of his dog, and he handed the animal to the manager's wife.

Yelena Vassilyevna sat down and put the little dog on her lap. It went on shivering either because it was cold or because it was afraid. Immediately the dog professed a most violent devotion to his new mistress and the enthusiasm with which he showed it was, to say the least, absolutely astonishing. When, for instance, the manager stretched out a hand to stroke his new lodger, the tiny dog immediately bit his forefinger and, what was more remarkable, set up such a loud squeal that it seemed as if someone had caught him by his tail and was pulling hard at it. The row went on for a long time, the dog yelping and choking himself with suppressed fury, its body shivering all the time, as if it was not he who had bitten the manager, but the manager who had bitten him.

Wiping the blood from his finger with a handkerchief, the disgusted Trofim Mikhailovich said, looking closely at his wife's new guardian: "Plenty of noise, but no hair!"

Hearing the squealing and the yelping, Nellie, Boris and Trubach came running into the office, while Mishka the cat jumped on the window-sill and the rook, which was dozing on top of the open casement, woke up. The new domestic pet treated them all as the mortal enemies of his beloved mistress and challenged them immediately to a fight. For some reason he picked out the ram first and bit him painfully in the leg. Boris leapt on the ancient office couch and hid himself behind the cushions. Nellie and Trubach fled from the little terror to the dining room and the cat Mishka, who was next to be attacked by the intrepid fighter, thought it beneath his dignity to flee and, arching his back, he gave voice to the well-known, venomous, feline war-song.

"Well," said Trofim Mikhailovich, "it seems he has found his match at last. Plenty of noise, but no hair!" And, flinging the insulting remark again in the face of the little bully, he prodded the cat encouragingly with his foot and said, "Now then, Mishka, spit at him!"

Mishka raised his war-song to the highest pitch and was about to spit when he noticed that the little dog was not in the least put out by his war-song, but that, on the contrary, his huge, bulging, ant-like eyes were blazing even more furiously than before. This so unnerved the cat that he jumped first on the window-sill and then out of the window, taking the rook with him.

Having won so famous a victory, the conquering hero returned to his mistress's lap as if nothing unusual had happened.

"What's the little darling's name?" asked Yelena Vassilyevna, looking very pleased with her new pet.

The Chinese replied simply, "Lemon, ma'am."

No one thought of finding out what the word "lemon" meant in Chinese, for everyone, of course, assumed that since the dog was yellow and so tiny, Lemon was the most appropriate name for him.

Henceforth the little bully began to tyrannise and lord it over all the animals in the house, none of those friendliest and most inoffensive creatures daring to offer the slightest resistance to him. I was staying at the manager's house at the time and four times a day I took my meals in the dining room. Lemon conceived a terrible hatred for me and the moment I appeared in the dining room, he would jump off his mistress's lap and hurl himself against my boot and, as the boot gave him a slight push, he would immediately fly back to his mistress's lap, inciting her against me by the loud squealing he set up. As a rule he would stop howling a little during dinner, but as soon as I, forgetful of the consequences, went up to Yelena Vassilyevna to thank her, he would start barking again.

My little room was separated from the rest of the house by a thin partition and I found it almost impossible to read or write for the incessant yelps of the little brute. Once I was awakened in the middle of the night by such an ear-splitting yapping in one of my host's rooms that I thought that burglars or murderers had broken into the house and, snatching up my gun, I rushed into the dining room. The other lodgers in the house also came running to the rescue armed with guns, revolvers, axes and pitchforks. The cause of the terrible din was Lemon, who was having a fight to the death with the hedgehog.

Many such incidents occurred amost daily and life was becoming so unbearable that Trofim Mikhailovich and myself began to hatch all sorts of plots for getting rid of the little nuisance. One day our chance came. Yelena Vassilyevna had to go out somewhere and for some reason she did not take Lemon with her, leaving him for the first time in the house without her protection. It was then that a plan of action suddenly occurred to me. I picked up my hat and went straight to the dining room.

"Well, sir," I said to Lemon, "your mistress is away and it's all over with you now. You'd better surrender at once."

Letting him bite my heavy boot, I suddenly covered him with my soft hat. Then, folding the brim, I picked him up, turned my hat over and looked into it: inside lay a silent little bundle, looking at me with a pair of enormous and—so it seemed to me—melancholy eyes.

I felt even a little sorry for him, and I confess I thought with some embarrassment: what if his little heart should break from fear and humiliation and he died? What on earth should I say to Yelena Vassilyevna then?

"Don't be angry with me, Lemon," I said in a kindly voice, trying to comfort him. "Let's be friends."

I stroked his head. He did not object. I went on stroking his head and he still did not protest against it, although he did not look particularly happy, either. I got worried in good earnest and put him down on the floor. Almost swaying on his little legs, he went silently to the bedroom. Even the two large dogs and the ram pricked up their ears and followed him with a surprised look in their eyes.

At lunch, at tea and at dinner that day Lemon did not utter a sound. Yelena Vassilyevna was beginning to get anxious about his health. Next day I went up to my hostess and had for the first time the pleasure of kissing her hand: Lemon seemed to have his mouth full of water.

"What did you do to the poor thing while I was away?" she asked.

"Oh, nothing," I replied. "I daresay he's getting used to me and about time, too!"

I did not dare to tell her that Lemon had been in my hat. But I confided the secret to Trofim Mikhailovich in a whisper and he was not at all surprised that Lemon should have lost all his ebullition of spirits in my hat.

"All bullies are the same," he said. "They talk big to you, they scream at you, they throw dust in your eyes, but put them in your hat and all their spirit goes: plenty of noise, but no hair!"

How I Taught My Dogs to Eat Peas

Lada is an old pointer—she is ten years old—white with brown spots. Travka is a reddish, shaggy-haired Irish setter and she is only ten months old. Lada is a quiet and clever bitch, but Travka is very excitable and she does not understand me at once. If I go out of doors and shout, "Travka!" she looks quite stupefied for a moment. Every time that happens, Lada just turns her head to Travka and all but says in so many words, "You silly fool, don't you hear your master calling you?"

To-day I went outside and shouted, "Lada, Travka, the peas are ripe! Come out quickly and have some peas!"

Lada had heard me say those words for the past eight years and she knew their meaning very well. She likes peas and as a matter of fact she eats not only peas, but also raspberries, strawberries, bilberries and even radishes, but she draws the line at onions. I would be eating peas in the garden and she, clever dog! would be watching me and next time I looked at her, she would be tearing off one pod after another. She'd fill her mouth with peas and, while she chewed them, peas would be dropping from either side of her mouth, like grain from a winnowing machine. Then she would spit out all the pods and start picking up the peas from the ground with her tongue to the last pea.

So now I picked up a fat, green pod and offered it to Travka. Lada, the old lady, did not of course relish the idea that I should show any preference to Travka. The shaggy setter took the pod in her mouth and spat it out. I offered her another, but she spat that out, too. I gave the third pod to Lada who accepted it. Then I again offered one to Travka. She, too, accepted it. And so it went on: one pod for Lada, another pod for Travka. I gave them ten pods in all.

"Come on, chew! Work away with your jaws!"

So away their jaws went, grinding the peas like millstones, peas scattering on the ground as they dropped from either side of the mouths of the two dogs. At last Lada began to spit out the empty pods and Travka did the same after her. Lada began picking up the scattered peas from the ground. Travka tried it, too, and then the whole uncomplicated business dawned on her and she began to eat peas with the same enthusiasm as Lada. Later Travka learnt to eat raspberries, strawberries and cucumbers. But the reason why I was so successful in teaching Travka all that was because she was so fond of me: Lada was jealous of Travka and she ate, and Travka was jealous of Lada and she, too, ate.

I expect if I organised a competition between them, they would soon be eating onions, too!

THE BLUE BAST-SHOE

A broad highway is being driven through our woods with separate roads for motor-cars, motor-lorries, carts and pedestrians. At present only the trees have been cut for the road. I like to look along that wide avenue: two green walls of the wood and a patch of sky at the end! When the trees had been cut, the large tree-trunks were taken away, but the small branches and twigs—the brushwood—were stacked up in large piles at either side of the avenue. They had intended to take away the brushwood, too, and use it as firewood for the factory, but they had no time for it and the piles of wood remained along the whole avenue through the winter.

In the autumn our sportsmen complained that the hares seemed to have vanished somewhere, and some were of the opinion that their disappearance was in some way connected with the tree-felling: the cutting down of the trees had created a terrible din, and now the hares had been frightened away. At the first snowfall, however, when the prints of the hare's pad exploded that theory, the tracker Rodionych came to me and said, "The blue bast-shoe is hiding under the piles of brushwood!"

Rodionych, unlike the rest of our sportsmen did not call the hare "a squint-eyed devil," but always spoke of it as "the blue bast-shoe." There is nothing strange about that, since the hare looks no more like a devil than a bast-shoe, and should anyone tell me that there are no blue bast-shoes in the world, then my reply would be that there are no squint-eyed devils, either.

The rumour that the hares were hiding under the piles of brushwood immediately spread all over our little town and on the eve of the free day all our sportsmen, headed by Rodionych, began to assemble at my place.

Early next morning we went out to hunt the hare without dogs: Rodionych was such a master at his trade of tracking down animals that he knew better than any dog how to lure the hare to the hunter. As soon as it was sufficiently light to distinguish a fox's track from that of a hare, we followed the hare's trail and, sure enough, it brought us to one of the piles of brushwood. The pile was as high as one of our wooden houses with an attic.   Somewhere under that pile a hare was crouching and, putting up our guns, we stood round in a circle.

"Come on," we shouted to Rodionych, "make a move!"

"Come out, blue bast-shoe!" shouted Rodionych, pushing a long stick under the woodpile.

The hare did not jump out as we expected.   Rodionych looked dumbfounded.   After a moment's reflection, he went round the pile slowly, examining it from every side.   Then he went round the pile a second time: not a single track led away from the pile.

"He's here all right," said Rodionych confidently.   "Take up your positions, lads!   Ready?"

"Get on with it!" we shouted.

"Come out of there, you blue bast-shoe!" Rodionych shouted and pushed such a long stick under the pile that he nearly knocked a young sportsman on the other side off his feet with it.

But there was nothing doing—the hare did not jump out that time, either.

Our eldest and most respected tracker had never suffered such humiliation in all his life; he seemed to take it to heart, for his face looked rather drawn.   We, on the other hand, began to rush about discussing the whole matter in little groups, each man advancing his own pet theory and each trying to help in the search for the missing hare, walking all over the snow and obliterating all the tracks and, generally, making quite sure that we should never be able to get to the bottom of the mystery of the whereabouts of the cunning hare.

Then I noticed that Rodionych's face suddenly brightened up. He sat down on a tree-trunk, looking very pleased with himself, rolled himself a cigarette and began winking at me to go over to him.   I, of course, twigged and, unobserved by the rest, went up to Rodionych, who just pointed to the top of the high, snow-covered pile of brushwood.

"Look," he whispered, "what a clever trick the blue bast-shoe is playing on us!"

It took me some time before I could distinguish two black dots— the hare's eyes—on the snow and two more little dots—the black tips of his long white ears.   That was his head sticking out from the top of the woodpile.   He was watching our sportsmen closely: where they went, there his head turned. . . .

I had only to lift my gun and the life of that clever hare would come to an instantaneous end.   But I felt sorry for him.   Were there not enough stupid hares crouching under the woodpiles?

Rodionych guessed my thoughts without my having to tell him: he made himself a tight little snowball, waited until our sportsmen had crowded together at the other side of the woodpile and, taking good aim, flung it at the hare. . . .

I never thought that our common white hare when he suddenly stood up on a woodpile and leapt about four feet in the air, thus standing out against the background of a clear sky, would look like a giant on a huge cliff! And those sportsmen of ours! Why, the hare had practically fallen in the midst of them straight out of the sky and to kill him seemed as easy as anything: they had only to put up their guns and shoot! But everyone wanted to be the first to kill the hare and everyone, of course, fired without bothering to take careful aim. No wonder the hare escaped safe and sound in the bushes.

"Good for you, blue bast-shoe!" Rodionych shouted after him delightedly.

Our sportsmen tried their luck again in the bushes.

"Killed!" a young voice shouted excitely.

But, as if in reply to that "Killed!" a hare's tail flashed among some distant bushes. Our sportsmen for some reason always speak of the hare's tail as a "flower."

The blue bast-shoe just waved his "flower" at our sportsmen from the far away bushes.

THE HOOF

Exactly twelve years ago, in 1926, I arrived in Sergiev (now Zagorsk) and wasted several days there in vain attempts at flat-hunting: nobody wanted to take me in with five dogs. I was forced at last to buy a little house with a piece of wasteland attached and settled there for many years. Mrs. Tarassovna, my right hand neighbour, kept goats and my left hand neighbour was a horse-butcher. He used to slaughter old and infirm horses, made use of the meat himself, sold the hides to the tanners and let stray dogs carry away the bones. (Now this is all finished and my neighbour is employed as a night-watchman at a slaughter-house.) There were no fences between our lots. Hundreds of bones, picked clean by dogs and bleached by the weather, lay about on my piece of land. Mrs. Tarassovna's goats grazed on my plot of land and on the plot of land of my neighbour the horse-butcher. The goats and the dogs were the cause of constant quarrels between my neighbours. I immediately built a stout fence of oak posts all round my piece of land, threw out the bones, ploughed up the wasteland and in this way separated the dogs from the goats. At the time I had the following hounds: Yarik, an Irish setter, Kent, a German pointer, Kent's puppies—the one-year-old Nerl and Dubetz and a foxhound—Solovey. All these dogs had the run of the fenced-in land, regularly dug up horse bones and played about with them, growling at each other. Every time I saw one of my dogs playing with a bone, I'd take it away and throw it over the fence into my neighbour's yard. So all the traces of past disorder were little by little obliterated, after which we acquired a cockerel and everything was as it should be: the cock began to crow and our house came to life.

In summer, in the interval between the spring and autumn hunting seasons, I wrote my stories beneath the only lime-tree in our kitchen-garden, near the fence, using an ordinary deal table for my writing desk. Over my table I put up a trapeze, so that, my writing over, I could pull myself up and down on it, turn somersaults, or else water my cucumbers, have my tea, do a bit more writing. In short my life passed just as I wished. One thing, however, was not so good: my dogs kept on interfering with my work. I was, of course, the centre of attraction for them and I could hardly blame them for that: they played their games and fought out their battles beside me, raising a terrible dust. I should really have driven them away, but I could not, somehow, bring myself to be very severe with my best friends, all the more so since I sometimes found it more amusing to watch their games than to write. The dust they raised at their games used to choke me and when they quarrelled, the dogs whose feelings had been hurt used to run to me and press against my knees. They naturally enough expected me to pass sentence on the guilty ones and punish them. So, I'm afraid, being rather weak, I allowed my relations with my dogs to deteriorate, which made me feel angry with myself and interfered with my work.

One day Kent happened to dig out of the ground not far from the lime-tree a hoof of a horse, long ago picked clean, without a vestige of anything resembling food on it. It was an utterly denuded hoof with a rusty iron shoe with "horse" nails, knocked through the "crown" and bent over on the outside. Seeing such rubbish, I was about to throw it over the fence to my neighbour, but the frightened look in the eyes of my clever pointer Kent stopped me. She regarded the old, weather-beaten hoof with an expression of superstitious awe with which children and uneducated people regard anything that appears incomprehensible to them. Kent's strange behaviour drew the attention of all the other dogs to the hoof and they all began to draw nearer to it, slowly and rather apprehensively. As the dogs came near her, Kent bared her teeth and growled, which made the other dogs stop dead in their tracks. After a moment's hesitation Kent opened her mouth so wide that I could not help being amused. Seizing the hoof, she crawled under my table, where she lay down in the attitude of a lion, placing the hoof between her fore-paws. The dogs moved slowly towards the table, looking as if they were hypnotised, reached some invisible line, placed themselves in a semicircle round it and, their eyes fixed on the hoof, assumed the same attitudes of couchant lions as the possessor of the newly-found treasure. If any of the dogs tried to overstep the mysterious line, Kent growled furiously at the violator of the frontier, forcing him to retire to his original position with his tail between his legs.

I soon came to the conclusion that the quiet that now reigned round my table was neither an accidental nor a passing occurrence. If the hoof had in any way been fit to eat, the tension among the dogs would have been too great and at the first slip made by Kent a dog fight would have started and, besides, Kent herself would have begun to gnaw the hoof and, in the end, it would have been treated by the dogs as just an ordinary bare and weather-beaten bone. It was possible that the hoof's substance, which was impervious even to a dog's teeth, exuded some kind of strangely seductive animal smell which no dog could resist and that it was only because of the existence of such a smell that Kent's authority over the other dogs was exercised in such dead silence, with such an absence of bad temper and over such a long time.

My dogs have no doubt at all about the existence of a god: I am their god and everything on earth, including the hoof, comes from me. God giveth and God taketh away. So after I had finished my work, I picked up the hoof and took it away with me. Next day I fetched the hoof, which I kept in a wicker basket, together with my papers and books from the house. Not wishing to hurt the feelings of any of my dogs, I entrusted the hoof to the safe keeping of each dog in strict rotation. Having picked out the dog whose turn it was to lord it over the rest, I put the hoof under the table by my feet and the other dogs, having come to know the established order well, disposed themselves near the table in a semicircle, adopting the same leonine attitudes which gave them the opportunity of jumping up immediately and snatching the hoof away the moment its master for the day let his attention wander. Having placed my dogs in that order I opened up the "safe," took out the treasure, the dog whose turn it was to be king for a day entered upon his reign and I, in the ensuing silence, worked away at my stories about the habits of animals.

Twelve years have passed. All my dogs—Yarik, Kent, Dubetz, and Solovey—have been described by me. Thousands and thousands of books about them for grown-ups and for children have circulated all over our country and some of them are even beginning to cross the frontiers. Nor is that all: I have met sportsmen who have named their dogs after mine, and the number of friendly letters I get! The

H

number of friends my books have made me! All that is, of course, excellent; one thing, however, is not so good. The dogs I have described in my books are no longer alive. They have made me many friends among all sorts of people, but they themselves have gone for ever. Kent died of heart disease and soon after her death Nerl and Dubetz died suddenly of the same inherited malady. Solovey died the way all the best foxhounds die: the old chap got a stroke while running full speed after a fox. To tell of Yarik's death is still too painful to me. So all my dogs have gone and of the famous "safe" only the wicker-basket—a product of Vyatka—remains. The hoof not only disappeared, but I forgot all about it. In all probability a member of my family, going through my accumulated rubbish, had thrown it into the dustbin.

The other day I was sitting under the lime-tree at the same writing table. Osman, a four-months-old puppy, a pointer with a beautiful black coat, was playing about with his mother Lada and the Siberian husky Biya. Even the young foxhound, the fleetfooted Anglo-Russian Trubach, was taking part in that never ending romp. The air was full of dust. I could hardly breathe. Suddenly the game came to a stop and Lada began to dig away furiously with her feet. Her son Osman was imitating her very comically. The other dogs stood around, looking bewildered. Then with the same strange expression that Kent had once had, Lada looked down into the hole, chased off the other dogs, bared her teeth threateningly and began to howl. Osman alone paid no attention and he got a good thrashing from his mother and, deeply hurt, ran to me squealing and clung to my feet.

Thus once again the famous hoof with the iron shoe had been dug up. I need hardly say, I put it away in the "safe" and every day I proceed to appoint one of the dogs in turn as lord and master of the hoof. I carry on with the writing of my stories about my new dogs in the complete silence of the little world which I have organised, but something, I must confess, is missing. Never shall I see my dear Kent again! It is only now that I understand the saying among old hunters that a hunter has only one dog. Somebody is knocking at my gate. Would Kent have ever left the mysterious talisman at the mercy of fate? She would have just growled, if anybody had been knocking at the gate. But Lada left the hoof and raced off to the gates, taking the other dogs with her. I was just in time to keep little Osman back. I pointed at the hoof, wishing to make him understand that now, while the other dogs were away, was his chance to seize power. I thought it would be great fun to watch the other dogs being lorded over by a little puppy with the help of the hoof.

Osman, however, remembered the hiding he had got from his mother because of that hoof only recently and he tried to get to the hoof without moving his feet, just with his nose. He wanted to smell it and, if nothing terrible happened, to remain where he was, but if something did happen, to run away.

"Go on," said I. He crawled forward a bit. "Courage!" I said.

Poor Osman began trembling all over. He stretched out his body as much as he could and inhaled the mysterious smell of the hoof which must always remain inaccessible to us. However, having acquainted himself with the scent of the hoof, Osman suddenly became strangely deflated and took to his heels with his little tail between his legs, hiding himself among the tall potato plants.

The dogs returned. Lada rushed back to the hoof, but I had finished my work and put the treasure away in the "safe." Only then did Osman recover from his terror and, poking his head from among the potato plants, began to yelp.

A Swift Brown Hare

We went out to hunt the white hare, but having been told in one village that a wolf had killed one of their dogs the night before, we were afraid to let our dogs chase the hares in the woods and decided to go after the brown hare. Soon we saw a brown hare, which, wishing to hide himself under the steep bank of a stream, began to cross it over the ice and fell through. Not in the least afraid, Solovey followed the hare's tracks, fell through the ice, got out, picked up the hare's trail and began to chase him. We fired and wounded the hare, but at first there was no sign of any slacking off in the hare's swift pace. The hare ran swifter than an arrow and soon disappeared behind some low hills on the horizon.

Everybody knows the way a brown field hare runs: he rouses the whole district, shows himself in every village and every man who owns a gun will immediately snatch it up and go racing after the hare.

"A hare, a hare!" the village boys scream at the top of their voices.

And everyone in the village joins in the chase, one man picking up a piece of wood, another an axe and a third a stone.

The hare rarely falls into the hands of the man who raised him in the first place.

Our wounded hare ran with his last strength, past fields, ravines, copses and villages. In some village he would run straight through the streets with every dog in the village after him. Our own experienced dogs never let go and the desperate hare tried to hide himself in Pakhom's barn in the village of Dubovitzy. Pakhom

himself was at the time sitting in his barn near the stove, putting logs
on the fire. Suddenly something burst into the barn—a kind of a
devil with long ears—and crash! straight into the flames, so that
poor Pakhom was covered with sparks and burning logs.

Terrified out of his wits, Pakhom rushed out of the barn and
there he saw a pack of hounds in full cry bearing down on him. Now
he realised what kind of a devil it was that came flying into his barn
and, naturally, when we asked him where the hare had run off to,
he told us a tall story about the direction he had seen the hare take.
The freshly fallen snow covered the countryside in deep drifts and
Pakhom no doubt knew very well that it would take us a long time
to find out that he had misled us and that we should consequently
not be coming back too soon. Having snatched our hare practically out
of the mouths of our hounds, he took it to his cottage and told his
wife to bestir herself and put it in the pot. By the time we had
reached the spot Pakhom had pointed out to us and disentangled the
tracks round the barn and, finally, realised what had happened, the
hare was cooked. We thanked Pakhom and his wife for their treat,
they thanked us, and that was the end of our hunt.

THE RESOURCEFUL WHITE HARE

We arrived in a village to hunt the white hare. In the evening
the wind rose, but Agafon Timofeyich reassured us: "There won't be
any snow," he declared confidently. A little later it began to snow.
"It isn't snowing very hard," he said. "It's sure to stop." It began
to snow heavily and soon a blizzard was howling outside. "It won't
interfere with you," said our host. "It's sure to stop at midnight,
then the hares will come out and, as they won't have much time to
run about, you'll find it easy work to hunt them out by following their
tracks in the snow. Mark my words, whatever happens is for the
best!" When we woke up in the morning, the snow was still coming
down in large flakes. We asked our host to account for it and he told
us a story about a priest in the old, old times.

A country squire, Agafon said, once had a favourite horse and
that horse suddenly died. The priest came and said, "Don't worry,
all's for the best." Next day another horse belonging to the squire
died. Again the same priest came and said, "Don't worry, all's for
the best." The poor squire put up with it for a long time, but when
his tenth horse died, he summoned the priest to him, intending to
give him a good beating or, perhaps, even to murder him. It happened,
however, that the roads were flooded at the time and on his way to
the squire the priest fell into a hole full of water. So he had to go
back home to dry himself on his stove. When the priest arrived next

morning, the squire's anger had gone. The priest told him how he had fallen into a water hole the day before. "Well," the squire said, "I must say you have cause to be grateful to your God that you fell into a hole full of water yesterday." "Of course I have," replied the priest, "didn't I tell you that whatever happens in the world is all for the best?"

"And what's the moral of your story?" we asked Agafon.

"Why," said he, "the moral of my story is that you ought not to be complaining about the blizzard. Go hunting and you'll see that everything's for the best."

The snowstorm soon ceased, but the wind was still high. However, we decided to go out to stretch our legs. As we were crossing a field, we said to each other that even if we were lucky enough to start a hare, the hare, if he had any sense, would only have to cross a field for his tracks to be covered up with the drifting snow and the dog would lose his trail immediately. However, we thought that the chances of any hare doing that were rather slight, since he was much more likely to run to the woods, where we should eventually shoot him. Soon we entered a wood. Trubach accidentally stumbled against a hare and gave chase. We were very pleased that there were no other tracks on the snow, thinking that our dog would have no difficulty whatever in pursuing the hare and chasing it straight to the spot where we should be waiting for it. "Whatever happens is for the best!" we echoed Agafon's sentiment laughingly. Yes, we felt very happy and we hurried off to take up our position along the circular trail. But directly we had taken up our positions, the hunt came to an end. It seemed the white hare was indeed clever and acted as if he had overheard our conversation: he ran out of the wood into a field and his tracks were covered up by the drifting snow so thoroughly that we could not discover a single trace of him although we had gone round the entire field. So we came home empty-handed and said to Agafon, "Well, what do you say about that?"

"Why, everything's for the best, of course," replied Agafon. "The hare got away and by next spring he will breed hundreds of new hares. Yes, sir. Whatever happens in the world is certainly for the best!"

LADA

Three years ago I visited Zavidova, a farm belonging to the Military Hunt Society. The gamekeeper Nikolai Kamolov asked me to have a look at his nephew's year-old bitch, a pointer named Lada, which was kept in a little lodge in the woods.

As it happened I was looking for a dog at the time. Next morning

we went to see Kamolov's nephew. I examined Lada: she was a
little on the small side, her nose was perhaps just a shade too small
and her tail a shade too thick. Her coat she got from her mother,
a brown-spotted pointer, and her nose and eyes from her father, a
black pointer. It was quite fascinating to watch her: the dog was
on the whole light coloured, white with pale brown spots, but three
points on her head—her eyes and nose—were as black as coal. She
had a jolly head, quite lovely, in fact. I put the pretty puppy on my
lap and blew on her nose: she wrinkled her face, as though she were
smiling. I blew again and she tried to snap at my nose.

"Mind!" the old gamekeeper warned me and he told me that his
son-in-law, too, once blew like that on a dog and the dog snapped at
his nose and bit it off, leaving the poor fellow without a nose for the
rest of his life. "And," he added mournfully, "pity the poor man who
has to walk about without a nose, for you can hardly call him a man!"

Lada's master was very glad I liked her. He was not interested
in hunting and he was only too anxious to sell a dog he had no use for.

"What clever eyes she has!" Kamolov pointed out to me.

"She's a clever one all right!" his nephew concurred heartily.
"All you have to do, uncle Nikolai, is to flog her hard, thrash her
within an inch of her life and she'll understand everything!"

The gamekeeper and I couldn't help laughing at that piece of
advice. We took Lada to the woods to try out her scent and her
ability to search for and pursue game. We, naturally, paid no
attention to her master's advice and treated her with the utmost
kindness: we gave her a piece of fat for good work and just wagged a
finger warningly at her whenever she made a bad mistake. It took
the clever little dog only one day to learn all we had to teach her:
she must have inherited her wonderful scent from her grandfather,
Cambyses, who was famed for his quite extraordinary scent.

I felt very pleased on our way back to the farm, for it was not so
easy to find such a fine dog.

"Her name shouldn't be Lada, but Treasure, for she's a treasure, a
real treasure!" Kamolov went on repeating.

We both came back to the lodge in the best of spirits.

"But where's Lada ?" her master asked in surprise.

We looked round and, sure enough, Lada was not with us. She
had followed us all the time, but as we approached the lodge, she
seemed to have sunk through the ground. We called and called,
both coaxing and threatening, but without avail. So we went away
feeling rather down in the mouth and Lada's master did not feel too
good, either. The whole thing turned out most unfortunately.

I wanted to give some money to Kamolov's nephew, but he would not accept any.

"And fancy us going to call her a treasure," said Kamolov.

"Well," his nephew laughed as he took leave of us, "I suppose some wood goblin must have carried her off!"

But we had only walked about two hundred yards in the woods without Lada's master when the dog suddenly jumped out of a bush and came running to us. What joy! We, of course, retraced our steps, but the moment we turned back, Lada again vanished—just as if she had been swallowed up! We did not waste our time looking for her, for now we understood the reason for her disappearance. Her master whipped her, while we were kind to her and had taken her out on a hunt. That was why she had hidden herself: she did not want to go back to her master. And, to be sure, no sooner did we turn back, than Lada again jumped out of a bush. On our way home, Kamolov and I laughed heartily as we recalled her master's words: "Thrash her within an inch of her life and she'll understand everything!"

So she did!

I have had Lada now for the fourth hunting season and she has shown herself to be an excellent hound both in the marshes and in the woods. Her favourite game was the fat and long-billed double snipe. In hunting the double snipe everything depends on the dog's scent and its ability to range over a long area. Thousands of sportsmen are after the double snipe and it is therefore of the utmost importance to scour through as many of its haunts in the shortest possible time. I usually use one gesture: I wave my hand in a wide arc all over the horizon and Lada rushes off, widening her circles more and more. When she comes to a point at some distance from me and sees that I am not in a particular hurry, she just lies down and waits for me. I like to let any of my visiting sporstmen see that. The moment my friend notices that Lada has found a double snipe and has lain down, he begins to shake with excitement and starts running, but I pull him back by the sleeve and say smilingly, "Calm yourself, my friend! There's no need to be in a hurry with that dog."

I offer him a cigarette and, as we walk leisurely along, I usually tell him a funny story.

"What a dog!" he'd say. "At what distance from the hunter does she lie down like that and wait?"

"Oh," I reply, "when she's half a mile away, or even a mile, she just lies down and waits. If the day happens to be hot, I am not in a hurry and I walk along slowly while she, bored with waiting so long, just rolls up in a ball and remains lying like that until she can see me.

By the time I arrive, the water is oozing out of the swamp where she's been lying, but it makes no difference to her even if she is lying in a pool of water. I can't help laughing at that and I say to her, 'Haven't you heard of the Russian proverb: Under a lying stone even water cannot run ? . . .' "

My guest usually bursts out laughing at that.

"She's a marvellous dog all right," he says. "I am not disputing that and I can well believe that she lies down and waits half a mile or even a mile away, but that she should curl up in sight of a bird, that, old man, I shall never believe!"

Well, of course, I don't feel like confessing that, pleased with my friend's commendation of my dog, I had been exaggerating a bit, and to justify myself I repeat to my friend the well-known sportsman's yarn—everybody has heard it, but I have not met one man yet who could not listen to it again and again. I daresay you, too, must have heard the yarn of the sportsman whose dog came to a point just as he reached the swamp. The double snipe was his for the asking, but just at that moment a telegram was handed to him and, forgetting everything, he rushed off to his horse. A long time afterwards he remembered that he had left his dog in a swamp, but he gave up the dog for lost. A year later he came to the same place with another dog and there he found the skeleton of his dog in the same attitude as when he had left it and the double snipe, too, had died there and become a skeleton.

"Now that is the way to tell a tall story," I say to my friend, "but that Lada curls up and. . . ."

"Well," my friend replies, "personally I would rather believe the story of the skeleton than that any dog would curl up, lie in a pool of water and stay there waiting for its master under the very nose of the bird."

THE QUEEN OF SPADES

A hen is unconquerable when, disregarding danger, she rushes out to defend her chicks. My hound Trubach could easily bite the head off such a hen by just closing his jaws, but the big bloodhound who would give a good account of himself even if he had to fight a pack of wolves, runs back to his kennel with his tail between his legs when challenged by an ordinary domestic hen.

We call our black brooding hen the Queen of Spades for her extraordinary parental fury in defending her chicks, and for her sharp beak. Every spring we put her on a clutch of wild duck's eggs and she hatches out ducklings instead of chicks for us. This year, as it happened, we were rather careless: we let the hatched out ducklings walk over the cold dew and they caught a chill and all died save one. We soon noticed that the Queen of Spades was this year a hundred times more bad-tempered than any other year.

What could be the explanation of that?

I don't believe a hen resents the fact that her fledglings are ducklings and not chicks. I can only suppose that a hen's feeling of duty, her "I must," never comes into conflict with her "I want" as it does with people. Once a hen has sat down on the eggs without noticing that they are not her eggs, she feels it her duty to sit on them until they are hatched and then, of course, she just has to look after her fledglings, defend them against their enemies and so on to the very end. This is why she takes them out for a walk and does not permit even a shadow of a doubt to cross her mind as to whether they are really hers or not. For such questionings of a personal kind as "I want—I don't want" and "I like—I don't like" man alone seems to have been created, but she is just a hen and she has to do what nature tells her to, what "must" be done.

I think therefore that the reason why the Queen of Spades was in such a temper this spring was not because she had been deceived, but because her ducklings had perished and, particularly, because she was worried about the chances of survival of her sole remaining duckling. The last point needs no explanation, for do not parents as a rule worry more about a child if it happens to be their only one?

Oh, my poor, poor little rook Grashka! I found him in my kitchen garden with a broken wing and he was already beginning to get used to his wingless existence, which to a bird must be about the worst thing on earth that can happen to it. He had even learnt to come running to me every time I called him by his name, when one day, while I was away, the Queen of Spades began to suspect him of wishing to kill her duckling and chased him out of the kitchen garden. He never came back.

But why talk of a poor rook? My pointer Lada, now rather an aged bitch and one of the best tempered dogs in the world, waits for hours behind the back door for a chance of going out for a run without being pounced on by the hen. As for Trubach, the dauntless challenger of wolves, he never leaves his kennel before making quite sure with those sharp eyes of his that the coast is clear and that that terrible black hen is nowhere near.

And what about myself, let alone my dogs? The other day I took out my six-months-old puppy Travka for a walk and I had barely gone round the barn when I saw the duckling right in front of me. The hen was not about anywhere, but the mere thought that she might peck out one of Travka's beautiful eyes made me run back and how pleased I was with myself afterwards! To think that I was so pleased because I was too terrified of a hen!

Last year we also had some remarkable experience with that bad-tempered hen of ours. When the hay-making had started on our meadows on the clear and cool nights, I decided to take Trubach for a run after a fox or a hare in the woods. I let the dog loose in a dense fir wood at the crossing of two green paths and he immediately poked his nose into a bush, roused a young brown hare and, barking at the top of his voice, went chasing him along the green path. It was the close season for hares, I did not have my gun and I was just going to give myself up to the enjoyment of what is surely the sweetest music to a hunter—a hound's loud cry during a chase. But somewhere near the village my dog suddenly lost the hare's track and he came back to me, looking very sorry for himself, his tail trailing mournfully behind him and with blood on his light brown spots (his coat is a dappled brown on a reddish background).

Everybody knows that a wolf will never touch a dog when there are sheep in the fields. But if it was not a wolf, whence the blood and why did Trubach look so down in the mouth?

A queer thought flashed through my head: I imagined that at last one hare had been found among all the hares in our woods, all of them such timid creatures, who was really brave and who was ashamed of running away from a dog. "I'd rather be dead," my imaginary hare said to himself, "than be chased by a dog!" and, turning round on his heels, he charged his enemy. When Trubach saw that a hare was running *towards* him, he immediately took to his heels in terror and, rushing through a thicket, scratched himself. So it was the hare who had chased the hound straight back to me, or was it?

Well, no. I really didn't think that was possible.

I once knew a very timid man, who, when mortally insulted, rose and annihilated his enemy in the twinkling of an eye. But that was a man: hares do not behave like that.

I left the woods, following the same path along which Trubach had chased the hare, and as I came out into the meadow I saw the hay-makers laughing and discussing something excitedly. Seeing me, they began to call me to join them quickly, as people usually do when their hearts are overflowing and they wish to unburden themselves.

"Lord, sir, what goings on!"

"Why? What's been going on here?"

"Oh dear, oh dear. . . ."

Off they went, all telling the same story together so that I could not understand a thing, except the one phrase which was repeated again and again and which was the only intelligible sentence I could make out in the general hubbub of voices: "What goings on! What goings on!"

What had been going on was that on rushing out of the wood the young hare ran along the road in the direction of the grain barns. Trubach came running after him, his body stretched out to the utmost. It often happened that Trubach would overtake even an old hare on an open space (he was a fleetfooted Anglo-Russian breed) and to catch up with a leveret was child's play to him. The brown hare likes to conceal himself from a pursuing dog near the villages in ricks of straw or grain barns. Trubach caught up with the hare near one of those barns, opened his mouth to catch him when. . . .

It is a situation that often occurs during a game of cards when all your cards have let you down badly and you suddenly feel disgusted with the whole game and are about to give up, feeling that the game isn't worth the candle and that the best you can do is to throw in your hand and declare yourself beaten. Your opponent has seen through you, he has his answer ready, he knows the three cards that will give him victory: here's the three of spades.

The three of spades!

The three of spades takes your card.

Seven of spades!

The seven of spades takes your card.

The ace of spades!

But wait! Instead of the ace of spades, it's the Queen of Spades. That was exactly what had taken place under the very eyes of the haymakers. All Trubach had to do was to get hold of the hare, but suddenly a black hen flew out of the barn and threw herself furiously upon the dog, ready to peck his eyes out. Trubach turned tail and ran. But the Queen of Spades jumped on his back and began to peck him mercilessly with her sharp beak.

What goings on indeed!

That was why there were spots of blood on the light spots of my brown-dappled, red-coated hound.

A bloodhound pecked into ignominious flight by an ordinary hen!

GRANDPA'S FELT BOOT

What do Crawfish Whisper About?

I can't help marvelling at crawfish: what a confusion of seemingly useless odds and ends! How many feet they have, feelers, claws! He moves about with his tail first and that tail is called a neck! But what struck me most about them as a child was that, when placed in a pail, they began to whisper to each other. They went on whispering all the time, but what they were whispering about no one could tell.

When people say, "The crawfiish have finished whispering," it means that they are dead and that their life has passed out in a whisper.

In our little stream Vertushinka there used to be in my time more crawfish than fish. One day granny Domna Ivanovna came on a visit to us with her little grand-daughter Zeenochka to get some in our stream. They arrived in the evening and after a rest went to the stream, placing their wicker baskets in the river and sitting down on the bank to wait patiently for the crawfish to be enticed by the succulent bait.

Everyone in our village made his own crawfish baskets. A willow wand bent round in a circle formed the basis of the basket, the hole being covered with a piece of an old fish-net. For bait we used a morsel of meat or, better still, a slice of roasted frog which had rather a peculiar smell that the crawfish found quite irresistible. Thus baited, the net is lowered to the bottom of the stream and the crawfish, scenting the roasted frog, crawl out of their nooks and crannies and get themselves entangled in the net which is fished out at regular intervals. The catch is then removed and the net lowered again.

It is really a very simple business. Domna Ivanovna and her little grand-daughter spent the whole night drawing up their net and when they had filled a big basket, they went back to their village, which was about ten *versts*[1] away.

The sun had only just risen when they started on their long journey. Granny and her grand-daughter went on trudging along the dusty road very slowly and they were soon perspiring freely and quite overcome by fatigue. They were not thinking of their crawfish any more, being anxious to get home as quickly as possible.

[1] Six miles.

"I hope the crawfish haven't finished whispering yet," said the old lady.

Zeenochka listened and was glad to reassure her granny: they were whispering like anything in the basket on granny's back.

"What are they whispering about, granny?" asked the little girl.

"They are saying good-bye to one another before they die, dear," said Domna Ivanovna.

But the crawfish were not whispering at all. They were only rubbing their rough shells against each other as well as their claws, their feelers and their necks, and that created the impression that they were whispering. They did not dream of dying, either. Oh, dear, no: they had made up their minds to go on living. Every one set his legs working feverishly, trying to find a hole in the basket. Their efforts were at last crowned with success. They found a hole, big enough for the biggest one to crawl through. It did not take long for the biggest one to crawl through and after him the smaller ones had no trouble at all in getting out of the basket, hanging on to granny's short woollen coat with their claws, crawling from the coat to her skirt and dropping from her skirt on the road and then walking at their leisure from the road to the grass and from the grass it was only a little way to the stream.

The sun was blazing down from a cloudless sky and granny with her grand-daughter went on trudging along for mile after mile, while the crawfish went on crawling out of the basket and going back home to their stream. At last Domna Ivanovna and Zeenochka arrived at their village. Suddenly Domna Ivanovna stopped, listened to what the crawfish were doing in the basket on her back, but could not hear a sound. After a sleepless night and the long walk to the village the old lady was so tired out that she could not feel the weight of the basket on her back and was not aware that it was empty.

"The crawfish, dear, must have finished their whispering," said granny.

"Are they dead?" asked the little girl.

"Asleep," answered granny. "They don't whisper no more."

When they came to their cottage, the old lady took off the basket and lifted the rag from the top.

"Mercy, child, where are they?" Domna Ivanovna cried.

Zeenochka looked into the basket: it was empty!

The old lady looked at her grand-child and just sighed.

"Oh dear, oh dear," she said, "so that's what the crawfish were whispering about! I thought they were saying good-bye to each other before they died, but it seems they were saying good-bye to us, fools that we are!"

THE DECOY DUCK

I was rowing across a mere and my decoy duck Khromka was swimming after me. This duck was one of a brood of wild ducks and now she serves me, a man, and by her cry decoys drakes to my hunter's hut.

Wherever I go in my boat, Khromka swims after me and if she busies herself in some backwater and I have gone on and cannot be seen by her, it is enough for me to shout "Khromka!" and she comes flying to my boat and, once more, where I go, she follows.

We had a lot of trouble with Khromka. After the ducklings had hatched out, we kept them for some time in our kitchen. A rat got wind of it, gnawed a hole through the floor in one corner and raided our kitchen. Hearing the cries of the ducklings, we rushed to the kitchen and were just in time to see the rat dragging a duckling by its leg to her hole. The duckling got stuck in the hole and the rat ran away. We nailed up the hole, but our duckling's leg remained broken.

We did our best to mend the broken leg, binding it up and bandaging it, bathing it and powdering it, but it was of no use and our duckling grew up into a lame duck.

Now, a lame bird or animal has a very hard life, for birds and animals seem to have a kind of law, according to which the sick must not be cured or the weak pitied, but both must be killed. Our ducks, our hens, turkeys and geese all seemed to have conspired to have a peck at poor Khromka. The geese, especially, showed no mercy to the lame little duckling. You'd think a duckling could hardly be of any account to such a big bird as a goose, but no! even the geese seemed to have set their hearts upon finishing off the poor little thing and crushing it with their beaks, as with a steam hammer.

What sort of brains could a tiny little lame duckling have? And yet in spite of having a head no bigger than a walnut, the duckling understood that its only salvation lay in man.

We, for our part, were of course sorry for it in a purely human way: the merciless birds of every breed wanted to kill it, but was it its fault that a rat had broken one of its legs? And so we got to love little Khromka in a purely human way. We took it under our protection and it began to follow us about. When the duckling grew up into a duck, we had no need to clip her wings like the other wild duck who, being wild, always tried to fly away. But Khromka had nowhere to fly to from us, for man's home was the only safe place for her and it became her home. That was how Khromka became a decoy duck and that is why whenever I go for a row on the mere after wild duck, she swims after me. Left behind, she just rises from the water and comes down by the side of my boat. If she is busy fishing in some backwater and I go round some bushes, I have only to shout, Khromka!" and my bird comes flying to me.

THE LONG-EARED OWL

That merciless bird of prey, the long-eared owl, hunts at night and hides himself in the day. People say .that he cannot see well in daylight and that is why he hides himself. But I believe that even if he could see well in daylight, he would still not be able to show himself: so many enemies has he won for himself by his nocturnal raids.

One day I was walking along the verge of a wood. My small hunting dog, by breed a spaniel and by name Svat, scented something in a big stack of dry branches. He kept on running round the woodpile a long time, but dared not crawl under it.

"Leave it alone," I said. "It's only a hedgehog."

My dog has been trained by me to leave things alone when I say "hedgehog."

But this time Svat refused to obey me and, attacking the woodpile fiercely, he somehow managed to crawl under it.

"I shouldn't wonder if it wasn't a hedgehog," I thought.

But from the other side of the pile under which Svat had crawled there suddenly ran out a long-eared owl, a creature with quite enormous ears and huge cat's eyes.

The appearance of a long-eared owl in the light of day is a tremendous event among birds. When as a child I found myself in a dark room, I used to imagine all sorts of monsters hiding in its corners, but most of all I was afraid of the devil. Now all this is nonsense, of course, and there is no devil so far as man is concerned, but as regards birds there is a devil all right: it is their night raider— the long-eared owl. So I was not in the least surprised that when the long-eared owl rushed out from under the pile of brushwood it was, so far as the birds were concerned, the same as if the devil suddenly appeared among us.

A solitary crow happened to fly past just at the time when the terror-stricken long-eared owl ran from the stack of wood to the nearest fir-tree and hid himself under it. The crow saw the long-eared owl, sat down on the top branch of the same fir and said in quite a special voice, "Kra-ah!"

The crow has quite an astonishing range in spite of her rather monotonous call. A man needs so many words to express what he has to say, but the crows can only caw in one syllable and yet their "Krah-h!" can mean hundreds of different things, thanks to the infinite variety of ways in which they say it. This time the crow's "Kra-ah!" was identical with our own scream of terror expressed in the words: "A devil!"

The nearest crows were first to hear that terrible word and, having heard it, repeated it. In the twinkling of an eye a huge flock of crows, a whole cloud of them, came flying to the fir-tree with a shout of "Devil!" and in a flash the whole tree was full of crows which were sitting on every branch.

Hearing the tumult among the crows, the jackdaws also came flying to the tree, black birds with white eyes; the jays, brown with blue wings, followed and after them came the orioles, bright yellow, almost golden. There was no room for them all on the fir-tree and many trees all round the fir-tree were covered with birds, while many other birds kept on arriving: tom-tits, coal-tits, wagtaïls, goldcrests and every kind of wren.

In the meantime Svat, not realising that the long-eared owl had jumped out of the woodpile and slipped under the fir-tree, kept on barking and rummaging under it. The crows and the other birds all looked at the pile of brushwood, waiting for Svat to come out and drive the long-eared owl from under the fir. But Svat was still searching and the impatient crows kept on shouting to him their "Kra-a-a-ah!" which this time simply meant, "Fool!"

At length Svat got the new scent, rushed out from under the pile and, picking up the right scent quickly, ran straight to the fir-tree, while all the crows again shouted in concert: "Krah!" which now meant, "Quite right!"

When the long-eared owl at length ran from under the fir and took wing, the crows again shouted: "Krah!" which meant, "Get him, boys!"

All the crows immediately rose from the tree and after the crows came the jackdaws, jays, orioles, thrushes, wrynecks, wagtails, goldfinches, tits and coal-tits and all these birds flew in a black cloud after the long-eared owl and all of them shouted: "Get him, get him, get him!"

I forgot to say that when the long-eared owl took wing, Svat succeeded in catching his tail between his teeth, but the long-eared owl gave a mighty pull and Svat remained with only a few feathers and down in his mouth. Angered by his failure to hold the bird, the dog rushed across the fields after the long-eared owl and, at first, he ran in the same direction and almost at the same pace as the birds.

"Quite right, quite right!" several crows shouted at him.

Soon the whole cloud of birds disappeared over the horizon and

Svat, too, disappeared behind a copse. What the end of it all was, I don't know. Svat came back only after an hour, still with the long-eared owl's down in his mouth. But it was impossible to tell whether it was the same down out of the long-eared owl's tail pulled out when the bird was taking wing or whether Svat had lent a hand in the final reckoning of the birds with the evil-doer. . . . What I did not see, I did not see, and I certainly don't want to tell a tall story. . . .

STICKLEBACKS

A golden fretwork of leaf-shadows danced upon the water. Dark-blue dragon-flies were clinging to reeds and to the spikes of mare's-tail. Each dragon-fly had its own mare's-tail spike and its own reed: if he happened to fly away, he was sure to come back to it.

The restless crows had hatched out their fledglings and were now sitting down on the trees, resting.

A leaf, the tiniest leaf imaginable, floated down to the river on a gossamer thread and, having touched the water, it went on twirling round and round, spinning round this way and that.

I was going slowly up the stream in a little canoe, hardly heavier than that tiniest of leaves, made of fifty-two thin rods with canvas stretched between them. It had only one paddle, a long piece of wood scooped out at either end. Dipped into the water alternately at either side of the canoe, a mere touch was enough to send the canoe skimming the surface of the stream at a great pace, and so quiet was its progress that the fish were not in the least frightened by it. The wonderful things you see when you go sailing up or down the stream in such a canoe!

Yonder a rook, as it flew over the river, let fall a dropping into the water and that calcareous, white drop, as it touched the surface, immediately attracted the attention of hundreds of sticklebacks. Noticing this gathering of little fishes, a big, predatory fish swam alongside and beat his tail with such force on the surface of the water that the little fishes were stunned and floated about upside down. In another minute they would have come back to life, but the big fish was no fool. He knew that it was not often that a rook casts a dropping into the stream and that hundreds of silly fishes gathered round one such drop: he seized one, then another and in no time he had devoured hundreds of them, and those who were lucky enough to escape would know better next time and, if something tasty dropped down from the sky, they'd keep a sharp look out lest something dreadful befell them from below.

THE STOREYS OF THE FOREST

The birds and the little creatures of the forest have their own storeys: the mice live in the basement, the roots of the trees, various birds, like nightingales, build their nests on the ground, blackbirds and thrushes a little higher in the bushes; the birds that live in the holes of trees—woodpeckers, tits, owls—higher still, along the different storeys of the tree-trunk and on the topmost branches live the birds of prey—the hawks and the eagles.

I happened to observe one day that the birds and the small animals of the forest had quite a different arrangement about their storeys from what we humans have in our skyscrapers: we do not mind changing floors with somebody else, but with them each species always lives on its own floor.

While out hunting one day we came to a clearing with dead birches. It happens not infrequently that birches, having reached a certain age, fall into the sere and yellow leaf and die. Any other tree, when it is dead, sheds its bark on the ground and begins to crumble away and the whole tree falls down. The birch, however, does not shed its bark, which remains as an impervious cover for the tree with the result that the dead tree stands for a long time like a living one. Even when the tree has rotted away and the wood has turned into a crumble of dust, saturated with moisture and therefore rather heavy, the birch remains standing as if it were alive, its bark looking white and fresh. But one good push and such a tree suddenly breaks into big, heavy pieces and falls down. Felling such trees is good fun, but it is not entirely without danger; for if you are not quick enough, a piece from such a tree can give you a nasty crack on the head. But we who roam the forests in search of game are not really afraid of it and whenever we come across such dead birch-trees, we usually start a tree-felling competition among us.

Having come to the clearing with the dead birches, we felled one of them. It was quite a tall tree and, in falling, it broke into several pieces, in one of which was a nest of coal-tits. The tiny fledglings did not suffer from the fall of the tree. They just fell out of the tree holes with their nests. The fledglings were only covered with down and they kept on opening their red mouths and, taking us for their parents, chirped loudly and asked us for some worms. We dug up a few worms and gave them to the little birds, who swallowed them, but kept asking for more.

Very soon, however, their parents came back with worms in their mouths and lighted on nearby trees.

"How do you do, sweet little birds," we greeted them. "We are

very sorry such an accident should have happened, for we assure you
we did not know your little ones were in that tree."

The tits could say nothing to us in reply, but what was much worse
they did not seem to realise what had happened, where their tree had
gone to or where their fledglings had disappeared. They did not
seem to be in the least afraid of us, but they went on fluttering from
branch to branch in great alarm and distress.

"Here they are!" we pointed out the nests to them. "Can't you
see them? Listen to them chirping, calling for you!"

But the tits did not seem to hear anything and just went on twittering excitedly, looking terribly worried, but refusing to abandon
their accustomed perch on the storey of the tree which seemed to be
occupied exclusively by tits.

"Perhaps they are afraid of us," we said to each other. "Let's
conceal ourselves."

We hid ourselves, but it made no difference. The fledglings on
the ground went on chirping frantically and their parents were also
chirping and fluttering about, but they would not come down.

It was then that we realised that birds, unlike people living in
skyscrapers, could not change their floors: as far as they were concerned, their floor with their fledglings had disappeared into thin air.

"Good gracious, how foolish they are!" said my companion.
"What a pity and yet how funny! Such lovely birds, with such
sweet wings and puffed up white cheeks, but they don't seem to be
able to realise what's happened."

So we broke off the top of a neighbouring birch-tree, put the
fallen-off branch with the tits' nests on it, placing it at the right
height to which the destroyed floor belonged. We did not have long
to wait in our hiding place: in a few minutes the overjoyed parents
were re-united with their fledglings.

THE BEAR

Many people seem to be under the impression that you have only
to go for a walk in a forest where a great number of bears are known
to be for the bears to fall upon you and eat you up.

What utter nonsense that is!

The bear, like many other wild animals of the forest, walks very
warily in the forest and, scenting the presence of man, he runs away
so fast that you won't even catch a glimpse of his tail. Once in the
north I was shown a place which was known to be a regular haunt of
bears; this was on the upper reaches of the river Koda, a tributary
of the Pinega. I had no wish whatever to kill a bear and I had no

time to go hunting after one, either: bears are hunted in winter and I arrived on the Koda in early spring when the bears had already left their lairs.

I wanted very much to come across a bear when he was feeding in a clearing or when he was busy catching fish from a bank of the river or, perhaps, when he was resting. With a gun on my shoulder for any eventuality, I tried to walk in the forest as warily as any wild animal and when I came upon the fresh tracks of a bear I used to hide myself. Indeed, sometimes I was so near the bear that I seemed to smell him, and yet I did not succeed in catching sight of a single bear that time. In the end my patience gave out and, as it was high time I left, I went to the place where I had stowed away my boat with provisions. While dragging out my boat I saw a large branch of a fir a few yards away from me stir and begin to sway.

"Some little animal," thought I and, collecting my bags, I sat down in my boat and started rowing. Just opposite that place, on the other bank, which was very steep, there stood a little hut inhabited by a professional hunter. One or two hours later this hunter went down the Koda in his boat and, stopping at the little inn half way down the river, found me having a rest there. He told me that while I had been busying myself with my boat, a bear had come out of the forest only a few yards away from me. It was then that I remembered seeing a fir branch stir as if by itself, there being not a breath of wind at the time. I was sorry to have frightened away the bear, but the hunter told me that the bear had not been frightened at all, but, on the contrary, had had a good laugh at me. He did not go far, but hid himself behind some fallen tree and there, standing on his hind legs, he watched me calmly as I walked out of the forest, sat down in my boat and rowed away. After I had gone, the bear climbed into a tree and watched me for a long time going down the river.

"He sat there so long," said the hunter, "that I got bored watching him and went back to my hut to have my tea."

I felt annoyed that a bear should have a laugh at me, but it is much more annoying to hear silly people frightening children by absurd stories about the animals of the forest and spreading the impression that it is enough for a man to show himself in a forest without a gun to be pounced on and eaten up by them.

A HEN ON PILLARS

Last spring our neighbours made us a present of four goose eggs and we put them under our black hen—the Queen of Spades. In due course the Queen of Spades became the foster mother of four yellow goslings which squeaked and whistled in a way that was quite different from chicks and yet our grand-looking hen, her feathers ruffled, refused to acknowledge any difference and lavished as much maternal care on the goslings as if they had been her own chicks.

Spring passed away and summer came, the "clocks" of dandelions and goat's beard appeared in every meadow and field. The young geese were now almost the same height as their foster mother, especially when they stretched out their necks, but they still followed her wherever she went. It often happened, however, that when the Queen of Spades was digging up the ground with her claws and calling the goslings to come to her, they would be busy with the blow-balls, poking them about with their bills and letting the little seeds float in the air on their tiny parachutes. We thought that the time had surely come when our grand-looking hen would begin to suspect that something was not quite right about her goslings and, indeed, we seemed at times to catch her looking rather suspiciously at them. Still she went on digging furiously for worms, sometimes for hours on end, while the goslings did not pay the slightest attention to her, just whistling to themselves and nibbling the green grass. If a dog happened to pass anywhere near them at the time, the Queen of Spades would immediately rush at it and drive it off. But, having done her duty, she would cast a definitely queer look at the goslings, a look which spoke clearly of her dawning doubts.

We began to watch our hen in expectation of some event which would at last open her eyes to the fact that her supposed children were not at all like chicks and that it was therefore hardly worth while risking her life for them in driving off the dogs. One day the expected event took place in our yard. It was a sunny June day filled with the scents of flowers. Suddenly the sky became overcast and the cocks began to crow.

"Cluck-cluck!" the hen said in reply to the cock, calling the goslings to come with her to the shelter of the barn.

"Good heavens, look at that cloud!" the women shouted, rushing out to take the washing off the line.

It began to thunder and to lighten.

"Cluck, cluck!" the Queen of Spades called the goslings more insistently.

Their heads raised high like four pillars, the goslings followed the hen to the shed. It was quite wonderful to see the four goslings, almost as tall as their foster mother, obeying the hen's orders. They squatted down, making themselves look very small, and crawled under the hen's wings. The hen spread out her wings over them, covered them up completely and warmed them with true motherly solicitude.

The thunderstorm, however, did not last long. After a downpour of rain the cloud passed over and the sun shone once more on our little garden. When the water stopped coming down from the roofs and the birds began to sing again, the goslings heard it and, being young, they of course wanted to get out in the open.

"Let's go, let's go!" whistled the goslings.

"Cluck, cluck!" replied the hen, which meant: "Don't be in such a rush, it's still a bit too fresh outside."

"No fear," whistled the goslings. "We want to get out!"

Suddenly they rose on their feet, raising their necks at the same time. The hen was lifted up, as though on four pillars, and began to rock about in the air, high over the ground.

It was then that everything was finished between the Queen of Spades and the geese: henceforth she went her way and the geese went theirs. It seemed that now the hen at last realised the true state of affairs and refused to be raised on pillars a second time.

GRANDPA'S FELT BOOT

Grandpa Mikhey—I remember it well and I can vouch for it absolutely—has been walking in his felt boots for well over ten years. I cannot say, however, how many years he walked in them before I knew him. He used to glance at his feet and say, "My felt boots have got worn out again. I suppose I shall have to sew another pair of soles on." He would then fetch a piece of felting from the market, cut a pair of soles out of it and sew them on, and his felt boots would be as good as new.

So many years had passed that I was beginning to think that while everything in the world must come to an end, grandpa's felt boots were immortal.

Then grandpa Mikhey began to suffer from rheumatic pains in his legs. He had never been ill before and now he suddenly began to complain of his pains and even called in the district nurse.

"You have pains in your legs because you will stand in cold water," the district nurse said. "I'd advise you not to go fishing any more."

"But," said Mikhey, "I can't possibly do that. Fish is my only food. I just can't help getting my feet wet in the water."

"No need to get your feet wet," advised the district nurse. "All you have to do is not to take your felt boots off when you go fishing in the river."

This turned out to be a piece of very helpful advice for grandpa Mikhey. The moment he started to go fishing in his felt boots, the pains in his legs disappeared. But Grandpa Mikhey got spoilt and he wore his felt boots every time he went fishing with the result that they began to wear out very rapidly with rubbing against the sharp stones with which the bed of our river was generously strewn. Cracks appeared in his felt boots not only in the soles and heels, but higher up, where the soles joined the uppers.

"I suppose it is true enough that an end comes to everything," I thought to myself. "Even grandpa's felt boots refuse to be of use to the old chap any longer: the immortal felt boots are about finished."

People even began to draw grandpa's attention to the state of his felt boots.

"Time to give your felt boots a rest, grandpa! Time you gave them to the crows to build nests with."

But grandpa was not so easily defeated. To prevent the snow from coming through the holes in his felt boots, grandpa Mikhey dipped them in water and put them outside in the frost where, of course, they froze and in that way the cracks were covered up. After that grandpa dipped them in water a second time and this time the whole boot was covered with a crust of ice. Such felt boots are extremely comfortable to walk in, for they are both dry and warm: I myself walked in grandpa's felt boots across the unfrozen swamps in winter and they were perfect!

So once more I began to doubt whether an end would ever come to grandpa's felt boots.

But one day Grandpa Mikhey was again sick and when he had to go out he put on his felt boots in the cold passage, but forgot to leave them there on his return and crawled on the hot stove in his felt boots. The water from the melting felt boots dripped into a pail of milk, but that did not matter very much. What did matter was that the immortal felt boots were now definitely finished and done with. For the ice in the cracks of the boots loosened the felt and tore it into shreds and when it had melted the whole boot became a mass of rotting felt.

After he had recovered from his bout of illness, Mikhey, who was as stubborn as a mule, tried to freeze his felt boots again and even put them outside in the frost once or twice, but soon spring came, the boots dissolved into a shapeless mass in the hall, disintegrating beyond repair.

"I expect," grandpa said crossly, "the time has come for them to have a rest in some crow's nest!"

He flung one of his boots from the high bank of the river into an agrimony bush where I was at the time trying to catch goldfinches and some other little birds.

"Why give your felt boots only to crows?" I asked. "Every bird in spring is busy carrying to her nest bits of wool, feathers and straw."

"Aye," said Grandpa Mikhey who was just about to fling away his second felt boot, "every bird wants a bit of wool for her nest and

so does every mouse, squirrel and other little creature. They all
want it and they can all make good use of it."

However, Grandpa Mikhey remembered our professional hunter
who had long ago asked him for his felt boots to make wads with
to ram shot down his gun barrels, and he asked me to give his second
boot to this hunter.

Soon the time came when every bird was busy building its nest
and down below on the bank of the river all sorts of spring birds
went darting in and out of the agrimony bushes and, while pecking
away at them, noticed the discarded felt boot. Every bird saw it
and they all began to help themselves to little bits of felt. In one
week grandpa's boot had disappeared, providing building material
for countless nests. At last the birds finished their nest building.
The hens laid their eggs and began to hatch out their fledglings, while
the cocks kept on carolling from dawn to dusk. The fledglings
grew up in the warmth of the felt from grandpa's boot and, when it
grew cold again, left in large flocks for warmer countries. In the
spring they returned and many of them still found remnants of
grandpa's felt boot in the holes of trees and their old nests. Nor did
the felt used in the building of nests in bushes or on the ground perish,
for the bits of felt which fell from the bushes on the ground were found
by the mice which carried away what was left of the felt boot to their
nests under the ground.

PHACELIA

I. THE DESERT

In a desert men can have only their own thoughts. That is why men are afraid of the desert: they are afraid to be left alone with their own thoughts.

A CONFESSION

SINCE the early days of my youth I have been fighting against this loneliness of the desert, addressing myself in my diaries with appeals to an unknown friend. My entries, at first so naïve and purely matter of fact, become more and more mature with time and form the source of all my books which have brought me many friends to my desert. It is in this conquest of the desert that the chief aim of my writings lies and therein also lies the meaning of that "optimism" (joy in life), about which my critics have spoken again and again. I have never felt the temptation of writing for writing's sake (literature) and, if all that is unimportant in my books is disregarded, it will be seen that I am essentially an author who writes about his own first-hand experiences.

The friend I have been so long waiting for arrives at last. The two of us examine these stains on the pages of my life—my diary entries—and in them—just as sometimes in the stains on old wall-paper or in the frost patterns on window panes—we beheld the image of my love—Phacelia.

PHACELIA

It happened a long, long time ago, but the memory of it is still fresh in my mind and I shall keep it fresh as long as I live. In those far-away "Chekhov" days we—two agronomists, men who hardly knew each other—were driving in a peasant cart to the old Volokolamsk rural district on grass-sowing business. On our way we passed a whole field of flowering, mellifluous, rich-blue grass— Phacelia. On a sunny day amid the gentle beauties of field and copse of the countryside round Moscow, this lovely field of flowers struck us with wonder. It seemed as if blue birds had come flying from far-away lands, spent the night there and left that blue field after them. There must be thousands and thousands of insects humming in that mellifluous grass, I thought, but I could hear nothing because of the rattling of the cart on the dusty road. Carried away by that power of the earth to distil beauty, I forgot all about the grass-sowing business and I asked my companion to stop the cart.

I cannot say how long we stayed there, how much time I spent with the blue birds. Having flown about in spirit with the bees for some time, I turned to my fellow-agronomist and asked him to carry on with our journey. It was only then that I noticed that this corpulent man with the round, weather-beaten, rather coarse face was observing me with some amazement.

"Why did we stop?" he asked.

"Oh," I replied, "I just wanted to listen to the hum of the bees."

The agronomist started the horse. It was now my turn to observe him closely as I looked sideways at him and I could not help noticing something about him I had failed to notice before. I looked at him again and again and I came to the conclusion that that extremely practical man was also thinking deeply about something, having come to understand, through me perhaps, the exceeding loveliness of those Phacelia flowers.

His continued silence began to embarrass me. I put some totally unimportant question to him, just to break the silence, but he paid no attention whatever to my question. It looked to me as if, somehow, my impractical attitude towards nature or, perhaps, just the fact that I was so young, not much more than in my teens, brought back his own youth, when almost every man becomes a poet for a time.

To bring that fat, red-faced man with that bull-neck of his finally back to reality, I put a question to him which at the time was of some practical concern to all of us.

"In my view," said I, "our grass growing propaganda is a sheer waste of time unless we secure the support of the co-operative movement."

"Have you ever had your own Phacelia?" he asked me.

"What do you mean?" I asked in surprise.

"I mean," he said, "did she ever exist?"

I saw what he was driving at and I replied, as behoved a man, that naturally she existed and what else did he expect. . . .

"And did she come to you?" he continued his interrogation.

"Yes, she did. . . ."

"And where is she now?"

I felt a sudden, sharp pain in my heart. I said nothing, but just parted my hands slightly to indicate that she was no longer there, that she had gone. . . . Then after a moment's reflection I said about the Phacelia:

"It is just as if blue birds had spent a night on that field and left their blue feathers behind."

He was silent, regarding me closely. Then he summed up the situation in his own way.

"Well," he said, "that means that she will never come back."

And, glancing at the blue Phacelia field, he said:

"Only those sweet, blue feathers of the blue bird remain."

I felt as if by a superhuman effort he had at last succeeded in placing a heavy tombstone on my grave: I was still waiting for her to return, but now everything seemed at an end and she would never, never come back.

Suddenly my elderly colleague burst into tears, and I no longer saw his bull-neck, those roguish eyes of his which almost completely disappeared in lumps of fat and that meaty chin of his, and I felt sorry for that man, the whole of him, at a moment when life, like a flame, blazed out of his heart. I wanted to say something nice to him, I took the reins in my hands, drove up to some water, wetted my handkerchief and passed it across his brow. He soon recovered, wiped his eyes, took the reins from me and we drove away, as if nothing had happened.

After a little while I decided to explain my idea of grass-sowing which at the time seemed rather original to me, namely, that without the support of the co-operative movement we should never succeed in persuading the peasants to introduce clover in their regular crop rotation programmes.

"And did you spend any nights with her?" my colleague asked without paying the slightest attention to my business-like remarks.

"Well, of course," I replied like a real man.

He fell into thought again and—damn him!—asked again:

"You don't mean one night only, do you?"

I felt fed up with him and I nearly got angry, but, recovering my self-possession completely, replied to his question—one or two nights?—with a quotation from Pushkin:

"What is life itself but one night or two?"

BLUE FEATHERS

On some birches—on those which are turned towards the sun—catkins have appeared, glorious ear-rings not wrought by the hand of man; on the others the buds are only just swelling and on others still the buds have already opened up and they are sitting on the trees like little green birds, gazing with wonder at everything around them. Here—on these thin twigs—and there and yonder. . . . And to us, to men, they are not just buds, but fleeting moments of great happiness. If we miss them, they will never return, and from among the great multitudes of people there is perhaps only one lucky man who, when his turn comes, is not afraid to stretch out his hand and is just in time to grasp them.

A yellow butterfly is sitting on a low cranberry bush, her wings folded in one leaf: she is waiting for the sun to warm her before she can flutter away, for she cannot stir now and she does not even wish to save herself from my outstretched fingers.

A black butterfly with a thin white edging to her wings, the little nun, was numbed in the cold dew and, not waiting for the morning sun, fell to the ground like a piece of iron.

Has anyone seen how the ice on a meadow dies in the rays of the sun? Only yesterday this was a fast-flowing stream: that can be seen by the mud left on the sward. The night was warm and during the night the stream had carried away almost all its water and emptied it into the big river. What was left over, the frost seized in the morning and transformed into lovely lace patterns on the meadow. The sun, however, soon tore the lace into shreds and each tiny piece of ice died separately, shedding its golden drops on the earth. Has anyone seen those drops? Has it ever occurred to anyone that the life of those drops bears a close resemblance to his own life and that but for a touch of frost he, too, might have reached the world of creative human endeavour, a world as vast as the ocean?

It was yesterday that the bird-cherry began to bloom and the whole town went to the woods to fetch home the branches laden with white flowers. I know a tree in the woods: for years and years it has been fighting for its life, trying to grow higher and higher and so escape from the marauding hands of man. At last it succeeded and now the bird-cherry stands bare like a palm without a single branch on its trunk so that it is impossible to climb it, but on its very top it has shot out a spray of lovely white blossom. But another tree did not recover; it sickened, and now only a few dead branches are sticking out of its trunk.

It sometimes happens that a man yearns greatly for the companionship of a fellow man, but that life passes him by and he somehow misses every opportunity of establishing a close personal relationship with anyone. In the case of so fundamental a failure it is impossible to look for compensation in some other activity, whatever its nature, whether astronomy, or chemistry, or painting or music. For then the world becomes so sharply divided into an outward and an inward world that . . . well . . . that deprived of human companionship a man's or a woman's inner life is devoted to some lap dog, and the life of that dog becomes infinitely more important than the greatest discovery in physics, which holds out the promise of cheap bread in the future. Is the person who devotes all his human feelings to a dog to be blamed? Why should he be blamed if, when he wanted it most, he did not find the human companionship for which his soul yearned? Why do I still preserve in my soul the blue feathers belonging to the blue bird of my youth—my Phacelia?

THE CLOTHES BRUSH

An artist, a man with a heart of gold, had been brought to such a point of exasperation at home that he hurled a clothes brush at his wife. It was to this man who had devoted all his life and his art to his family that his wife, who had been hit in the face with the clothes brush, said: "Now I can see what you really are!"

The humbled artist went for advice to a man famed for his wisdom, and the wise man told him that it was not himself he had to thank either for his goodness or for his genius, but his forebears, and that it was therefore quite true that those qualities of his had nothing to do with "himself." As for throwing the clothes brush at his wife, that indeed was the expression of his inner self and to fight against that was his own personal affair from which he could not run away: for he could not run away from himself.

How much untruth is there in this wisdom! The untruth consists in the fact that someone makes use of it as a spider-web to catch his prey: you can't run away from yourself! And, no doubt, in some cases a man cannot run away from that kind of "self." If, however, this ancient method of intimidation is done away with, if the man is sufficiently strong, then the best he can do after having thrown the clothes brush is to run away as far as possible "from temptation."

THE PARTING

What a lovely morning! Dew and mushrooms and birds. . . . But this is already autumn, remember. The birch-trees are turning yellow and the trembling aspen whispers: "There is nothing really to hold on to in poetry—the dew will dry up, the birds will fly away, the firm mushroom will crumble to dust. . . . There is nothing to hold on to. . . . And I, too, must reconcile myself to this parting and fly away somewhere with the leaves."

THE CUCKOO'S LAST CALL

The cuckoo went on calling incessantly, the pauses coming only when enforced by the laws of rhythm and after the bird had promised many more years of life to the man who was counting her calls, each call being an additional year to his earthly span. I had no wish to ask the cuckoo the same question. I was perfectly satisfied not to have reached the end of the road this year and that I could still write down my thoughts in the woods to the cuckoo's call, when suddenly—as happens only very rarely—the cuckoo just uttered one short "cuck" and did not finish her call.

I forgot the train of my thoughts.

So it will be with me one day: my last "cuck" will sound and everything will be at an end.

THE WOODCOCK'S RETREAT

I had gone out woodcock shooting, but the woodcock did not come flying to his customary retreat, although all the omens were favourable. I became lost in my memories. . . . Just here, on this very spot, the woodcock did not turn up and many, many years ago *she* did not come, either. She loved me, but that did not seem enough to her to respond fully to my great passion. So she did not come and I just went away from that "retreat" of mine and never met her again.

How lovely this evening is! The birds are singing, everything, everything is so lovely, but the woodcock does not come. Two ripples dash against each other in the little stream, there is a splash and nothing more: the water runs rippling as gently as before over the spring meadow.

But later, I went on reflecting, it so happened that the fact that she did not come led to the happiness of my whole life. What happened was that while, as the years passed, her image became vaguer and vaguer in my mind, my feeling for her remained, it lived on in the endless searches for that vanishing image and, failing to find it, it clung lovingly to every manifestation of life on our earth and, indeed, in the whole world. So instead of one face, *everything* became like a face and all through my life I scanned the features of that boundless face with a feeling of rapt animation, adding something to my observations every spring. I was happy and the only thing that marred my happiness was that I wanted everybody in the world to be as happy as I was. Indeed, it seemed to me that everybody could be as happy as I if only everybody refused to grasp "the sweet little hoof" [1] and transmuted this feeling into a word, and whoever does that will surely not lack readers.

Now, I believe that happiness does not at all depend on whether she comes or not, that happiness depends only on love, on whether there was love or not, and this love cannot be separated from "genius."

[1] *See* "The Root of Life," p. 87.

I kept on revolving these thoughts in my mind until it grew dark and then I suddenly realised that the woodcock would not come any more and a sharp pain shot through me and I whispered to myself, "O hunter on the hill, hunter on the hill, why did you not grasp her by the hoof?"[1]

ARISHA'S QUESTION

When the woman left me, Arisha asked me:
"And who's her husband?"
"Don't know," I said. "I did not ask her. What does it matter who her husband is?"
"What do you mean it doesn't matter?" said Arisha. "You've been sitting with her and talking to her for hours and you don't know who her husband is! I should have asked her."

Next time when she came to see me I remembered Arisha's question, but again I did not ask her who her husband was. I did not ask her because something about her pleased me and, as a matter of fact, I am inclined to think that it was her eyes that pleased me so much, for they reminded me of the girl I once loved as a young man, my lovely Phacelia. Whether it was that or something else, I liked her for something for which I had also liked Phacelia: yet she did not arouse any desire for intimacy in me; on the contrary, the interest I took in her precluded my taking any interest whatever in her private life. No, I was not interested in her husband, or her family, or her home. . . .

When she was about to leave, I felt like having a walk myself, being in need of a breath of fresh air after my day's work, and I asked her if she would mind my going out with her or perhaps even seeing her off home. We went out. It was a frosty evening. The black river was freezing over, wisps of mist rose from the ground and a strange rustling noise came from the ice-covered banks. The water in the river looked so terrible, such a bottomless depth of water, that it seemed to me that anybody contemplating drowning himself in that river had only to look at the water to go back home feeling happy and, after starting the *samovar*, say to himself, "Drown myself indeed! What silly nonsense! In the river it is worse than here, for here I can at least make myself a cup of tea!"

"Have you any feeling for nature?" I asked my new Phacelia.
"What's that?" she asked in her turn.
She was an educated woman and she must have read and heard

[1] *See* "The Root of Life," p. 87.

a hundred times about a feeling for nature. But her question sounded so sincere that there could be no doubt at all about it: she really did not know what a feeling for nature was.

"Why indeed should she know," I thought to myself, "if she herself, she—my Phacelia, is that very 'nature' ?"

This thought rather surprised me.

Once more I wanted to look into those lovely eyes with that newly-won understanding and through them into the very soul of that "nature" of mine, so passionately desired and for ever virginal and for ever re-born.

We were crossing a large iron bridge at the time and the moment when I opened my mouth to ask my lovely Phacelia Arisha's question, I heard iron footsteps behind me. I did not want to turn round and see who the giant was, striding behind me on the iron bridge. I knew who he was: he was the power that came to castigate me for the futility of the dream of my youth, the poetic dream which once more took the place of real human love in my heart. When he over-took me, he just touched me and I was hurled over the side of the bridge into the black, yawning, bottomless abyss.

I woke up in my bed and reflected: "Arisha's commonplace question is not so silly as I thought, for if in my youth I had not preferred my dream to love, I should not have lost my Phacelia and now, many years later, I should not have dreamt of the black abyss."

THE ABYSS

If a man says that the abyss is drawing him on to throw himself into it, then it means that he, the strong one, is standing at its edge and is holding back. A weak man is never drawn by an abyss, but is thrown back by it on to the calm, safe shores.

The abyss is a test of strength for every living creature, a test of that strength which nothing can replace.

But, O strong of heart and sinew, remember: the hour may come when such an abyss will open up at your feet that you will say to yourself, "Go back, you can't resist its pull any more!" It is necessary to draw back from the abyss in time, preserving your last ounce of strength for the supreme and last eventuality, and to live to your last breath, realising always that even if it is for the last time, you can do it! Then it might well happen that man could conquer even death by this last, passionate desire for life.

11. THE CROSSROADS

A signpost stands at the crossing of three roads: whether you take the first, or the second, or the third—different troubles await you on every one of them, but at the end of each road you will find one and the same doom. Luckily, I am not walking in the direction where the roads diverge, but back from there—for me the roads of doom do not diverge, but converge, at the signpost. I am glad to see the signpost, and I am returning home by the only safe road, recalling all my troubles at the crossroads.

THE DROP AND THE ICE

THE ice is hard beneath the window, but in the sun it is growing warmer and warmer and icicles are forming under the roof—drops of water begin to drip as the ice and snow begin to melt. "I! I! I!" each falling drop sings as it dies; its life is but a fraction of a second. "I!" is merely the exclamation of pain, which expresses its utter helplessness.

But see! there is already a hole in the hard ice, a hole scooped out by the drops of water falling from the roof. The ice is melting, the ice is gone, but from the roof the clear drops still fall ringing to the ground.

THE GRAMOPHONE

I felt the loss of a dear friend so deeply that even strangers remarked on how low-spirited I looked. My landlady noticed it and asked me what I was so worried about. She was the first human being to take a real interest in my sorrow and I told her everything about Phacelia.

"Well," said my good landlady, "I know of an excellent cure for you!" and she told someone in the house to take her gramophone to me in the garden.

The lilac was in bloom and nightingales were singing everywhere. There was also a field with Phacelia there and the rich-blue flowers hummed with bees. My landlady brought me a record and put it on for me. From the gramophone came the voice of Sobinov, a singer who enjoyed great popularity at the time, singing Lensky's aria from Chaikovsky's opera, *Eugen Onegin*. The woman looked at me with her rapt, kindly eyes, ready to help me in any way she could. Every word sung by the singer to the accompaniment of the singing of the nightingales breathed with love, was impregnated with the sweet fragrance of the Phacelia flowers and exuded the scent of the lilac.

I

Many years have passed since that day and every time I hear
Lensky's aria, everything comes back to me: the bees, the blue
Phacelia, the nightingales, the lilac and my kind-hearted landlady.
At the time I did not realise it, but now I know that she really did
cure me of my fit of hopeless melancholy, and when I hear people
talking of the vulgarity of the gramophone, I just say nothing.

THE HUNCHBACK

Nikolai is walking beside us—Nikolai is a hunchback—and he has
a most cunning way of always getting something from us. I cannot
help feeling a kind of loathing for the man and yet I know that I,
too, once carried a hump inside me. So if I am myself inwardly a
cripple and if I have devoted most of my life to straightening my own
hump, why should I feel such a loathing for a man who tries to arouse
the pity of charitable people by his deformity or even to feign such a
deformity? No doubt, I thought to myself, the reason why I dislike
Nikolai is because he reminds me of my own hump, concealed in my
spiritual world.

APPETITE FOR LIFE

A distraught man came to see me, introducing himself as "one
of my readers," and asked me for a word that could save his life.

"You are a servant of the word," said he, "and I can see from your
writings that you know of such a word. Please, I pray you, tell me this
word!"

I told him that I never kept such words for any special occasion
and that if I knew such words, I would tell them to him gladly.

But he refused to take no for an answer: I must produce the magic
word instantly! He was so distraught that he even began to weep
and when he went at last and saw in the hall the bundle with his
boots, he cried even more bitterly. He explained to me that as he
was putting on his felt boots at home, it occurred to him that a thaw
might be starting while he was out and it might be wise to take his
boots with him.

"That must surely mean," he said, "that I still have a certain
appetite for life, for otherwise I should never have thought of keeping
my feet dry in case of a spring thaw."

When he said that I suddenly remembered how I had once got
over my troubles—a bitter loss I had suffered—by a similar expectation
of spring, and how many words of sweet comfort I had later obtained
from it, and I felt overcome with happiness. I know many words
of comfort and I have written them down, but I was unlucky in my
reader.

Then I remembered something and I told my unknown visitor what I could.

THE KEY TO HAPPINESS

Nothing in the world is alien to us, but we are so made that we can only see what affects us; one man sees more, another man sees less, but all men see what affects them and nothing more.

You achieve self-realisation usually by examining something that is of little importance, but through which you enter that world where "I" becomes the soul of everything. I have spent many years thinking about that little detail, that thing of no importance which is the gate through which you enter the world you long for. I can remember many such memorable occasions, but what are the conditions for the emergence of that overflow of feelings, in which all nature seems to fuse into one whole, and why it happens, I cannot even to this day say for certain. I daresay there is really no such key and there can be none: for that would have been the key to happiness. All I know is that one has to try many different keys and turn them until the lock opens.

Should you afterwards want to open the gate again with the same key, it will not open and you will find that the lock will open by itself. Yet you must go on turning one key or another in the keyhole, for therein lies your whole secret: to turn the key, to labour with faith and love, for then the lock will surely open by itself.

To-day in the confusion of flowers and sounds in the gorgeous meadow of the blue Phacelia, one sunbeam fell on a little floret of stock, and it blazed forth with a ruby flame which roused my inner sense to the oneness of nature and to the beauty of the whole world of flowers and sounds. At that moment the tiny floret of stock became the key to my happiness.

GOETHE WAS WRONG

For the first time to-day I noticed that the song of the oriole differed in every bird and I remembered Goethe's saying that whatever nature creates was impersonal and that only man is personal.

I'm afraid I don't think so. In my opinion it is only man who is capable of creating totally impersonal mechanisms, whereas everything in nature is highly personal, not excluding even nature's laws: in living nature those laws, too, change.

Thus even Goethe was sometimes wrong.

A NUPTIAL DAY

A quiet, sunny morning. The early morning frost had tidied everything up, dried up here, smartened up there, trimmed up yonder. The sun, however, very soon destroyed all the frost's morning work, sparing no pains, and where it shone hottest the sharp blades of the green grass began to blow their bubbles beneath the water of the puddles.

I do not know, neither do I want to know, the name of the tree upon which I saw the sweet tufted buds, but as soon as I caught sight of them, all the springs I had ever experienced became as one spring to me, one feeling embraces them all and all nature appeared like a nuptial dream come true.

Early spring takes me back to the day when all my dreams began. For a long time I thought that this poignant feeling for nature remained with me ever since I, as a child, first met nature face to face; but now I know full well that the feeling for nature itself arose as a result of my meeting with man.

This began when the thought first flashed through my mind that perhaps it was necessary to part from my love, and that thought gave me, at the same time, both exquisite pain and a delightful consciousness of great peace and boundless joy. It seemed to me to be so easy to exchange my pain for devotion to man's thrice blessed work wherein dwell both beauty and joy.

It was then that I remembered and I saw myself a child in nature. In a foreign land my native country, wretched and poor, seemed to me exceeding fair and beautiful and it was then, at that first meeting with her, that nature appeared to me in all her glory and my dear countrymen in my own dear native land also appeared beautiful to me.

HAPPY MOMENTS

In early spring nature is so fickle that it is only in brief snatches that one can feel happy. To most people early spring means wind and rain, cold and dirt, but to the few chosen ones such moments of intense happiness are granted, the like of which do not occur again during the whole year.

In early spring no man can adapt himself to the vagaries of the weather: grasp each moment like a child and be happy! The trouble with people is that they get so used to everything that their senses get dulled.

In early spring it seems to me every time that not only I, but everybody could be happy and that creative happiness could become the religion of humanity. Creative happiness? But what other happiness is there? I am afraid I made a mistake—not creative happiness, but just happiness, for non-creative happiness is merely the complacency of a man who lives behind seven locks.

HIDDEN STRENGTH

Hidden strength (so I shall call it) determined my authorship and my optimism: my joy resembles the sap of coniferous trees, that aromatic resin which seals up a wound. We should have known nothing of that resin if the coniferous trees had no enemies who inflicted wounds upon their trunks, for every time such a wound is inflicted the tree exudes an aromatic balsam which covers up the surface of the wound.

As with trees, so with men: in a strong man spiritual pain sometimes brings forth poetry, as a tree gives forth resin.

THE MOUSE

During the spring flood a mouse swam long in the water in search of land. At last she saw a bush sticking up out of the water and climbed to the top of it. Until now the mouse had lived like all other mice: She had observed her fellows and did everything they did. But now she was asking herself: how shall I live? A red ray from the setting sun strangely illumined the mouse's forehead, like a human forehead, and the beady little black eyes of the mouse shone like a flame. A thought flashed in them; the thought of a mouse abandoned by all, of that particular mouse which had come but once into the world and realised that if she did not find a means of salvation no mouse like herself would be born in the countless generations of mice to come.

In my youth the same thing happened to me, only it was not water, but love—also an element—which engulfed me. I then lost my Phacelia. But my misfortune brought me understanding. When the love-flood had abated, I came to men with my word of love as to a bank of salvation.

BIRCH-TREES

Beneath the dead leaves and dead blades of grass, green grass is pushing through. The leaf had lived, the grass had lived and now, having lived well, they pass into new green life as fertilizer. It is a terrifying thought to put oneself on a level with them; to realise one's value as manure. In relation to man it makes nonsense. I have but to choose something and to love it, be it leaf or grass or those two sister-birches, and the chosen objects cannot completely fall into the category of fertilizer like their predecessors. Neither do I know for certain whether it was I, who had breathed a living soul into them or whether, on the contrary, having watched them closely and having come to understand them with that inner sense of kinship of all nature, I had deepened my own perceptions and was thus able to discover their own soul.

The two sister-birches I have chosen are still small, the size of a man. They grow side by side as if they were one tree. While the leaves have not opened up yet and the swollen buds look just like beads, the whole delicate fretwork of the little branches of those two intertwined birches stands out clearly against the background of the sky. For several years now I have been admiring the graceful traceries of the living twigs at the time when the sap begins to rise in the trees; I make a careful note of the appearance of new twigs, try to penetrate into the life history of the exceedingly complicated organism of the tree which so resembles a whole kingdom united by the power of the trunk. I can see much that is wonderful in those birches and I often think of a tree which goes on growing quite independently of me and which, for all that, enriches my own spiritual life when I approach it closely.

It is a cold evening and I am feeling a little out of sorts. To-day my precious speculations about the "soul" of a birch -tree appear to me the æsthetic ravings of a man in a delirium: it is I, only I, who am surrounding the birches with a kind of poetic aura and discover a soul in them. Actually, there's nothing there. . . .

Suddenly a drop fell on my face from a clear sky. I raised my head thinking of some bird that might have flown past, but there was no bird. Then another drop fell on my face from a cloudless sky. It was only now that I saw that high over my head a twig of the birch beneath which I was standing was broken and it was the sap of the birch dropping on me.

Then, fully alive again, I returned in my thoughts to my two birch-trees, and I remembered a friend who saw a Madonna in the woman he loved; when he got to know her more intimately, however, he became disillusioned and called his former feeling a sublimation of sexual love. I had often pondered over that in many different ways and now the birch sap gave quite a new direction to my thoughts of my friend and his Madonna.

"A man does not always act as my friend did," I thought. "Sometimes a man, like myself, never parts from his Phacelia, but carries her image in his heart, doing his work with the rest, but concealing his love from everybody. But where there is love, there is also 'soul'; in fact, 'soul' is everywhere, your beloved has it and your birch-tree has it."

So that evening, under the influence of the rain of sap from the birch-tree, I understood that my two sister-trees have their own "soul."

AUTUMN LEAVES

Just before sunrise the first frost descends on the glade. Let me conceal myself, let me stand at its edge and see what is happening there in the forest glade!

Invisible forest creatures arrive in the half-light of dawn and they begin to unroll white sheets upon the whole of the glade. The first rays of the sun, however, immediately roll up those sheets, leaving green patches where there were white patches before. Slowly the white vanishes and only in the shades of the trees and mounds do white strips of mist linger.

You cannot make out what is happening in the blue sky among the gold-tinted trees: is it the wind that is carrying away the leaves, or have little birds gathered in flocks and are they flying away to warm, far-away countries?

The wind is a careful husbandman. During the summer he visits every place and he knows every leaf even in the densest brakes. But now that autumn has come, this careful husbandman has begun to gather his harvest.

As they fall, the leaves whisper to each other, bidding a last farewell: for once a leaf is torn off its tree, it is good-bye for ever to its native wood, it is the end.

And how is it with us?

Again I remembered Phacelia and on that autumn day my heart was filled with joy as on a day of spring. I felt as if I had torn myself away from her like a leaf, but I was not a leaf, I was a man. Perhaps this had to happen to me: perhaps because I had torn myself away from her, just because I had lost her, I began to draw closer and closer to the whole world of men.

TREES IN CAPTIVITY

With its top spray the tree, as if with the open palm of a hand, gathered the falling snowflakes until so big a snowball accumulated that the top of the birch-tree began to bend. During the thaw more snow fell and the snow clung to that large snowball, the topmost branch on which it hung, bending the whole birch in an arc till, at length, the top of the tree with that huge ball of snow was borne down to the snowy ground, and in this way became a captive until the coming of spring. All through the winter wild animals and men on skis passed under that arc. Close by the proud firs looked down upon the arching birch as people born to command look down upon their subordinates.

In spring the birch-tree rejoined those firs, but if it had not bent in that very snowy winter, it would have remained among the firs both in summer and in winter, while now it bends even on a day when very little snow falls and, in the end, it bends in an arc over the woodland path all the year.

To walk through a wood of young trees in a winter of heavy snow-falls is an eerie experience. Besides, to walk through such a wood is well-nigh impossible. The path along which you used to walk in summer is impassable now: on either side of it trees are bent so low that only a hare can manage to run under them. But I know of a simple, almost magic way of walking along such a path without having to bend double. I break off a large, heavy stick and with it I give each bent tree a sharp rap. Immediately the snow with all its weirdly shaped figures falls off the tree which leaps up into the air and makes way for you. In this way I walk along the path and free the trees from their captivity by a touch of my magic wand.

LIVING SMOKE

I have just remembered how I woke up last night in Moscow and, looking through the window, guessed the right time by the smoke rising from a chimney: it was just the hour before dawn. The smoke rose from a house somewhere in the city, from a chimney barely distinguishable in the darkness, straight up like a column that rises tremblingly in a mirage over the desert. Not a living creature stirred, save that living smoke, and my living heart fluttered just like that living smoke and my soul was uplifted in the great silence of the sleeping city.

So I passed some time alone with that smoke in the hour before dawn, my forehead pressed against the window pane.

THE STRUGGLE FOR EXISTENCE

It is the season when the birch-trees are shedding their last leaves of gold on the firs and the sleeping ant-hills. At such a time, even when alone with my sorrow I am not inclined to grieve or mourn, for I am not the only one to grieve, the whole world is grieving and even death loses its terrors in a crowd. Life is especially sweet before the end, life is so precious then. Now I even notice how the fir-needles glow in the rays of the setting sun and I walk on and on along the woodland path, my heart full of joy, and the woods are to me like an ocean, and the verge of the wood like the shore of the sea, and the glade in the wood like an island. A few firs are huddling together on this island and I sit down for a rest under them. All life, it seems, is concentrated on the topmost branches of these firs. There among the profusion of fir-cones a squirrel is busying herself, and crossbills, too, are very busy there and hundreds of other creatures, no doubt, creatures quite unknown to me. Below, however, beneath the firs, everything is gloomy as in a dark passage and all you can see is the husks dropping from above.

If you look at life with an eye of wise understanding, and if your heart is full of compassion for every little creature, you can read nature's magic book even here in the gloom of the twilight hours of an autumn day. Look, for instance, at those seeds of the fir-tree which drop as the squirrels and crossbills are extracting them from the cones. Once such seed fell under a birch-tree, between its bared roots. The fir, protected by the birch from the blistering sunbeams in summer and the frosts in winter, began to grow, moving slowly among the outer roots of the birch, came across new roots and could go no further because of them. In such a predicament the fir raised her roots above those of the birch-tree, went over them and pushed her roots into the earth on the other side. Now that fir-tree has overtaken the birch and stands side by side with it, her roots intertwined with those of the birch.

A WIDE SHEET OF WATER

Goethe says somewhere that man contemplating nature bestows the best of himself on it. Then why—as sometimes happens—when you approach a wide sheet of water, is one glance at it enough for your drab little soul, made drabber still by some petty domestic trouble, to expand and become full of forgiveness?

A NOTE FOR OLD AGE

From the moment we entered the boat at Vyezhi until our arrival in Zagorsk we did not exchange a cross word with anyone, and the whole journey passed off without a hitch and with no voice raised in contention. As you grow older, you should remember that every quarrel with people, every "loss of temper" costs you something, that it is, in fact, the most useless waste of your energies and that you ought to shun it more than anything else in the world. You may find it hard work to keep out of such quarrels, but it is surely not harder than changing over to a vegetarian diet, when such a thing becomes necessary.

I*

A WRETCHED THOUGHT

It grew warm suddenly. Petya went to the peaty pond to catch fish. He put in the net for carp and made a mental note of the place: on the other side of the pond, just opposite the net, stood about a dozen small birches, none of them taller than a man. The sun was setting, its disc looking enormous as it hung on the rim of the horizon. Petya went home and lay down to sleep. The frogs were croaking, the nightingales were singing: the night was one of those "tropical" nights which are full of all sorts of delights. Unfortunately, as often happens when everything around is so lovely, a poor chap gets a wretched thought into his head and that thought prevents him from enjoying the beauties of such a tropical night. Last year somebody had stolen Petya's nets on just such a night and now it occurred to him that somebody had been watching him at the pond and stolen his net. Early next morning he rushed to the pond and he saw a crowd of people standing at the very place where he had put in his net. He ran angrily to the place, ready to fight them all, but suddenly he stopped dead in his tracks, a broad grin on his face: those were not people at all, they were the birches which had put on their clothes during the night and were standing there looking for all the world like people.

SINGING DOORS

Watching the hives with the bees rushing back and forth in the sunshine—empty from the hives and laden with pollen on their way back—one cannot help thinking of the world of men and things so commonplace, so utterly familiar that, like the doors in Gogol's story *Oldfashioned Landowners*, they "sing."

Whenever I find myself among hives, I always remember those oldfashioned landlords, just as Gogol saw them and as people do *not* see them: in that funny old couple with their singing doors Gogol seemed to see the possibility of the existence of harmonious and perfect love among people on earth.

A VICIOUS CIRCLE

Time was when I could not help wondering why baldheaded people were not ashamed of themselves and what they were thinking about when they combed up their few remaining hairs over their bald pates, going even so far as to plaster them firmly with something or other. Bald, paunchy men in evening dress, old maids with yellow cheeks, gems sparkling on their velvet dresses. How was it that they were not ashamed to show themselves among people, decked out in all their finery?

Twenty, thirty years have passed and I, too, began to comb up my hair from the back of my head until somebody one day brushed them back and said, "Why are you covering up your head? You have such a fine forehead, such a lovely bald head!" So slowly I got reconciled to my bald head as well as to all my other short-comings which, as the years rolled by, became more and more evident. . . . I got even reconciled to the loss of my youthful love, Phacelia.

Bald men, paunchy men, yellow-faced men, sick men no longer haunt me: it is only men with trivial minds I cannot abide. But I cannot help thinking that even genius is like a bald head: genius, too, can disappear, you don't want to write any more—you get reconciled to it; for it is not you who have created your genius: it has grown up with you like your hair and if you neglect it, it will also fall out like your hair—the writer will "write himself out." It is not genius that matters so much, as the man who is in control of it. *That* one cannot afford to lose, for the loss of it would be irreparable: for *that* is not a bald head or a big belly, *that* is I! And while *I* still exist, it is folly to cry over what one has lost. Isn't there a Russian proverb, "It's no use crying over a man's hair, if he has lost his head?" I should like to add to that, "Keep your head and your hair may grow again."

The Parting and the Reunion

It gives me great pleasure to watch the beginning of a torrent. A tree stood on a little hill, a very large fir. From its branches the raindrops gathered on its trunk where they increased in size, jumped over the bends of the trunk and vanished in the thick, bright green lichen which grew on the tree. At the bottom the tree was twisted and from there the drops from under the lichen fell straight down into a tranquil pool of water full of bubbles. In addition, hundreds of raindrops fell into the pool straight from the branches, each falling with a voice of its own.

While I was watching it, the little pool beneath the tree burst its banks and the torrent of water rushed under the snow towards the road, which had now become a dam. The newly born torrent rushed with such violence that it burst through the dam of the road and dashed furiously down the fields with the magpies towards the little stream.

The alder bushes on the banks of the stream were soon under water and from every branch drops were falling into a little backwater, giving rise to numerous bubbles, which moved slowly across the backwater towards the torrent, where they were suddenly caught up and carried along the stream together with the foam.

Some kinds of birds kept on appearing and disappearing in the mist, but I could not make out what birds they were. They twittered as they flew past, but in the noise of the rushing stream I could not recognise their voices. They lighted on a group of trees some distance away, not far from the bank of the river. It was there that I hurried to find out who those early visitors from the warm countries were.

Under the noise of the bubbling stream, and the ringing music of the drops, a thought about myself entered my mind, as happens sometimes when listening to real, human music. It concerned a painful spot which had not healed for so many years. . . . Little by little the murmuring led me to think distinctly about the beginnings of man. He that gives himself up to the search for happiness and lives with these streams and bubblings and birds is not yet a man. Man begins when he takes leave of all that: therein is the first step of consciousness. Thus, step by step, forgetting everything, I began to ascend through my pain to man detached.

I became once more conscious of my surroundings when I heard the song of the chaffinch. I could hardly credit my ears, but I soon realised that those early visitors, the birds which I had seen flying through the mist, were all chaffinches. Thousands of chaffinches were flying about, lighting on trees and on the ploughed up fields. But what I was chiefly conscious of on coming across those welcome little birds was fear that, absorbed in my own thoughts as I was, I might have missed them if there had not been so many of them.

'To-day I should have missed the chaffinches,' I thought to myself, 'and to-morrow I might miss a good man whose whole life might depend on my sympathy with his troubles and on the feeling of brotherly concern with which I treated him.'

It was then that I understood that there was the seed of great evil in the thought of man in the abstract. It was none the less also true that the chaffinches were dearer to me now because earlier I had bidden good-bye to the rushing stream and the birds; that was why I felt their presence now so much more poignantly, more triumphantly. This sweet reunion came to me only after the sorrow of parting. 'This means,' I thought, 'that there is nothing wrong about parting and that this kind of parting really is man's first beginning, save that I must always come back to the original thought: it began with the chaffinches and it must end with the chaffinches. Most probably it means that one has to return to oneself, to one's own original thought; and the evil does not lie in the fact of the parting, but in the fact that you have lost yourself in thoughts that were not your own and have not returned to yourself.'

PHACELIA'S DAUGHTER

I lost sight of her completely and many years have passed since the day I saw her last. I have forgotten even what she looked like and I should not have recognised her by her face if I had met her again. Only her eyes, so like two northern stars, I should have recognised—her eyes only.

One day I went into a shop to buy myself something. I was lucky to find the thing I wanted and I bought it. I then queued up with a cheque in my hand next to another queue of people who wished to change their notes as the cashier had no change. A young woman in that other queue asked me if I could change her a five rouble note: she wanted two roubles to pay for her shopping. I only had two roubles in small change and I gladly offered it to her. . . .

I expect she probably did not realise that I wanted to give her the money, to make her a present of it, or, maybe, she was so sweet a girl that she had overcome the feeling of false pride and did not wish to be a slave to convention. Unfortunately, as I was handing her the money, I glanced at her and immediately recognised those same eyes, the two northern stars—Phacelia's eyes. In a flash I saw through her eyes into her very soul and it occurred to me that perhaps she was "her" daughter.

But after the glance I had given her she would not accept my money. Or was it only now that she realised that I, a stranger, wanted to make her a present of the money ? To think what a fortune I was offering her—two roubles! I stretched out my hand with the money.

"No, thank you very much," she said. "I can't possibly accept it from you."

The moment I recognised her eyes I was ready to give her everything I had and, at a word from her, I should have run any distance and brought her more and more.

I looked imploringly at her, as if I were the poorest of the poor, and I begged her: "Please, take it!"

"No, thank you," she repeated.

But as I looked so unhappy, like a man broken in mind and body, a homeless wanderer on the face of the earth, she smiled her first sweet, Phacelia-like smile and said, "I'll take your two roubles if you'll agree to take my five roubles in exchange."

I was delighted to accept her five roubles and I could see that she understood and appreciated my delight.

THE OLD LIME

I was thinking of an old lime-tree with its bark torn by thousands of crevices. How many years, I wondered, had she comforted her old owner as she was now comforting me without giving a thought to either of us.

I consider her selfless service to man and hope, like a fragrant lime flower, opens up in my heart: one day perhaps I, too, shall blossom like her.

III. JOY

Sorrow, accumulating more and more in the heart of one man, may one fine day catch fire, like hay, and burn everything up with flames of great joy.

THE LAST SPRING

This spring is perhaps my last. Why, of course, every man, whether young or old, cannot but think, as he welcomes a new spring, that it may be his last and that he will never see another. Such a thought increases the joy of spring a thousand times and every little thing, a chaffinch or just a stray word that reaches you from who knows where, comes to you with its own countenance, its own demand for a right to existence and its own part in what may be also for them their last spring.

A NEAR PARTING

In the autumn everything around whispers of a parting that cannot be long delayed and on a joyous, sunny day a challenging note steals into this whisper: "It may be my last one, but it is all mine own!"

I cannot help thinking that perhaps all our life just passes like a day and that all life's wisdom comes to one and the same thing: only one life, one only, as in autumn one sunny day—one day only, but mine own!"

The Cuckoo and the Birch

A cuckoo sat somewhere quite near to me as I was resting on an uprooted birch-tree, and with a kind of breathless emphasis, as if she wanted to say, "Well, try and see what happens!" said, "Cuckoo!"

"One," said I, beginning to count automatically how many more years I had still to live.

"Two!"

No sooner had she begun her call for the third time and no sooner had I got ready to say, "Three!" than "Cuck!" she said and flew away.

So I did not say "Three!" after all. I had, it seemed, only a short time to live and I felt a bit taken aback as I thought of the important business I was going to embark upon when, no sooner was I ready to start, than "Cuck!" . . . and all was over.

Was it really worth while?

'No, it certainly isn't!' thought I.

But as I rose to go I threw a glance at the birch-tree and instantly everything seemed to burst into flower in my heart: this beautiful, uprooted tree was opening up her resinous buds for her last, her only spring—this spring!

The Smile of the Earth

Among great mountains, as in the Caucasus, there remain everywhere traces of the titanic upheavals in the life of earth's crust, which in a way resemble the traces left on a human face by suffering and terror. There, under your very eyes, water rends asunder mountains, stones are precipitated into valleys and gorges, rocks are gradually disintegrating. Perhaps in ancient times there was also such an upheaval of the earth's crust in our Moscow district, but ages separate us from that time, and water has so tempered the elements that it looks that here at last the earth, as it were, is smiling with her green, wooded hills.

You let your eyes roam over some of these dear little hills and sometimes, as you remember your past, the thought comes to you— 'No, I don't want to go through it again! I don't want to be young again!' and you smile together with the earth and feel happy.

The Sun in the Wood

The wood is so dense that you cannot see the sun all at once and it is only by its fiery shafts and splashes of gold that you guess it is hiding yonder behind that large tree and from there throwing its oblique early morning rays into the dark wood. . . .

From the glade, ablaze with sunshine, you enter the wood as if it were a cave, but as soon as you have had time to look round—how beautiful it is! It is impossible to describe the beauty of a dark wood on a bright, sunny day. No one, I think, could help giving full freedom to his thoughts there, preoccupied as they may be with all sorts of petty worries. Then your thought bounds happily from one pool of sunshine to another, embracing on its way a dear little fir-tree on a sun-splashed glade, soaring upwards like a tower, enticed by a silver birch, like an innocent little girl, hiding its flushed face in the green foliage and away it will speed, flashing in the sunbeams, from glade to glade.

THE OLD STARLING

The starlings have hatched out and flown away and their nests have long ago been occupied by the sparrows. But on a fine, dewy morning an old starling still comes flying to the old apple-tree and bursts into song.

It is queer, isn't it? Everything, it would seem, has come to an end, the hen starling has long since hatched out her brood, the fledglings have grown up and flown away. . . . Why then should the old starling come flying every morning to the old apple-tree where his spring has been spent? Why should he sing there?

I could not help being surprised at the starling and sometimes, with a kind of vague hope, I myself begin to write something to the strains of the old starling's song, so tongue-tied and so comic.

A LITTLE BIRD

A tiny little bird sat on the topmost finger of the highest fir-tree and it seemed as if he were not sitting there in vain—he, too, was glorifying the sunrise; his little beak kept on opening up, but his song did not reach the earth. From the look of the bird you could see that his sole business was to glorify the sun, not that his song should reach the earth and glorify him.

FLOWERING GRASSES

When the rye in the fields begins to flower, all the grasses in the meadows are also flowering, and when an insect shakes a spikelet, it is enveloped in pollen as though in a golden cloud of dust. All the grasses are in flower and even the plantain—and you could hardly call the plantain a grass, could you?—is smothered in tiny little white beads.

Snake-root, lungwort, all sorts of spikelets, buttons and little cones on thin stalks welcome us. How many of them have perished during our lifetime and yet you can hardly tell—they seem to be the same spikes and awns, such old friends! Good morning to you, my dear, dear friends, once more good morning to you!

THE BLOSSOMING DOG-ROSE BUSH

A dog-rose has, most likely since last spring, climbed up the trunk of a young aspen and now when the time has come for the aspen to celebrate her birthday, it has burst forth in a glory of sweet-smelling pink flowers. Bees and wasps are humming busily in the dog-rose bush, humble-bees add their bass voices to the chorus, all of them fly to the aspen to wish her many happy returns of the day, to sip some honey at her birthday party and to take some home with them.

BIG, FAT BUBBLES

It had been raining the whole day and it was steamingly hot. The tit's song does not sound as before; it is no longer a nuptial song while the bird is basking in the warm sunbeams. Now in the rain he sings with scarcely a pause and he seems even to have gone thinner because of it: how slender he looks on the bough yonder! The crow refuses even to fly to a tree and stands cawing in the middle of the road, bowing, choking, rattling, panting with desire.

This spring the waters began to flow in rushing torrents. The snow in the fields and on the meadows became granular and it was possible to walk over it, sliding forward one foot at a time like skis. Each fir-tree in the woods has a quiet pool of water under it. The spring showers do not raise bubbles on the puddles in the open glades. But beneath the fir-trees, the raindrops that fall from the boughs are heavy and, as it hits the water, each drop produces a big, fat bubble. I love those bubbles. They remind me of little children who resemble both father and mother.

RHYTHM

There is in my nature a constant craving for rhythm. Sometimes when I get up early and walk out into a dew-bespangled world, I am seized with such happiness that I decide there and then to take such a walk each morning. But why *each* morning? Because one wave follows another. . . .

WATER

Nothing in nature knows the secret of concealment so well as water, and it is only when a beautiful sunrise fills the heart of a man with boundless joy that you seem to divine this secret of water: you try to be as quiet as a mouse and you steal forth and then, as it were, you reach out to the hidden depths of your own being, to the conduit which unites you with humanity at large, and you draw up a bucketful of living water from there and go back to our world of men, where an azure stretch of calm water meets you, wide, blossom-strewn, vast! . . .

YOUNG LEAVES

The red candles of the firs are in flower and their yellow pollen is dispersed by the wind. I sat on the ground, leaning against a huge old tree-stump. Inside, this stump is just a crumble of dust and it would doubtlessly have disintegrated completely, if its outer covering of wood had not split up into little planks and each plank had not rested against the crumbling wood-pulp and kept it together. From the midst of that crumble of dust a birch grew out and now its buds have opened up. A multitude of little bushes and wild plants, smothered with blossoms which in good time will become berries, have grown up round that huge old tree-stump.

I lingered for some time by that tree-stump, sitting beside the birch and trying to catch the rustle of her trembling leaves. But, try as I might, I could catch no sound. The wind, though, was quite strong and the music of the woods passed over the fir-trees and reached me in loud, widely separated waves. As one such wave sped away, going afar and not returning, a curtain seemed to descend and shut out the noise; for a moment or two complete silence reigned and a chaffinch immediately made use of this intermission to burst out into a joyous, exuberant song. To listen to him filled me with sheer delight: oh, how glorious it is to live on earth! But I wanted to hear the whispering of the pale-yellow, fragrantly-sparkling and still so very small leaves of the birch-tree. But all in vain: no sound came from them. They are so tender that all they can do is to tremble, glitter and scent the air: they know not as yet how to rustle.

BESIDE THE OLD TREE-STUMP

It is never empty in a wood and if it looks empty to you, it is your own fault.

The huge, old tree-stumps of the old, dead trees in the woods are enveloped in complete silence; the hot sunbeams that come tumbling through the branches pierce the darkness that enfolds them and, as the old tree-stump absorbs warmth from the sun, everything round it also gets warm and is set in motion; the tree-stump becomes overgrown with every kind of vegetation and it is covered with every kind of flower.

Beside one such tree-stump, in a small pool of bright sunshine, where the ground was very hot, ten grasshoppers, two lizards, six large flies and two beetles have crowded together. Round about the old tree-stump tall ferns have gathered like a group of guests and it is very rarely that even the gentlest breath of the wind that is blowing somewhere in the wood will burst in among them; then in the guests' parlour beside the tree-stump one fern bends over another and whispers something, and that one whispers to a third, and so all the guests exchange thoughts.

BESIDE THE BROOK

The little birches have long since donned their dresses and now they are standing waist-high in the tall grass; but when I photographed them it was early spring, and in the snow beneath that birch yonder the first brook was only just starting to flow, dark against a blue sky. Since then, while the little trees were putting on their dresses and the different grasses were growing up beneath them with their different spikes, cusps and stalks of various flowers, much water has flowed under that birch and the brook itself has become so overgrown with the dark-green thicket of impenetrable flags that I cannot tell whether there is any water left in it now.

I, too, am like that brook: how much water has flowed since we parted, and to look at me no one could tell that the brook of my soul is still alive.

THE WATER'S SONG

Spring water gathers every sound that in the least resembles its own sounds: sometimes you cannot for the life of you say whether it is the sound of rippling water, or the muttering of black grouse, or the croaking of frogs. Every sound merges into the one song of the water and over it, in harmony with every other sound, the snipe utters its deliberate *chip-per*, the woodcock screeches and the bittern booms mysteriously. All those strange notes of the birds emerge from the song of spring water.

THE AEOLIAN HARP

The dense long tree-roots which overhang the steep slope have now been transformed into icicles beneath the dark vaults of the river bank and, growing larger and larger, they have reached the surface of the water. When the ripple of wavelets raised by even the gentlest spring breeze reaches the icicles under the sloping bank, they begin to stir and, as they knock against each other, they also begin to ring, and this sound is the first sound of spring—an Aeolian harp.

To an Unknown Friend

The morning—all sun and dew—is like an undiscovered land, like an unexplored vault of heaven, such a unique morning: nobody has risen yet, nobody has seen anything yet, and you yourself are seeing it for the first time. The nightingales are finishing their spring songs, the blow-balls are still untouched in the places which are shielded from the wind and, perhaps, somewhere in the damp and the dark shade a lily-of-the-valley gleams white. To the aid of the nightingales have come the gay summer birds: the wrens, and the oriole's flute is especially enchanting. From every side comes the busy twitter of the thrushes and a woodpecker, tired out with looking for live food for its fledglings, sits down for a rest at a distance from them on a bough.

Get up, my friend! Gather up into a bundle the rays of your happiness! Be brave! On with the struggle, help the sun! Listen, yonder the cuckoo sounds her call, ready to help you. Look, a hen-harrier skims the surface of the water: it is not an ordinary hen-harrier, for on this morning he is the first and the only one; and there the magpies, sparkling with dew, have gone for a walk on the path—to-morrow the glitter of their feathers will not be the same: the whole of to-morrow's day will be different and the magpies will not come out for a walk on the path. This is a unique morning, not a single soul has seen it yet: you alone and your unknown friend see it.

For thousands of years people have lived on this earth and during all those years they have been treasuring up their joy and handing it on to each other so that we might come and pick it up: gather a quiverful of her arrows and rejoice. Be brave my friend and get up!

And you, my enemy, you don't know and, if you ever did know, you will never understand from what kind of material I have woven this joy for people. But if you do not understand what is best in me, why do you cavil at my mistakes, and on the ground of such trifles level your accusations against me? Pass by and do not interfere with our joy!

Once more my soul expands with joy: how lovely the firs are, how sweet the birches! I cannot tear my eyes away from the green candles on the pines and the young red cones on the firs. Oh, you lovely firs, you lovely birches—how wonderful everything is!

The Topmost Sprig

Yesterday's snow still lay on the ground this morning. Later the sun peeped out for a moment and all day a cold north wind blew and dark clouds scurried across the sky, threatening clouds which disclosed the sun only for a fleeting moment and immediately covered it up again. . . .

In the wood, however, there was no breath of wind and everything there was quiet and the life of spring went on without any interruption. What a wonderful sight the woods present when from all the different storeys of the trees branches are hanging down, meeting, intertwining, branches still bare, but hung with blossoming catkins and with long, green, swelling buds. The bird-cherry with green braid, the elder tree hung with dense clusters of flowers shaped like red hairy disks, on the early willow minute yellow florets are sprouting from under its earlier hairy catkins, which will later look like yellow chicks that have just chipped through their shells.

Even the trunks of the young firs are covered with green needles, like a fur, and on the topmost finger of the topmost sprig the new knot of the future sprig can be seen. . . .

I do not say that we complex adults should return to childhood's days, but we should keep a little child alive within us; our lives should grow like a tree: the immature sprig always on the topmost branch, in the light, while our maturity is the strength, the trunk. . . .

Come down, come down, oh, snows of May! Let every living creature remember Jack Frost and hide himself away, and there in his crevice, in his hole, in his nook let him dream of the green, topmost sprig in the rays of the great sun: this is no idle dream, this means that we go back to the trunk and the little children—to growth.

A Grain of Wheat

Now even Shakespeare's power of imagination does not depress me as a writer. I know perfectly well that if I were successful without any imagination, but just by dint of patient digging, finding in myself that little grain by which all people live and telling about it, then Shakespeare himself would have invited me to his hunting lodge like a brother, and it would never have occurred to him to set off the great power of his genius against the grain of wheat of my faith in a friend.

Secret Life

Here, in this blossoming glade, people lived a long time ago: there you can see the ground has been dug round, yonder the sward has been trenched, yonder still the house must have stood and here was the cellar, and by the strip of dark-green sward it is possible to recognise a path along which a man long since dead once walked.

I am walking along this strip of sward and I perceive that because of some unimportant event my feelings can undergo so great a change, something so strange can happen to me, that I am able to recognise in myself the man who long since is dead, and I can see both how he walked along that path and how he is now walking along that dark-green strip of sward.

When that man came to life in me beneath the big oak-tree, I perceived along the lush, green grass the dark image of another tree, a tree which was also of enormous size. A little reflection and I realised that that other oak, which had grown for many years alongside the still standing oak, had long since fallen, crumbled into dust and fertilized that dark-green strip of grass on the sward.

THE EVENING OF THE CONSECRATION OF BUDS

The buds are opening up, dark brown with green tails, and on each little green beak hangs a big, transparent, luminous drop. You take a bud, rub it between your fingers and for a long time after your fingers smell of the aromatic resin of the birch or the poplar or the strangely evocative fragrance of the bird-cherry: it recalls to your mind how you used to climb to the top of the tree to gather the shiny, black, lacquered cherries, how you used to eat handfuls of them, swallowing them with their stones and, somehow, this had no ill effect on you whatever and you got nothing but pleasure out of it.

It is a warm evening and everything is so still that you are waiting impatiently for something to happen: surely, you say to yourself, something must happen in such a stillness. And then this thing you are expecting happens: the trees begin to whisper to each other. One silver birch calls to another silver birch from a distance, a young aspen, standing like a green candle in a glade, finds another such candle, a bird-cherry stretches out her branch with opening buds to another bird-cherry. So, to draw a parallel between the trees and ourselves, *we* talk to each other by sounds and *they* by their fragrance: now each species of tree is enveloped in its own fragrance.

When dusk fell the buds began to disappear in the darkness, but the raindrops still glittered on them and even when it became impossible to distinguish anything at all, the drops went on sparkling in the gloom of the thick bushes, the drops and the sky were the only remaining centres of light: the drops borrowed their light from the sky and lighted us on our way in the dark wood.

It seemed to me as if I was wholly gathered up into one resinous bud and yearning to burst open and welcome my only unknown friend, a friend so fair and beautiful that by only waiting for him all my enemies crumble to dust beneath my feet.

THE WOODLAND BROOK

If you wish to penetrate into the very soul of a wood, you must find a woodland stream and follow its course, either up or down. I am walking along the bank of my favourite woodland stream in early spring and this is what I see and hear and am thinking about.

I can see that where the stream is rather shallow its flowing waters meet an obstacle in the roots of firs. In overcoming this obstacle, the stream dashes noisily against the roots and produces countless bubbles, which, as they rise, race furiously along. Some of them burst almost immediately, while the greater part crowd together at the next barrier into a snow-white ball of foaming froth which is visible from afar.

The water meets with new and ever new obstacles, but that makes no difference to the stream, which merely gathers itself into currents, like muscles tensing for the inevitable fight.

The tremulous ripples, reflecting the sun, throw shadows across the trunk of a fir-tree and across the sward, and these shadows race along the trunks and the grass. In those vibrating flashes of light sound is born and it seems as if the blades of grass grow to the accompaniment of music and you can see how harmoniously the shadows blend.

From its wide but shallow bed the stream rushes into a narrow gully and there its silent yet animated movement creates the impression that the water has tautened its muscles; the sun reflects this movement and the shadows of the rippling wavelets dart quickly over the tree-trunks and the sward.

Further on the stream meets a big obstruction and the water here seems to protest and the splashing of wavelet against wavelet can be heard a long way off. But this does not denote weakness or despair, nor is the stream complaining: water knows none of these emotions, each brook is quite sure that it will reach free water and even if a mountain of the size of Elbrus should bar its way, it will cleave Elbrus in twain, and sooner or later, it will reach its goal. . . .

The rippling surface of the water, caught by the sun, throws back its rays and a shadow like a wisp of smoke darts perpetually across the sward and the trees, and the resinous buds of the birch open up to the sound of the brook, and along its banks the grass rises from the water.

Here is a quiet pool with a tree fallen into it and here the sparkling water-boatmen ripple the still surface of the pool.

To the sound of the restrained murmur of the water, the wavelets glide along confidently and they cannot help calling to each other in their joy; a myriad currents meet and coalesce into a big one and, as they meet and mingle, they talk and call to each other: this is the roll-call of the coming and going currents.

The water flows over the buds of newly-born yellow flowers and, as it touches them, tremulous ripples are born of the flowers. So life passes on in bubbles or foam or in a joyful exchange of greetings among flowers and dancing shadows.

A tree had lain so long and so firmly across the stream that it grew green with time, but the stream found a way beneath the tree and it rushes along, purling and casting tremulous shadows.

Some grasses have long since emerged from the water and now, in the midst of the fast flowing current, they bow continually and reply together to the dance of the shadows and the rush of the stream.

What if an obstruction bars the way! Who cares? Obstacles lend life to the stream: without them the water would have at once flowed lifelessly into the ocean, just as a lifeless body passes into incomprehensible life.

On its way the stream meets a wide and rather deep depression. Without a thought, it fills it with water and races on, leaving that backwater to live its own life.

The winter snows have bent a big bush over and many of its branches are under water. It looks like a giant spider, a brown one at that, sitting in the stream and moving its long legs about.

The seeds of fir-trees and of aspens, too, are carried down the stream.

The whole course of the stream through the woods is one long struggle and it is thus that time is born here. The struggle goes on for so long that in this length of time life is born, as well as my own consciousness.

To be sure, if the stream did not meet obstacles at every step of the way, the water would have flowed away at once and there would have been neither life, nor time.

In its struggle there comes a time when the stream intensifies its headlong rush and then it seems as if its muscles become tautened, but there is no doubt that sooner or later it will reach the ocean, and that "sooner or later" is that self-same time and that self-same life. Looking at that running stream I cannot help thinking that I, too, will sooner or later reach the big water and even if I were the last one there, they would certainly receive me as if I were the first one; for there in the big water, in the ocean, all are first because life has no end there.

The different currents in the same stream, straining between the narrow banks, each pronounce its "sooner or later." And while there is still a drop left in the stream, while the stream has not dried up, the water will go on repeating incessantly: "Sooner or later we shall get to the ocean."

Just beyond the stream, cut off by one of its banks, is a small, round pool and in it a jack pike remains a prisoner.

Then suddenly you come to a place where the stream runs so noiselessly that you can hear a bullfinch twittering all over the woods or a chaffinch rustling in the dead leaves. Or again you come to a rapid where the whole stream rushes at an oblique angle and dashes itself with all its might against the sloping bank, strengthened by hundreds of strong roots of a century-old fir.

The spot was so pleasant that I sat down on the roots of the fir-tree and, as I was having my rest, I listened how under the steep slope below me the rushing waves called confidently to each other, vociferating, exchanging their slogan: "Sooner or later" and I completed their sentence for them: ". . . we shall come to the ocean and we shall conquer the mighty tree and uproot it on its big hill."

The water widened into a lake among an aspen underwood and, gathering its several streams in one corner of it, precipitated itself over a height of about five feet, and the noise of the waterfall could be heard a long way away. So the stream burst into loud talk, while on the surface of the small lake the water rippled along calmly and the dense uprooted aspens under the water coiled and twisted like snakes that could not run away from themselves.

The stream has bound me to itself and I cannot leave it, for every time I do, I feel depressed and lose my confidence that sooner or later I shall reach the wide, limitless expanse of free water.

I came out on a woodland path and the grass on this path was the shortest grass imaginable, but it was also of so bright a green that it looked almost venomous and the two ruts at either side of the road were filled with water.

The fragrantly resinous buds on the small birches are green and they shine brightly, but the wood has not put on its spring garments yet, and to this still bare wood a cuckoo came this year: a cuckoo in a bare wood is considered a bad omen.

For twelve years I have been taking a walk along this wild woodland glade with its stumps of felled trees when only the primroses and the anemones are in flower. I know each bush and tree and even tree-stump so well that this wild glade is like a garden to me. For have I not cherished every bush, every sweet pine and fir and have they not all become mine? Is it not the same as if I had planted them myself, as if this were my own garden?

From "my garden" I returned to the stream and was in time to witness a great woodland event: a huge, ages-old fir-tree, undermined by the stream, crashed with all its old and new cones and lay across the stream with all its branches, and now the wavelets beat against each branch and, as they rushed past, they called to each other: "sooner or later. . . ."

The stream ran out of the dark wood and spread itself over a glade in a wide sheet of water under the open, warm rays of the sun. It was here that I saw the first yellow flower appearing from under the water. The spawn of the frogs lay thick on the surface like honey-combs and so far advanced were the frogs' eggs that through their transparent shells the little black tadpoles could be seen. Here, too, just above the surface of the water, hovered incalculable multitudes of little bluish flies, almost as small as fleas, and here they also fell into the water; they seemed to come flying from nowhere and then they just fell into the water and that, it seemed, was the whole of their brief existence. A little water beetle, shining as if made out of burnished copper, began to spin round and round on the calm surface of the water, while an ichneumon-fly skimmed over the surface rapidly without touching the water. A yellow butterfly, large and dazzlingly bright, fluttered over the wide stretch of calm water. The small puddles round a backwater were overgrown with grasses and flowers, and the fat catkins on a pussy-willow were full out and looked like little chicks covered with yellow down.

What happened to the stream? Half of its water went in a separate stream in one direction and the other half in another. Perhaps in fighting for its faith, for its "sooner or later," the stream became divided: one half of it said that one road would bring it nearer to its goal, while the other half saw its journey's end looming nearer the other way, and so they parted; and, making a wide circular detour, they joined up again, enclosing a large island, for they had realised that for water there were no different roads, that, sooner or later, all roads led to the ocean.

My eye dwells joyfully on this scene and my ear constantly catches the water's refrain—sooner or later—and both eye and ear and the fragrance of resin and the buds of birch-trees—all merge into one another. I feel the happiest man in the world and there is no other place where I had rather be. I sink down between the roots of a tree, lean closely against its trunk, turn my face towards the warm sun and it is then that my wished for moment comes and lingers on and, the last man from the earth, I am the first man to enter this blossoming world.

My stream has reached the ocean.

RIVERS OF FLOWERS

Where the spring torrents used to rush, there are now everywhere torrents of flowers.

I felt very happy as I walked across that meadow, for I thought to myself, "So it was not for nothing that the turgid torrents rushed across this meadow in spring!"

Then reflecting on my experience of life, I thought: "Man has to learn humility from the snake-root which transmits its life to a snake-root so much like it that it seems to us as if it had been living for ever and will go on living for evermore."

But can man so humble himself? I don't think so. But how is one to go on living without believing that sooner or later all the turgid streams of human life will inevitably become rivers of flowers?

LIVING NIGHTS

Three or four days ago spring entered into its last and most important phase. The warmth and the rains transformed our countryside into a hothouse; the air is heavy with the scents of the resinous leaves of poplars, birches and the flowering willow. The real warm *living nights* have begun.

It is good to look back from the height of fulfilment of such a day and to realise how necessary the cold days of sleet and rain are for the creation of these beautiful living nights.

A REVIVIFYING SHOWER

The sun just put in a brief appearance at sunrise and then retired softly behind the clouds, and it began to rain. The rain was as warm and revivifying for the plants, as love is for us.

This warm shower falls with such infinite tenderness upon the resinous buds of the reviving trees and so softly does it touch the bark, which changes colour the moment the raindrops come in contact with it, that you cannot help feeling that this warm heavenly water is the same for the trees as love is for us. It was that self-same love that, as with us, washed and caressed the roots of a tall tree and because

of that water the tree crashed to the ground and became a bridge
from one bank of the stream to the other, and the heavenly love-
shower continues to fall on the fallen tree with its bared roots; and
its buds are now opening up because of the same love which felled it,
they scent the air with the fragrance of resin, and it will flower this
spring like the rest of the trees and transmit its life to others.

THE BIRD-CHERRY

Full of pity for a fallen birch-tree I sat down on it to have a rest
and I kept on looking at a big bird-cherry, sometimes forgetting it
and sometimes coming back to it with a feeling of amazed wonder;
for it looked to me as if, before my very eyes, the bird-cherry was
putting on its transparent garments, made, as it were, of the green
noises of the woods.

The bird-cherry alone was green among the still bare grey trees
and many bushes, and through its tracery of green I could at the
same time see a copse of silver birches behind it. But when I got
up and wanted to take my leave of the bird-cherry, I could no longer
see the silver birches behind it. What could it mean? ·Had I dreamt
about the birches or . . . had the bird-cherry finished dressing while
I was having my rest?

A GULP OF MILK

A bowl of milk stood in front of Lada's nose, but the dog turned
away. They called me. "Lada," said I, "you must drink." She
raised her head and began to wag her tail. I stroked her coat and
my caress brought life back into her eyes. "Drink, Lada," I repeated,
pushing the dish nearer to her.

She stretched out her nose to the milk and began to lap it up.
Through my caress, therefore, life was added to her. Perhaps those
few gulps tipped the balance in favour of life.

The matter of love, too, is decided in our world by such a gulp
of milk.

LOVE-DUTY

I am reading Tolstoy's diary for 1910. Tolstoyan "love" is
indistinguishable from duty. But love means being in love with, just
like the impact of a first glance, a child's glance, it is a state of mind
when all people appear to be beautiful and the whole world an

indivisible whole in man's creative effort. Why should one not regard such love as the basis of the creative impulse of life ? It will be objected that such love passes and that it is, therefore, impossible to put any reliance on it. But this is where I disagree: love has passed away because you yourself have destroyed this great gift. Your personal guilt has been concealed in duty-love, it was entirely through your own fault, through your own sin, that your creative love was transformed into duty-love.

LATE SPRING

The lilies-of-the-valley are first to flower, then comes the dog-rose—everything flowers in its own good time. But it sometimes happens that a whole month has passed after the lilies-of-the-valley have stopped flowering, and yet you can still find one in full flower in some dark nook of a woodland brake, scenting the air all around it. This happens to man, too, though almost as rarely as it happens to the lily-of-the-valley. Sometimes in some quiet nook, in life's deep shadows, there lives an unknown man about whom people usually say, "He has seen his best days!" and pass by. But see! he comes to life suddenly and bursts into flower! . . .

THE DAISY

What great joy it is to come across a daisy, quite an ordinary daisy—"he loves me, he loves me not"—in a meadow in the woods! Such a joyful meeting made me think again that the wood reveals itself only to him who can feel that all its creatures and plants are his kindred.

That first daisy, for instance, seems to try to find out on catching sight of a passer-by whether "he loves me or he loves me not." If a man does not notice it and passes by without seeing it, then the answer is: "he loves me not"—he loves only himself. But if he does, then, oh, what joy! "he loves me! . . ." If he loves me, everything is forgiven: he can even pluck me!

LOVE

No trace of what people call love could be found in the life of that old artist. He had dedicated all his love, everything by which people live, to his art. Rapt in his own visions, enfolded in the veil of poetry, he remained a child, for ever haunted by those obstinate questionings of sense and outward forms and filled with the aching joys and dizzy raptures which the contemplation of nature evoked in him. In a short time, perhaps, he would have been dead, convinced to the very end that life on earth was just that and nothing else.

But one day a woman came to him and it was to her and not to his vision that he murmured his "I love you."

They all say that. But Phacelia, who expected something better and more original from an artist, asked him, "But what does 'I love you' mean?"

"It means," he replied, "that if I had only one morsel of bread left, I would not eat it, but give it to you, that if you were ill, I should not leave you, and that if I had to work for you, I should work for you like a slave."

And he went on speaking to her in the same vein, telling her what people endure because of love.

Phacelia waited in vain for him to say something original.

"Give up your last crumb of bread, nurse a sick person, work like a slave," she repeated. "Why, there's nothing original in that! Everybody does it. . . ."

"That's exactly what I mean," said the artist. "I want to be like everybody else. That is why I am telling you this, for I want you to realise that I, too, am at last experiencing the great happiness of not being a man apart, of not being alone any more, but of being as good as the next man."

THE END